CHAPTER 1

1939

'Are you going to join up when war is declared, Daddy?' I asked my father, after we had boarded the early ferry back to England.

'They wouldn't have me this time, Mary, not with only one lung, don't forget I was gassed in the last war and I'm grateful to be alive,' he replied, 'but I'll have plenty of work to do at the War Office I expect.'

Our family holiday in Normandy had been cut short when my father received a phone call to warn him that war with Germany was imminent and that we should get home, as quickly as possible.

As I looked back at the French coast, it felt strange to think that I had only been playing and laughing with my brothers on the beach the day before. I wondered if we would ever be able to return.

'Will they let me do something to help?' I asked eagerly. 'I can't just sit at home and do nothing.'

'I've never seen you do nothing!' my brother William giggled, sitting next to me. 'Perhaps you could dig up the garden and plant potatoes?'

Although William was only eleven, four years younger than me, he played a first-class game of tennis and very often beat me. He had even managed to beat my elder brother Peter once, which didn't go down well with him at all, as he liked to win at everything – even Monopoly. Peter was eighteen and due to go to Cambridge soon.

When we were back in England and on the road home to Woking, my father pointed to a roadside café with several lorries parked outside it. 'That's a good sign,' he said 'it means the food is good. Let's stop here and have some breakfast.'

'Well it's not exactly the Ritz is it?' my mother said, as we pulled in. 'Let's just hope it's clean.'

'Now children,' my father warned, 'keep your voices down when we go in, as some of the lorry drivers might object to people who drive a Daimler using their café.'

'Why?' William asked, 'What's wrong with our car?'

'It's not the car, but us,' Peter explained to him 'it would be like barging into the servants' dining room while they are eating. They would be just as put out as we would be, if they suddenly came in and sat down in our dining room while we were eating.'

'Oh,' William said glibly, 'I see.'

'Oh My Goodness!' my mother cried suddenly as she was about to get out of the car.

'What's wrong darling, have you got cramp?' my father asked her.

'No I've just realised that there will be no food in the larder and no one to cook for us when we get home!' my mother exclaimed. 'They won't be expecting us home until next week.'

'We'd better go to Sainsbury's on the way home then,' suggested my practical little brother.

Sainsbury's had just opened their first shop in Woking, which William loved as it all seemed so different and such fun, everything was sold in such huge quantities and there was a variety of food in colourful tins. My mother would sometimes take him with her if she was shopping there as a treat, although she told me that she still always preferred her own little grocer's shop that she'd been using for years.

'Let's make a list of the things we need to keep us going for the next twenty-four hours while we have breakfast,' my mother said as we followed her into the cafe.

My father found us a table near the window, and then he and Peter went to place our order with the woman behind the counter. There was a tough-looking man standing next to her who must have noticed our car in the car park piled high with luggage as I heard him say to my father in a rather sarcastic tone. 'You running 'ome quick from France then, Guv? 'Fraid them Huns were behind you and want to steal your fancy car?'

'We've come home early from our holiday to see what we can do to help.' my father told him firmly 'I served in the last war, so I want to do my bit in this one too.'

A broad grin crossed the tough man's face and his tone then changed completely, 'Well done, Guv, we'll all do the same.'

Breakfast was served on chipped plates, but it was hot and delicious.

BRAVE FACES

BRAVE FACES

BRAVE FACES

MARY ARDEN

Matador
9 Priory Business Park
Kibworth Beauchamp
Leicestershire LE8 0RX, UK
Tel: (+44) 116 279 2299
Fax: (+44) 116 279 2277
Email: books@troubador.co.uk
Web: www.troubador.co.uk/matador

ISBN 978-1784623-388

British Library Cataloguing in Publication Data.
A catalogue record for this book is available from the British Library.

Typeset in Aldine 401BT Roman by Troubador Publishing Ltd
Printed and bound in the UK by TJ International, Padstow, Cornwall

Matador is an imprint of Troubador Publishing Ltd

Brave Faces is dedicated to my mother and father
who were always there for me when I needed them.

There were doorsteps of hot buttered toast and the tea was poured from a metal teapot, which to our surprise tasted better than tea poured from the china teapots we were used to at home. My mother ordered a coffee, which she quickly regretted as she'd been spoiled while we were in France with much better quality. My father told her that she would have to get used to drinking far worse coffee once we were at war.

'I'd better send telegrams to the servants to tell them to return at once,' my mother said looking at my father.

'That isn't fair, Mummy,' I said, 'think of how hard they work all year round. This is the only holiday they get. Perhaps we could ask Pansy to come and help out instead?'

Pansy lived locally and worked for us on an hourly basis when we had visitors, or at other times when extra help was needed around the house. She would always arrive on her bicycle and I knew that she would be only too happy to have a few extra hours work, as her family were very poor.

'Good thinking,' my father said smiling at me.

My mother said that she was worried that if the threat of war escalated some of the staff wouldn't be able to return. Nancy, our cook, was only in Portsmouth so she should be able to catch a train; and Alice, the housemaid, lived in Devon so she would be able to do the same; but Agnes, our parlour maid whom we all called 'Aggie', was staying with her family in Ireland, so she might not be able to get back to England and without her the house wouldn't be run properly.

'What a disaster that would be!' my mother exclaimed.

'Perhaps Kay might like to earn a little extra money, Mummy?' I suggested, 'She's good at doing everything in the house and she is always willing to help.'

Kay was my ex-governess, and I loved her like an elder sister. Kay and her husband, Jack, lived only fifteen minutes from us, so we were able to keep in regular touch with one another. As we were driving the final leg home I asked my father if he would tell us about some of his experiences in the last war, a subject he seldom talked about.

'When war is declared I will tell you about it, but I'd rather not right now as it brings back some rather unhappy memories my dear. Let's play 'I spy with my little eye' instead,' he suggested.

This passed the time for about half an hour until William said in a loud voice that he was bored and hungry and asked if we had remembered to put chocolate biscuits on the shopping list, which made us all laugh, as if eating chocolate biscuits was an international sport William would certainly win the gold medal.

As usual we ended up buying far more than was needed, so when we got back in the car, Peter and I had bags of shopping on our knees, while William clutched a leg of lamb to his chest.

When we finally arrived home it took almost an hour to open up the house, remove the dustsheets and carry in all the cases, golf clubs and tennis rackets, plus all the food we'd just bought. The only things we didn't take into the house were the heavy trunks and our rather fishy-smelling bathing costumes.

Lunch was the next priority. Peter was put in charge of the sausages. My father opened two tins of baked beans, while William was sent out to the garden to see if there were any ripe plums and vegetables worth harvesting. I offered to lay the dining room table but couldn't find the silver. I opened all the sideboard drawers and even looked in Agnes's pantry but couldn't find it anywhere and started to get worried, so I asked my mother where it was.

'Oh goodness, it's in the bank!' she said, 'I'd quite forgotten. We'll have to use the kitchen things.'

'So why don't we eat in the kitchen then Mummy?' I suggested. 'It seems silly to carry it all through from one room to another. It'll be like a picnic.'

After lunch, my father tried in vain to get the boiler to light, but smoke belched out of it instead of going up the chimney.

'I could go next door and ask Mrs Derwent if it's all right with her if we borrow Brown for half an hour. I'm sure he would be only too willing.' Brown was the Derwent's handyman and always seemed happy to help anyone in need.

'Good idea,' my father said coughing and opening a window to let the smoke out.

We were great friends with the Derwents, and their children were in our house as much as in their own. I ran along the terrace, down the steps to the lawn and then down again to the tennis court that adjoined the Derwent's orchard, pushing myself through the hole in the hedge, as I had done many times before. When we'd first come to live at Woking, the gap in the hedge had been tiny, but over the years, as all us children had grown up, the gap had become big enough to walk through. Bullen, our gardener, had often promised to put a gate there but he had never had enough time to do it.

As I ran towards the house, I wondered whether Edward and Robert, the Derwent boys, would be at home and then thought that if they were perhaps their cousin Andrew or Edward's best friend Henry might be there too. When I got there I saw Brown, the handyman, standing on top of a ladder picking damsons.

'Hello Miss Mary,' he said smiling down at me.

'Hello Brown,' I replied still a little out of breath, 'Do you understand boilers? If so, do you think you could come and help my father? He says to tell you that he gets the kindling lit, puts on the coal but then it goes out.'

'It 'be those there dampers,' Brown said as he descended the ladder, 'You go tell Mrs Derwent you be 'ome, Miss Mary, and I'll go clean up me 'ands and call you when I'm ready.'

Mrs Derwent, or 'Aunt Nora' as I called her even though she wasn't a relative, was in the kitchen with the family's nanny, an old lady who had long since retired but still lived with them and was more like an old friend than staff now.

Aunt Nora gave me a hug and asked after my parents, and then told me that Edward and Robert were away at some sort of camp and would not be home for several more days. I then explained why we had come home early and the reason for my visit.

'May we borrow Brown for half an hour to get our boiler going?'

'Keep Brown for as long as you need him. Boilers can be the very devil; you have to know how to work the dampers and Brown seems to be the only one that does!' Aunt Nora said laughing just as Brown knocked on the kitchen door to tell me that he was ready. I suggested that we go to our house through the hole in the hedge to save time.

'After you, Miss Mary,' Brown grinned as he forced his big body through the hole in the hedge, 'this 'edge could do with a clipping it could, make it look more tidy-like.'

I guided Brown up the steps, past our seesaw, to the back door of the kitchen where the recalcitrant boiler was. My father was thankful to see him and apologised for having no idea how to light his own boiler. After taking a close inspection, Brown confirmed it was just the dampers.

'You have to pull 'em up and then pull 'em down,' he advised my father, demonstrating at the same time, 'to help the air go up the chimney.'

Half an hour later, the boiler was red hot and began to heat the water. Brown offered to fill the hods with coke and coal and asked if there was anything else he could do for us. My father asked him for a hand to get the roof rack off the car.

'Shall I switch on the immersion heater in the nursery bathroom?' Brown asked.

We all looked at him in amazement, as everyone had completely forgotten that we had such a thing. It was good that we did, as it meant that at least three baths could be run one after the other. As Brown left, my father gave him a pound, which he took reluctantly, saying he'd put it towards a new bicycle.

By the time we'd all unpacked, put everything away, sorted the laundry and carried the dirty shoes down to the gardener's shed, it was nearly teatime.

'Mary dear, make me a cup of tea will you darling?' my mother asked me, 'and then be a good girl and go over to Kay's house and ask her if she'd be willing to come each morning to help cook the lunch and prepare something light for supper. Tell her I'll need her for a week until the servants come back and that I'll pay her two pounds a day. Then come straight back again as I'll need you to help me cook the dinner.'

I cycled over to Kay's house and passed on my mother's request. She leapt at the chance to earn some extra money, as she wanted to buy a new carpet for their sitting room. I promised I'd help her as much as I could and be her kitchen maid, 'I'd better hurry back now to help Mummy cook the joint, as she's never cooked one before!'

'Good luck,' Kay said laughing, 'and if you need any advice just give me a ring.'

When I got home, my mother was already in the kitchen and I was amused to see her with an apron on, as I had never seen her wear one before. I found a roasting tin and the lard we'd bought from Sainsbury's, and then William climbed onto a chair, pulled down Mrs Beeton's cookery book, and found the chapter on how long to cook lamb. Meanwhile Peter was sent to see if there were any potatoes ready to be dug up.

'What do we do if there aren't any?' William asked worriedly.

Having carefully weighed the joint, William said it needed to cook for two hours and that if we planned to eat at the usual time of seven-thirty, then the joint needed to go in the oven within the next hour. My mother sprinkled salt on the joint and then attempted to light the oven. When a big flame popped up at the back she gave a sigh of relief. As the oven needed to heat up before the joint went in, my mother told us that she would go and listen to the news for half an hour with a gin and Dubonnet and a cigarette.

William and I decided to pick some peas and runner beans in the garden and found Peter out there digging up enough potatoes for what looked like at least a week. When we all went back inside we found our mother asleep on the sofa with her feet up and her shoes on the floor. The sound of us laughing woke her up with a start.

'I had no idea where I was for a moment!' she said, now laughing too 'I wasn't sure whether I was still in France or safely back here at home. Now, William what do you think we should we do with the potatoes? Should they go in with the joint or in a separate tin?'

'Put the joint in first, Mummy,' he instructed, 'then the roast potatoes take about an hour in their own tin... but you have to cook them in really hot fat.'

While our dinner was cooking, I asked if I could ring my cousin, Jane, who lived in London. When I got through to her, I asked, 'Does your father think there's going to be a war too?'

'Fraid so,' Jane replied, 'that's why we've come back early.'

'I did miss you in Normandy, Jane. What was it like in Wales; did it rain all the time?'

'No we were lucky and there were riding stables attached to the hotel so I was able to ride every day and Bridget found a couple of boys who took her out in a boat on a nearby lake and they danced together every evening in the hotel ballroom.'

'Sounds like fun! What did you do in the evening?' I asked.

Jane giggled and told me that as there was nothing else to do once she'd read a story to her little brother Tim, she had gone to the ballroom too and that there was a gorgeous looking man who was a dance instructor so she'd learned how to dance the tango and the rumba. 'I'll teach you how to do both when you come to stay,' she promised.

'I can't come for at least a week as I need to help Mummy with the cooking.'

'Your mother cooking!' Jane giggled. 'Now that's a sight I'd pay to see!'

After I had put the receiver down I looked up and saw Peter walking towards me looking very worried.

'There's something wrong with the oven,' he told me. 'Come and have a look. The joint hasn't even started to cook. Poor Mummy is near to tears.'

I peered into the oven and guessed that it must be something to do with the gas pressure because the flame at the back was now very low. 'Mummy, did you turn the gas tap on full?'

'Of course I did!' she answered crossly.

'Is there a tap on the wall?' William suggested 'somewhere you can turn up the gas pressure. Shall I go and fetch Dad?'

'Your father wouldn't be much help, think how hopeless he was with the boiler!' my mother snapped.

'Why don't I call Kay?' I said quickly. 'She'll know all about the gas pressure and that sort of thing.'

When I rang Kay and explained the situation to her she told me to go and check the regulator knob and see what setting it was on, so I returned to the kitchen and went over to the stove. The regulator knob was on zero. No wonder our dinner wasn't cooking! I immediately turned the knob to number six and then went back to tell Kay what had happened. She roared with laughter.

'I'm afraid dinner will be a little late tonight,' our poor mother announced, 'but at least the water will be hot by now so we can all have baths, get changed and forget about this beastly kitchen for a while!'

It was eight-thirty by the time we sat down for dinner, and we were all so hungry by then that we'd have eaten the meat raw but, as it turned out, the lamb was just right, the roast potatoes crisp, the vegetables done to a 'T', and the gravy that William had made was rich and smooth.

'Well done darling!' my father said blissfully unaware of the earlier drama. 'You see it's not so difficult is it?' My mother looked as if she was about to pick up her plate and throw it at him, but somehow managed to restrain herself and gave my father a triumphant smile instead.

A week later the household was back to normal: Nancy, our cook, was back at the helm in the kitchen and she couldn't help but chuckle over my mother's mistake with the regulator knob; Agnes was cleaning the silver in the pantry that had been recently returned from the bank and Alice was cleaning the house thoroughly, tut-tutting as she went over Pansy's half-hearted efforts.

One morning after breakfast I decided to walk over to the Derwent's house to see if the boys were back yet, as I hoped they'd come over to play tennis with us or come one evening and play silly card games. When I got there I saw a lovely red MG sports car in their drive, which I knew belonged to Edward's best friend, Henry. I'd known Henry Neville ever since we'd moved to Woking, as he often spent part of the holidays with the Derwent family. The last time I saw him I thought how good looking he was, tall with sandy red hair, blue-green eyes and a husky voice with a drawl just like a film star. I had a bit of a crush on him. His father had given him the MG for his twenty-first birthday and I longed to have a ride in it but realised that a man of his age was unlikely to take much notice of a fifteen-year old schoolgirl.

Just as I was going into the house, Henry walked out. He was wearing an old pair of shorts and an open necked shirt and was carrying a bucket full of water. I suddenly felt so shy that I could hardly look at him let alone speak.

'Well hello Goldilocks!' he said teasing me. 'Just in time to help me clean the car!' Henry took the wet sponge from his bucket and tossed it at me. I ducked and it narrowly missed me. I then threw it back at him and got a direct hit. His shirt was absolutely soaked. He took one look at himself and then grinning at me from ear to ear said, 'Right, this is war!' He dipped the sponge back into the bucket and threw it back at me with full force. This time it landed right in the middle of my chest and I was now dripping wet too. We both pointed at each other and laughed and then seeing how wet I was he pulled out his handkerchief and began to dab my shirt dry.

Suddenly he stopped mid dab and staring at my breasts said, 'My goodness Goldilocks you have grown since I last saw you!'

I began to blush and seeing my discomfort Henry kindly changed the subject, 'Oh, by the way, I heard that one of the first television sets is being exhibited in the music shop in Woking. Edward and Robert have taken their father there to have a look at it. If you'd like to see it too, I'll run you into town.'

I didn't care a fig about the television set but longed to climb into Henry's sports car and here was my opportunity, what bliss!

'I'll have to go home and change out of my wet blouse first,' I replied.

I quickly ran home, had a pee, changed out of my wet blouse, and then decided to do something about my hair. As I brushed my long blonde curls in front of the mirror the memory of Henry calling me 'Goldilocks' made me smile. A moment later I heard his MG pull up in the drive and the thought having a drive in it got me so excited that I had to go for another pee and then in my haste to get back downstairs I decided to slide down the banisters, hitching up my skirt before I did so. I went flying down, only to be met at the bottom of the stairs by Henry.

'Agnes let me in,' he said grinning from ear to ear. I stood there, stunned, my skirt now up to my waist.

'Are they strong enough for me to have a go?' he chuckled.

I was too embarrassed and busy pulling down my skirt to reply for a moment but, once I had recovered, begged, 'Please don't tell my mother that I slid down the banisters, I'm supposed to behave like a lady!'

'In that case,' Henry replied, looking at me with a bit of twinkle in his eye, 'I'd better behave like a gentleman and pretend I didn't see what I saw.'

I climbed into Henry's car mindful that my mother was most probably watching from the window and careful not to show more bare flesh than necessary. I tucked my skirt between my legs, which made Henry smile, 'Done just like a lady!'

We drove very slowly out of the drive but once we had gone past the Derwent's gate he put his foot down and the car took off. I loved the thrill of driving so fast.

When we arrived at the music shop Henry came round and opened the car door for me, offering me his hand, as I climbed out of the car. He was teasing me of course treating me like a lady, but he did it so nicely that I gave him my hand and did a little curtsey.

'I may as well come in and see the television as I'm here,' he said as we spotted Edward and Robert and their father gazing in awe at what appeared to be a screen full of snow.

'Wait a minute! It has to warm up first,' said Edward excitedly as Henry and I entered the shop together. Edward came over and as usual pecked me on the cheek, but Robert simply nodded.

We all stood watching the television until eventually an image of a man emerged out of the snow: his mouth was moving as if he was talking but we couldn't hear a word, only static. Then, suddenly, a very clipped BBC voice was audible. He was talking about the history of television and how Yogi Baird had discovered it.

'It's early days,' the commentator said, 'but before too long, everyone will have a television set in their sitting room.'

Mr Derwent was all for ordering a television set immediately, which Henry warned against doing, saying that if war was declared, all research would have to stop as the resources required to develop it would be directed towards armaments, planes and better radio equipment.

The shop owner turned off the television and turned on a wireless set. We were all just about to leave when suddenly we heard the voice of Neville Chamberlain, the Prime Minister, on the wireless. We stood still and listened anxiously.

'This morning the British Ambassador in Berlin handed the German Government a final Note stating that, unless we heard from them by 11 o'clock that they were prepared at once to withdraw their troops from Poland, a state of war would exist between us. I have to tell you now that no such undertaking has been received, and that consequently this country is at war with Germany.'

After Chamberlain had finished speaking I glanced across at Edward, who had gone as white as a sheet. Mr Derwent put a hand on his son's shoulder and looking at all of us said, 'I think it's time we went home now.'

As we left the shop I looked up at a calendar on the wall.

The date was the 3rd September 1939.

When I asked my mother how I could help the war effort she told me the best thing we could all do for now was to try to carry on as usual, which for me was to work as hard as I could towards my School Certificate exam.

All we seem to do at school was work, work and more work. So much so that everyone started to complain of headaches. There was a huge sigh of relief when our Head Mistress announced that each form was to put on a short play to entertain the other forms, but it was soon followed by a huge groan when she added that my form had to produce its play in French! We were not amused but at least our French teacher agreed to allow us to read the English translation so that we could understand the plot.

Exhausted after doing so much intense work, I was very happy when we broke for half term and I was allowed to go home to see my parents for a few days.

As soon as I got back I went into the garden to look for my father. I was horrified to see that half the lawn, where Alice our housemaid usually hung out the washing, had now become a second vegetable patch. I found my father with several workmen discussing plans to create an air raid shelter, next to the steps that led down from the rose-garden, so that when there was an air raid there would be somewhere safe for us to go. Before that moment I had thought air raids would only happen in London or possibly some of the bigger cities, and it had never crossed my mind that a bomb could fall in Woking, let alone near our house. I suddenly felt really afraid.

I asked my father what plans he had made if the house was bombed.

'What if everybody is killed except me? Where will I go?'

'I've discussed it with Aunt Edith and we have both agreed that if any of us adults are killed, then the others will look after the children. But don't worry, Mary, it won't happen to us.' I wasn't sure if I believed him but desperately wanted to. The idea that any of my family could be killed was unthinkable.

My father told me that he had recently joined the newly formed Home Guard and that the few weapons they had were mostly relics taken as souvenirs from the First World War. As it would take time to turn the factories that usually made cars and tractors into armaments factories they had been told by the War Office that they would have to improvise so they were lashing carving knives onto broom handles to use as bayonets and they had asked the local man who used to sharpen knives in the street to sharpen all the axes, scythes and sickles they could muster. I hadn't realised that my father might have to fight the Germans in hand-to-hand combat and the idea really scared me.

I wished my brothers were at home for half term but my mother told me that Peter was too busy studying at Trinity College, Cambridge to have any time off and that William wouldn't be home until the following week so I decided to see if any of the Derwent boys were at home. They weren't but their cousin Andrew, who was in his mid twenties so a lot older than all of us, was there as he had taken a week's leave and he, like me, was feeling a bit lonely because no one else was at home. He told me that he loved being in the RAF and was now training as a Pathfinder pilot. I was intrigued and asked him what that was. He explained that when bombers had a target to get to he would be the one that went on ahead of them to guide them there.

'Gosh, that sounds dangerous!' I said, 'Aren't you scared?'

'Scared enough to wet my trousers if I get caught in search lights!' he replied, 'you see, Mary, when you're caught in the searchlights, you're completely blinded and can't see a damn thing. Bombers can zigzag to get out of the way but a Pathfinder has to stick to its course come what may.'

'Did they make you do it, or did you volunteer?'

'Well, someone has to do it and I'm older than most of the others. I've been flying since I was seventeen, so I'm really one of the most experienced pilots they have. By the way, what are you doing this afternoon?' he asked, changing the subject.

'Nothing much, just resting my brains, I've been swotting for School Cert.' I explained.

'Would you like to come to the cinema with me? It'll rest my brains as well! I've no idea what's on but it's a good way of forgetting about the war... at least for a couple of hours.'

The film was a comedy and it made us both laugh. On the way home, Andrew asked me how school was going. I told him that although I was working very hard I didn't expect to pass the maths exam.

'I'm quite good at maths so I could pass on a few tips when I am here over the Christmas holidays,' Andrew kindly offered.

'Won't you be going to your parents?'

'Not this year, Mary, The war will prevent me going to Singapore to see them so I'll probably stay with the Derwents.'

'How's Edward by the way?' I asked.

'Did you know he's thinking of offering his services as an ambulance driver to avoid having to join the army?' he said shaking his head, 'I can tell you that Uncle Christopher was not at all pleased but when I told him that Edward could have just registered as a conscientious objector he quietened down a bit, but Edward knows that his father is ashamed of him and he's very upset about it.'

'It's not fair, Edward isn't a coward; he's more the sort of person who should be a clergyman, if you know what I mean. He hates the idea of killing his fellow man.'

13

'We haven't any choice when it comes down to it,' Andrew said bitterly 'that's what war is all about – it's either him or me.'

I thanked Andrew for taking me to the cinema and then ran back home thinking, 'Take care, dear Andrew, please take extra care.'

As I helped Agnes lay the table that evening, I asked her what she was doing for the war effort and she told me that she was now working some mornings and a few afternoons at the 'Munitions', meaning the ammunition factory.

'But you'll still live here with us won't you Aggie?' I asked anxiously.

'I will Miss Mary,' Agnes replied. 'Your father very kindly told me that I must think of this as my home and asked me not to go back to Northern Ireland as I'm needed here. I did offer him my war-work wages to cover the extra expense of having me here,' Agnes said lowering her voice, 'but your father wouldn't hear of it. He said 'we all have to pull together to win the war'.'

I watched Agnes as she polished the glasses and said, 'I do admire you, Aggie, for the war work you're doing. Once my wretched exams are over, I plan to do some sort of war work too.'

'Good for you Miss Mary… meanwhile as your mother keeps saying 'Carry on as usual'.'

Before I knew it, I was back at school and 'carried on' studying as hard as I could until it was time to go home to my parents again for Christmas.

I hadn't seen my old governess, Kay, since the summer, so decided to go and see her on my first day back. When I got to her house and she opened the front door to greet me I was horrified to see that she had a very swollen tummy. Tears ran down my cheeks: 'Oh Kay, your poor tummy; are you ill?'

'Never better!' she said happily. 'Surely you've seen a woman carrying a baby in her tummy before?'

'Never!' I gasped, 'Oh Kay, does Jack know?'

'Of course he does, silly girl. It's his fault I'm like this,' she said laughing.

'Oh? What do you mean it's his fault?' I asked, not understanding what she meant.

'Well, when married couples share a bed… well sometimes babies just come – you know? They must have told you at school in biology lessons, all about the birds and bees… about pollination and fertilisation?' Kay ventured.

'Oh that! But that's for trees and plants,' I replied, 'not for people… is it?'

'Oh yes it is, it's much the same. You'd better ask your mother to explain it a bit more,' Kay said, smiling at my innocence.

Later that evening at dinner as Agnes handed round the bread sauce, I announced to everyone, 'Kay's been pollinated!… or is it fertilised? – I forget which exactly – but she's expecting a baby in the spring and she looks like a huge balloon and I told her that I hoped she wouldn't burst!'

My father put his napkin over his mouth but I could see he was laughing so hard he was almost crying, while my mother looked totally bemused, my brother Peter let out a loud snort and William stopped mid-way as he was about to put some bread sauce on his chicken. It was Agnes who spoke first: 'I'm delighted to hear the news Miss Mary, I've always been very fond of Mrs Kay.' Agnes was a staunch Catholic who always seemed to us to be very prim and proper but she didn't seem in the least bit shocked with my talk of Kay being 'pollinated'.

'Yes that is wonderful news darling,' my mother added, 'Let's buy some wool tomorrow and then you can knit a cardigan for the baby, and the next time you see Kay, please tell her that I would like to pay for the Moses basket.'

'Why does Kay need a Moses basket?' William asked with interest. 'Is she planning to float her baby down the river?'

As my mother kissed me goodnight later that evening she said that perhaps it was about time she had another talk to me about 'the birds and bees,' but that first we'd better get Christmas over with.

Surprisingly, Christmas didn't feel very different from the previous year. There were blackout regulations of course, which meant people couldn't put lights on their Christmas trees and we couldn't see the decorative shop-displays, which I particularly liked, as all the windows were obscured by anti-blast tape but apart from that it was much the same as it always had been. Food hadn't been rationed yet but Agnes told me that bacon and butter would start to be rationed from January.

As Aunt Edith and her family, the Godburys, were staying with us for Christmas, as well as their refugee cook, every room would be taken. This meant that my cousin Jane would have to share my room, which I was looking forward to, as we were so close that we were almost like sisters.

As usual when the Godburys were staying with us, all the children would put on a Nativity play for the adults. This gave Jane's elder sister, Bridget, a chance to be the director, which was perfect for her as she loved bossing everyone about and Peter would get the opportunity to be a lighting engineer, which he loved doing. William would be in charge of making the programmes and doing the prompting and Jane and I would get to sing songs from the latest musical shows and dance. We all learned our parts as quickly as we could and by Boxing Day we were ready to put on a performance.

The old billiard room had been turned into our theatre, as it had an enormous bay window, which made a perfect stage for our play. The audience included Jane's and my parents, the Derwents and their houseguests, Andrew and Henry who were both on leave.

I took my place on stage as the Virgin Mary with one of my dolls as Jesus and Jane stood near me as the Angel Gabriel, because she had long, straight fair hair and looked the part. William and Jane's little brother, Tim, were the shepherds, while Bridget played Joseph. Meanwhile, Peter was balanced on a ladder behind a screen, as he was responsible for moving the star of Bethlehem on a long pole over our heads.

Everything went smoothly right up to the last scene but then suddenly there was a dull thud as the star fell off the pole and landed on Joseph's head, nearly knocking him (Bridget) out in the process and as she bumped into me I tumbled over and dropped baby Jesus but fortunately William must have seen what was happening and grabbed the doll one handed like a cricket ball before it landed on the floor.

'Oh well caught that Shepherd!' yelled Henry and everyone laughed.

When it was time for our neighbours to leave, Edward Derwent noticed some mistletoe hanging from the light in the hall and pulled Bridget under it to give her a long lingering kiss. Then he turned to me and gave me a gentle peck on the cheek, as he and his brother Robert usually did to say goodbye, so when Henry bent down to do the same thing I was a little surprised when he whispered in my ear, 'I'll give you a real kiss when you're sixteen!'

'Like they do in the cinema?' I whispered back, blushing.

'Oh I think I can do better than that!' Henry teased in his husky deep voice, 'Don't let anyone else kiss you, I want to be the first, promise?'

'Who would want to kiss me?' I asked innocently.

'All the boys will Goldilocks, you'll be fighting them off just you wait and see.'

After they had all left Jane came up to me and asked, 'What was Henry whispering to you about?' She sounded jealous, 'That man is the most gorgeous being I've ever seen, and in his RAF uniform, I could swoon and let him kiss me without the help of any mistletoe.'

'Jane!' I said, shocked, 'He's far too old for you.'

'I don't mind how old he is,' Jane insisted. 'Surely that isn't the same little boy that we used to play Hide 'n' Seek with in the garden, and whose mother lives in France?'

'It is,' I confirmed. 'He has become rather nice looking hasn't he?'

It was lovely to spend a few days with my cousins and my family over the Christmas period and after they had left to go back to London the house felt very empty, and quiet. A few days later it was my sixteenth birthday. My mother had said she wanted to buy me some clothes but what I really wanted was a new bicycle. When I came down for breakfast on my birthday, my parents were sitting at the table but there was no sign of my brothers who I thought must be sleeping in. Suddenly the front door bell rang and my father asked me if I would mind going to see who it was and when I opened the front door Peter and William were standing there holding a brand new bicycle with a large basket at the front. I was so excited that I squealed with delight. My mother, who was now right behind me, wished me a happy birthday and gave me a hug and then my father and my brothers joined in and we nearly toppled over, which made us laugh. It was a very special moment that I knew I would treasure forever, whatever happened.

I rode my new bicycle straight over to the Derwents to show it to the boys, or more importantly to Henry, but none of them were there, so Henry's promise of a proper kiss when I turned sixteen would have to wait for another day.

CHAPTER 2

1940

Rationing was introduced on 8th January 1940. It didn't matter how wealthy you were, any available food was shared equally at fair prices, so my family, like everyone else's, had to adjust to the privations of war, putting up with the shortages of food, standing patiently in long queues at the butchers and fishmongers, sometimes for up to two or three hours at a time. My mother told me that while they all waited, they discussed ways and means of making their meat rations go further, like adding dough-balls or dumplings to stews, or adding canned beans and slices of apple to a curry.

A week later I was back at school, and although rationing applied here too, which meant that we had to use less butter and sugar than usual, the only thing I really missed was sweets. The first morning in our classroom, we all swopped stories of what we had been up to over Christmas and there was a lot of laughter in the classroom but then one of the teachers came into the room and told us that the head girl and her sister wouldn't be coming back this term because their father had been killed in action. The room went so quiet you could have heard a pin drop. The reality of war had suddenly hit us all.

That term my head was crammed full of revisions for the upcoming exams and the only light relief was when we were rushing up and down the games field playing lacrosse against other schools.

By the next holidays, I felt so tired and stressed that I burst into tears as soon as I got home. My mother was obviously worried about me and tried to help me feel better by saying, 'Only one more term, darling, and then I promise you we'll send you to the Finishing School we've been planning for you but unfortunately, it is no longer in Florence because of the war.'

'So where is it?' I asked.

'They have rented a house in Eastbourne,' my mother replied, 'You'll learn to sing, improve your languages, cook and study art there, as well as learning how to curtsey for when you 'Come Out',' She then curtseyed to me, which made me laugh and then laugh even louder when she pretended to fall over.

After I had been at home for a week, we received a call to let us know that Kay had given birth to a baby boy. I was thrilled to bits and cycled straight across the park between Kay's and our house to see her baby whom she had named Richard.

Holding the baby in my arms I said to Kay, 'He's lovely! I want to have twelve babies one day, six boys and six girls!'

As I snuggled Richard to my chest, I asked Kay if it was difficult to feed a baby.

'It's not difficult exactly, but it can be rather embarrassing at times, as I have so much milk that I feel like a cow!' Kay said smiling. 'What are you planning to do during the holidays Mary?'

'Well I'm thinking that I could help at the YMCA, make sandwiches for the soldiers, and help write letters home for them, that sort of thing, but I could still come and help you with the ironing if you like?'

'Thank you, Mary, we'll see about that but at the moment I'm managing fine.' Kay then touched my arm and said in a serious tone, 'Do be careful what you say when you are writing the letters for the soldiers.'

'What do you mean?' I asked.

'Well the first thing you need to do is to find out whether the letter will be for their mother, father, sister, girlfriend or wife, and then adjust what you write accordingly. What they really need you to do is to give who ever they are writing to some reassuring news from them like: 'I am very well' or 'the food is very good' or 'I have made some new friends', that sort of thing.'

'Oh I see, that makes sense,' I nodded. It was good advice and less than a week later I was helping my first soldier write a letter thanking his family for a parcel they had sent him and the next one wanted to tell his little sister about a film he'd seen. After that I got the hang of it and was soon in big demand.

Alice, our housemaid, had now left us to join the ATS but she'd left a pile of magazines behind full of soppy love stories, which I used as inspiration when a soldier wanted help writing to his sweetheart. I took sentences straight off the pages like, 'How I miss you my darling and cannot wait to hold you in my arms,' and 'The memory of the sweet smell of your hair makes me long to be home'. I really enjoyed helping to write these letters for the soldiers and they seemed very happy with the results. One of them gave me the biggest smile I had ever seen and said, 'Coo Miss, she won't 'arf love that!'

I decided that it might be a good idea if I brought some of my schoolbooks with me next time so that I could teach some of the men the rudiments of reading and writing, as I had been surprised by how many of them couldn't. I asked Kay's advice, and she lent me some of her old Froebel books. I only had two takers the first day, as the other chaps were most probably too embarrassed to be taught by such a young girl, but a week later when they realised I wasn't being judgmental, I had enough men to make a small class.

The following week, my mother surprised us all by joining the local Red Cross so that she could then pass her nursing exams and learn to drive an ambulance. We were amazed at her willingness to do such a thing and felt very proud of her. It made me determined to do my bit too and become a nurse, as soon as I was allowed to.

At the end of that same week, we heard on the radio that Germany had invaded Holland and Belgium and that Neville Chamberlain, the Prime Minister, had stepped down. Winston Churchill had now been asked to form a coalition government, which pleased my father, as he liked Churchill and thought that he was 'just what this country needs.'

The next morning he took me to one side to show me how to use his First World War pistol, telling me that this was 'just in case the Germans invade England and walk into our home'. I was shocked and felt sick at the thought that I might have to defend myself by taking another's life.

I was still feeling sick the next day and woke up with a sore throat and a rash all over my body but this was a real illness.

'It's German measles,' our family doctor announced. 'No school for you for two or three weeks young lady.'

Reprieve! I thought, and then started to panic when I realised that this enforced time off might mean I'd fail all my exams, as I hadn't revised everything I should have. However, my father came to the rescue and decided to take the train to my school in Haslemere to collect some of my schoolbooks for me so that I could keep revising while I was convalescing.

As I lay in bed recovering, I wondered why it was called 'German' measles and was concerned that it might be something the Nazis had concocted so was relieved when my mother told me that the virus' real name was Rubella and that it was only called German measles, as it was German physicians who had first described it.

After two weeks of being indoors all the time my mother told me that I could now go outside for short bicycle rides to get some fresh air into my lungs. In between bike rides I helped Bullen in the garden, planting peas and beans, and he told me that although he was too old to fight in this war he was more than willing to do his bit and 'Dig for Victory'.

One day as he and I were sitting in the warm sunshine having a cup of tea together, he said 'We be 'avin' some fowls Miss Mary next time you be home.'

'Fowls?' I asked, not understanding.

''ens Miss, so that Nancy can go on bakin' them cakes she does so well 'afore she gets called up,' Bullen chuckled, taking a big mouthful of cake that Nancy had served with our tea.

'Where will you put the hens?' I asked.

'Your father said he would remove the swing and see-saw, Miss Mary, as you be growing up, and can give 'em to Mrs Kay for when 'er nippers are bigger.'

That evening as I sat on the swing, the swing that I had sat on hundreds of times since I was a small child, I realised that the war was making everything different and even my beloved swing was going to have to make way for a hen run. A tear trickled down my cheek: I now understood that my childhood was over and it was time to grow up.

Very early the next morning I heard the telephone ring and after a couple of minutes I heard my mother yelling at me to get up straight away. I had no idea what was going on but could tell by her tone that something wasn't right and did as she asked. When she came into my room she told me that she was urgently needed at her first-aid post, as hundreds of wounded soldiers were being evacuated from the beaches of Dunkirk and that they needed to be taken to hospitals that had empty beds like the one she worked in. She explained that she would be busy all day, and that as my father wouldn't be back from the War Office until the evening I would have to fend for myself for the day. I told her that I would be fine, as I needed to swot up on my French verbs.

'Well, if you do go out anywhere,' my mother instructed, 'be sure to let Nancy know where you are, just in case there's an air raid.'

Nancy had worked for my family for eight years, so I had known her for half of my life and was very fond of her. She was due to marry her fiancé, who was in the Royal Navy, that summer and she had cried when she told my parents she would be leaving us after she was married and had promised to do her best to find a replacement, and swore that she'd write to us all often, as she thought of us all as her family. I got dressed and went to the kitchen to ask her if I could help her peel some potatoes but just as I got there the telephone rang.

'I'll get it!' I called out to Nancy. It was for my mother so I explained that she was out on an emergency call to drive the ambulance.

'Is that Mary who writes letters for the soldiers?' a lady's voice on the phone asked.

'Yes, that's me. Who is speaking please?'

'This is Betty Albright, dear. I did so hope your mother would be able to help us out at Woking station today, you see, we have dozens and dozens of our troops returning from Dunkirk in a very bad way and they all need refreshments and a cheery smile before going on to London or wherever. It's a bit of a shambles, I'm afraid to say, but there's nothing like tea and buns to cheer one up, and we need help urgently.'

I knew Lady Albright as she often came to the YMCA to supervise and check everything was going satisfactorily. She would always smile at me kindly and ask how I was doing with my letter writing for the troops.

'I could come and help instead, Lady Albright,' I suggested, 'I know how to serve tea and buns and I don't get tired like my mother does when standing on her feet, so I'll be just as useful, if not better!'

'Well dear, I don't know, your mother should really give you permission first but hold on a minute while I have a word with Mrs Brown.' I heard whispering at the other end of the telephone, but couldn't make out what was being said.

It was Mrs Brown came on the phone this time. 'Hello Mary. If you don't mind doing the washing-up and fetching and carrying things, so that one of us can keep an eye on you to make sure you're alright, then I'm sure your dear mother would have no objection to you helping out. Come as soon as possible and report to me in the car park where you'll see our YMCA van, and oh, please wear comfortable shoes, dear, as you'll be on your feet all morning.'

I felt excited to finally get a chance to do 'my bit' of war work at last. I ran upstairs and changed into my most comfortable shoes – my summer sandals – grabbed a cardigan, and then rushed into the kitchen to let Nancy know where I was going and that I didn't know what time I'd be back, but if I was late, not to worry.

When I arrived at the station car park, I propped-up my bicycle in the bike racks and went looking for Mrs Brown. When I found her she said, 'Go to Platform Three, dear, and report at the station café where the WVS has taken over.'

The cafe was like a madhouse: dirty trays everywhere, half-empty milk bottles and packets of sugar lumps, all mixed up with bags of buns waiting to be buttered and loaves of bread waiting to be made into sandwiches. No wonder Lady Albright had been desperate for extra help. Middle-aged women in green WVS uniforms were doing their best to restore order and I couldn't help admiring them. One of the ladies asked me to take over the washing-up, which I did happily.

Having restored a certain amount of order to the washing-up area, I then wiped the trays and put the teaspoons in the cups ready for the next train of returning soldiers to arrive. I filled all the kettles and put them back on the gas stove, but I didn't touch the urn, as I had no idea how to work it; I presumed it would need filling up though and hoped that one of the WVS ladies would see to it. Then I looked to see if there was anything to fill the sandwiches with and saw several tins of bully beef, spam and a rather sticky bottle of tomato chutney. I was rummaging about in a drawer for a tin opener and a bread knife when one of the WVS ladies entered the café and said in a rather loud voice, 'Good girl, you've done what I should have done half an hour ago!'

'Can I help you with the sandwiches?' I asked her.

'Yes you certainly can my dear,' the woman replied with a smile, 'We are going to need to make a mountain of them, as many of the soldiers won't have eaten anything for days.'

Five minutes later we were both spreading some rather soft and strange-looking butter onto the bread slices and putting some very thin slices of meat and a dollop of chutney between them to turn them into sandwiches.

'What's your name?' the woman asked me.

'Mary Arden,' I replied, 'what's yours?'

'Just call me Joy, ducky. Oh give me an 'and with the lid of this urn will you, luv?' she asked cheerfully, 'It's bleedin' 'eavy and hot!' We lifted the lid with a dishtowel and refilled the urn with the kettles of boiling water.

'Was it you that refilled the kettles love?' Joy asked and when I nodded she continued, 'Well you'd better fill 'em up again, as there's another train expected in five minutes and there will be many more after that.'

An hour later my back was already starting to ache so I was relieved when I was asked to go to Platform Three to collect any dirty cups and bring them back to wash-up before the next train arrived, as it gave me the chance to stretch my legs. On the way there, an empty porter's cart caught my eye and I thought it would be much quicker and easier if I piled all the dirty trays and crockery onto that but before I had time to do anything about it, another train arrived.

I could see half-naked men leaning out of the windows, their faces filthy and unshaven and one of them was staring into oblivion, as if he had been to hell and back. Perhaps he had, I thought. Another man's face was so dirty he looked like a chimney-sweep and another had blood running down the side of his cheek, but when they saw the WVS ladies coming with tea and buns, they all cheered and blew kisses, which brought tears to my eyes. I had no idea what these poor men must have gone through but realised that all of them must be in pain, whether physically or mentally, or both.

Then one of the men wolf whistled at me, which I found rather embarrassing so I looked away, but then when a couple of other soldiers whistled and waved at me I realised that this is what men did and there was no harm in it, so I might as well just smile and wave back. It didn't take long before I was running up and down the platform, shaking hands with the men and blowing kisses back.

After the train had pulled out of the station, I grabbed the cart I had spotted earlier and once I had piled the dirty crockery onto trays and carefully balanced them on the cart, I asked one of the Porters if he could help me push it over to the café, which he was more than happy to do.

An hour later everything was washed and stacked on clean trays ready for the next train. One of the WVS ladies then asked me to pop over to Sainsbury's to tell them that we needed some more milk, packets of sugar, butter or margarine.'

'Of course, I'd be happy to,' I said, 'but what's margarine?'

'It's imitation butter, dear, and it helps out with the rationing,' the WVS lady replied. So that was what the soft strange looking and odd tasting butter was I realised. Butter rationing had come into force in January, along with bacon and sugar, but as the war continued, other rations had followed and now included meat, cheese, eggs, milk, jam, canned fruit, tea, cereals and biscuits.

'I'm afraid I haven't brought any money with me, shall I ask them to put the things you've asked me to get on my mother's account?' I asked.

The WVS lady replied, 'That's very kind dear, but not necessary. Sainsbury's has offered to give us anything we need for the troops at no cost. Ask one of the errand boys to help you to carry it back, as the milk will be heavy for a little one like you, and it'll save time, we need you back here as quickly as possible.'

When I arrived at Sainsbury's, I asked for the manager and requested the items for the café. The order was promptly made up, and I was handed several packets of biscuits, as a treat for the soldiers. The manager wrote down the Woking branch telephone number and his name, and told me that if we needed any more supplies not to come back but to just ring up and someone would bring over whatever was required.

'That's very kind of you,' I said.

'Not at all. I'd do anything for those poor men after what they've been through,' the manger said quietly.

When I got back to the station, the trains were still coming and going thick and fast and we had to ring up Sainsbury's almost every hour for more supplies. Then some of the local people began to turn up with whatever spare provisions they had at home. Some brought biscuits, others sandwiches, cigarettes and sweets, and some brought warm jumpers and even a few blankets. Word must have spread that our brave soldiers were returning from Dunkirk and were passing through the station.

I noticed two soldiers standing close together, one was only wearing a pair of underpants and the other had a blanket around his shoulders; but both of them clutched their rifles as if they were the crown jewels. The porter told me that the reason so many of the soldiers were no longer wearing uniforms was that they had got them drenched when they had come off the beaches and been forced to wade through the sea to get on board the small vessels that were then able to transfer them to the bigger ships that had brought them home.

'One of the men told me that they had been under constant attack from machine gun fire and that the explosions had sent shrapnel everywhere,' the porter said solemnly, 'It must have been chaos… poor bastards,' As soon as the porter had gone I started to cry but managed to pull myself together before going back to the café.

An hour later Mrs Brown came and told me that as no more trains were due to arrive, I could go home. My feet felt as if they were on fire and I was exhausted. I didn't even have the strength to ride my bicycle home, so I walked to the nearest telephone box to ring home and ask if someone could come and collect me, but just as I was about to put the money in the slot, I saw my mother's car pull up near where I had left my bike.

As I staggered towards her she put her arm around me and said, 'Oh, my poor little lamb. Nancy told me you'd been here all day and I thought I'd come and bring you home. We'll leave your bike here and you can collect it tomorrow.'

When we got home my mother made me put my blistered feet in a washing-up bowl filled with warm water and added a few drops of disinfectant, which stung so much that I cried out with pain. My mother gave me a spoonful of brandy 'for medical purposes only' and when my father got home, he took one look at my feet and decided he would have a swig of brandy too!

'Why on earth did you wear your summer sandals?' he asked me.

'It was Lady Albright,' I replied, 'She told me to wear comfortable shoes and as I couldn't wear my school walking shoes with my summer dress, I thought sandals would be nice and cool. I didn't realise I'd be on my feet for so long.'

The following morning, my mother told me that Lady Albright had phoned her and was full of praise for what I had achieved. She then took me to the local cottage hospital to get her doctor to look at my sore feet.

A few days later, on the 4th June 1940, Winston Churchill made an uplifting speech on the radio telling everyone to be prepared to fight when the Germans invaded our country, which my father told me was expected any day now.

'We shall go on to the end, we shall fight in France, we shall fight on the seas and oceans, we shall fight with growing confidence and growing strength in the air, we shall defend our Island, whatever the cost may be, we shall fight on the beaches, we shall fight on the landing grounds, we shall fight in the fields and in the streets, we shall fight in the hills; we shall never surrender…'

On 10th June, Italy declared war with Britain and France. My father came back from the War Office that evening, and told us that after hearing this news, Churchill had apparently said, 'People who go to Italy to look at the ruins won't have to go as far as Naples and Pompeii again.'

I then had to go back to school to sit my exams for my School Certificate, so the rest of that term it was all work and very little play. When it was finally all over, we broke up for the summer holidays and I went home again.

Much to my delight, the next weekend Henry turned up at our house.

'So Goldilocks, I hear you've left school and you're off to Finishing School in the autumn, is that right?' he asked, as we walked around our garden.

'Yes, but I'd much rather do some proper war work than go to a Finishing School and have to do all this silly 'Coming Out' business,' I replied. 'To be honest, Henry, all this nonsense about taking one's rightful place in society seems very wrong when there is a war going on. It's really just an excuse to get me married off to a suitable man, but if I want to marry the milkman I shall do it!'

'Lucky milkman!' Henry teased and then leant over and kissed my cheek, whispering, 'I thoroughly agree with you by the way, except about the milkman of course. You should at least aim for the farmer that owns the cows!'

'Have you got a girlfriend?' I asked him.

'Dozens!' Henry said laughing.

'Well they are not invited to the party tonight!' I joked back.

My father had agreed for Peter to put on a dance in the Big Room that evening for his friends, and my parents would avoid the noise by going next door to play cards with the Derwents. William and I were allowed to go to the party, as long as we helped get it all ready. William helped Peter choose the music and I helped Nancy bake some vol-au-vent cases and then filled them with chicken and mushroom in a white sauce. We then fried lots of chipolata sausages, which William cut in half and spiked with wooden sticks. We picked lettuce leaves, tomatoes, cucumbers and cress from the garden to make a huge salad and it all looked absolutely delicious. We then covered the ping-pong table with a sheet and put the plates, cutlery and glasses on it.

After we had done everything we could to help, I went upstairs to choose something to wear. I couldn't make up my mind between a long dress, which I thought might be a bit too formal for this occasion and a short one, which might be too casual and make me look younger than I was, but then I remembered that my mother's sister, Aunt Beth, had given me a very pretty Hungarian-style three-quarter-length skirt and a white embroidered blouse that she'd found in a box of discarded theatrical costumes.

I felt quite grown up in my new outfit but my confidence soon evaporated, when I saw to my dismay that most of the other girls were wearing much prettier and more sophisticated dresses than mine. I looked more like a twelve year-old child than a girl of sixteen.

'Lovely dress Mary,' I heard a voice say behind me, 'just right for dancing.'

It was Henry, which boosted my confidence considerably. However, the feeling only lasted briefly, as I then saw him flirting with a very attractive girl who had just arrived.

It didn't take long before the party was in full swing. William kept himself busy changing the records, while I kept running to the pantry to wash endless dirty glasses, checking the next batch of vol-au-vents was ready and generally making myself useful. But after a while, I got fed up of being 'invisible' and decided that I would have to do something about it. I ran upstairs to my parent's bedroom and on my mother's dressing table I found a lipstick, so I dabbed some of the colour on my finger and used it to blush my cheeks and then patted the rest on my lips. I then put a little blue eyes shadow on my eyelids and brushed some mascara onto my lashes. Admiring myself in the mirror, I thought that I now looked far more grown up and in a final desperate attempt to be more sophisticated I squirted some of my mother's most expensive perfume behind each ear.

Feeling much better about myself, I then went back downstairs to join the others in the Big Room. Peter walked straight past me not recognizing that I was his little sister at all, which made me smile. Within a moment or two I was invited to dance, first with one boy and then another. Hmmm… I thought, if it only takes a bit of makeup to look older, I might start using it every day.

I was happily dancing with a boy called Malcolm when he became a little too friendly and tried to fondle one of my breasts. Shocked, I immediately pulled away, muttering something about checking the vol-au-vents, and ran out of the room. Henry must have seen what happened, as he followed me into the kitchen, took one look at my face and then pulling out his handkerchief, he dragged me, protesting, over to the sink.

'You don't need to put paint on your face to look pretty Mary,' he admonished, running the corner of his hanky under the tap, and then washing the lipstick off my face.

'I wasn't trying to look pretty!' I protested 'I just wanted to look older so someone would dance with me.'

Before I could say anything else, Henry took me in his arms and holding me close whispered, 'I will dance with you.' We then danced together in a slow sleepy waltz and I felt as though I was in heaven until the spell was suddenly broken by Agnes who called out, 'Sir Henry, you're needed urgently on the telephone. It's Mr Derwent for you.'

Henry went into the hall where the phone was and after listening for a moment he then mouthed to me, 'Pen. Paper.' I found both under the telephone table and gave them to him; he quickly wrote down a telephone number, only saying 'Yes… Yes I understand… thank you,' and then he hung up the phone.

'May I use your telephone Mary? It's urgent.' I told him that of course he could and then went into the drawing room to give him some privacy but overheard him say, 'Yes Sir, at once. It will take me a couple of hours, I have to pack and then drive back.' When he joined me in the drawing room he immediately explained what the call was about.

'Mary, I've been recalled urgently. Apparently German bombers are collecting over the sea and heading towards England. They're aiming for London. All fighter pilots are needed right away to stop them.'

'Are you frightened?' I asked him.

'A little, but this is what we've been training for over the last few months.' He then looked down at my face 'Mary, there is something I have been wanting to do all evening so I'd better do it now just in case I don't make it,' He then lifted up my chin and very gently and slowly put his lips on mine. I felt for one wonderful moment that I was floating but then crash-landed quickly, as Henry grabbed my hand and we went back into the Big Room together. He switched on the lights, which made everyone cover their eyes to cover the glare, and yelled at his RAF friends, 'Tally-Ho, the fox has been spotted! Come on chaps, action stations.'

Andrew was the first to react saying to Peter. 'I'd better return to base too, thanks for a smashing party,' I hurried into the hallway to give him a kiss goodbye and said, 'Take care dearest Andrew.'

'You too Mary, and please say goodbye to your parents for me,' he then walked out and everyone else began to collect their things and get ready to leave too. The party was over.

Having heard the reason why the party had ended so abruptly, my parents quickly returned home and told us that we must prepare for the worst, as the invasion might begin that very night. My father carefully checked all the blackout curtains were in place, as he was frightened that if the Germans flew over Woking that night, we would all be killed if any house lights were seen from the air. My mother didn't think it was a good idea making the entire family sleep in the air raid shelter and told us that we should all get a good night's rest in our own beds tonight before we faced 'heaven knows what'.

Thankfully we had a peaceful night and the next morning everything remained quiet until about eleven when we could see white vapour trails begin to appear in the cloudless sky. My father said that it was a dog-fight, but you could have been forgiven for thinking there was a rugby match going on instead, as we all started to yell to our boys in their Spitfires to 'Give 'em hell!'

These dogfights became a regular occurrence and every time I heard a Spitfire fly overhead I wondered whether it could be Henry.

On the 20th August 1940 we heard Winston Churchill give another of his wonderful speeches referring to the brave RAF pilots who were fighting what we now called the Battle of Britain.

'Never in the field of human conflict was so much owed by so many to so few. All hearts go out to the fighter pilots, whose brilliant actions we see with our own eyes day after day, but we must never forget that all the time, night after night, month after month, our bomber squadrons travel far into Germany, find their targets in the darkness by the highest navigational skill, aim their attacks, often under the heaviest fire, often with serious loss, with deliberate, careful discrimination, and inflict shattering blows upon the whole of the technical and war-making structure of the Nazi power.'

Less than a month later, the Battle of Britain was over but the Germans were now dropping bombs on London every night. Many houses were completely destroyed or damaged and there had been many civilian casualties already. I was very concerned for Jane, as her family lived there, so rang her as often as my mother would allow me to.

'Is it very scary Jane?' I asked my cousin.

'Yes it's terrifying but we have got used to it somehow, and if I am going to die I would rather be with my family when that happens,' she said bravely.

I suppose I felt much the same but that we were most probably much safer in Woking than our cousins were in London.

The entire country was now asked to raise money, so that more Spitfires could be built to win the war in the skies. We were asked to put on Bring-and-Buy sales, clear our attics of saleable goods, and do anything possible to raise money for the war effort.

Agnes proudly announced one day that she was now making spare parts for the Spitfires at 'the Munitions'.

'What parts?' William asked her.

'Your guess is as good as mine, Master William, but every bit helps.'

As the weeks went by, I made myself more and more busy, frantically doing my nurse's training and practising bandaging on William. I soon became an expert at making a head bandage, which didn't slip or fall over his eyes. I also volunteered for extra hours at the YMCA and, when I had time, I would go to Kay's house and clean for her, look after baby Richard or help her with the ironing. All this activity filled my days and made me feel that at least I was doing 'something' towards the war effort but I couldn't wait until I could become a real nurse.

One evening after we'd listened to the news on the wireless, William switched channels to a different wavelength and we heard a very strange voice with a rather comic upper class accent saying, 'Jairmany calling. Jairmany calling.'

'Is he trying to say Germany?' I said. The comical voice continued, telling the public how many British fighter planes had been shot down. The number was so high that we all looked at each other in disbelief.

'He's lying again, we haven't got that amount of planes to shoot down,' my father remarked.

'Who is he?' I asked.

'I'm not sure exactly Mary, as there seem to be a few different announcers trying to demoralise us this way but they have all been given the nickname Lord Haw-Haw at the War Office. We soon realised that he… or they… were telling lies, because we knew from our own broadcasts that we were winning the war in the skies. These broadcasts are designed simply to undermine the morale of the British people, but it won't work.'

A week later the Germans were still bombing London every night and the residents had to seek shelter in the underground stations or wherever they could find it. The bombing only seemed to make the British people more determined to fight on. Every now and then Winston Churchill would address the people on the wireless to rally everybody to be brave.

'These cruel, wanton, indiscriminate bombings of London are, of course, a part of Hitler's invasion plans. He hopes, by killing large numbers of civilians, and women and children, that he will terrorise and cow the people of this mighty imperial city, and make them a burden and anxiety to the Government… Little does he know the spirit of the British nation, or the tough fibre of the Londoners… who have been bred to value freedom far above their lives. This wicked man, the repository and embodiment of many forms of soul-destroying hatred, this monstrous product of former wrongs and shame, has now resolved to try to break our famous Island race by a process of indiscriminate slaughter and destruction. What he has done is to kindle a fire in British hearts, here and all over the world, which will glow long after all traces of the conflagration he has caused in London have been removed.'

A few days later, Andrew turned up at the Derwent's house on leave but as none of his cousins were at home, he spent a lot of time with my family instead. One afternoon I took him over to Kay's house, and while I did some ironing, he mowed their lawn. Over tea, Andrew asked whether Kay's husband, Jack, was in the Army. She explained that Jack had a slight heart murmur and hadn't passed his medical, so he'd been told to join the Fire Service instead. Recently, he and his fire crew had been helping put out the fires in London.

'Good Lord!' Andrew exclaimed. 'Surely that's far more strenuous than going into battle.'

'We try not to think about it,' Kay said quietly. 'At least he's doing something to help and he manages to get home most nights. When you have a very small child it is a great relief to have a man about. It really would be far worse if I didn't know exactly where he was.'

On the way back from Kay's, Andrew told me that as a Pathfinder pilot he would have to guide our bombers over Germany soon, 'We'll be getting our own back soon, you'll see.'

After Andrew had left to return to his squadron, I thought that I'd better start praying for him now, as well as for Henry.

The following week my mother and I went up to London to stay with Aunt Beth at her flat in Queen's Gate. My mother was particularly keen for me to go to Finishing School, so that I would then mix with other girls who would also be presented at court, but I knew that her long-term plan was that she hoped I would make friends with girls from aristocratic families, who would then invite me to the 'right kind' of parties and that I would eventually marry an 'eligible young man', preferably no lower than an Earl's son. It wasn't so much that my mother was a snob, but coming from a fairly aristocratic family herself, she wanted no less for her daughter.

After breakfast we went to meet Mrs Estrada or, as I soon discovered she preferred to be called, 'Signora'. Her interview technique was a mixture of firing questions at me one after the other, presumably to discover how well educated I was, and then talking to me in French and then German to see what my language skills were like. I must have passed her tests as she then turned to my mother and asked, 'Who will be sponsoring Mary when she is due to be presented at Queen Charlotte's Ball?' When my mother said the name of my sponsor, who was a most respected aristocrat, Signora's face was a picture to behold and I was immediately accepted as one of her fifteen pupils.

To celebrate, my mother then went completely mad buying me all sorts of new clothes, getting fashion advice from Aunt Beth as we went from shop to shop. When I tried on a deep plum coloured evening dress, I immediately adored it although I was bit concerned by the low neckline. 'What if I lean forward Mummy? People will see my bosoms, look!' Seeing that I now had a woman's bosoms rather than a young girl's, my mother said that she had better add 'new brassieres' to her list.

When we got home to Woking, my mother telephoned the baker, who to her delight was only too willing to hand over a few of his daughter's clothing coupons in exchange for six eggs a week for the next month, which was highly illegal but everyone was doing it. The following day we went to Guildford and bought two white petticoats, four pairs of white knickers with two Kestos brassieres, and some stockings. I was now kitted out for at least a year.

That evening Robert Derwent came to our house to ask me if I could help him do a spot of fire watching in the evenings between our two gardens, as apparently an air raid warden had been to their house to say that they were expecting fire bombs any time now, and until they had time to recruit older people, they were asking anyone available to keep watch. When I asked my father's permission he agreed that I could patrol the two gardens with Robert between six and eight in the evening, as long as we took refuge in the air raid shelter during an actual raid.

As it turned out it wasn't a German bomb but English shrapnel from two Ack-Ack guns that landed in the Derwent's orchard.

A couple of days later, when I was in the garden helping Bullen in the vegetable patch, I looked up and saw another dog-fight going on so cheered the British pilot hoping that he would shoot down the German plane. Then suddenly the two planes collided mid air and exploded in a huge fireball.

When I got over the initial shock I then realised with horror that I had just seen two young men die before my eyes. I ran back to the house sobbing hysterically. My father who was clipping a hedge at the time, looked up as I came hurtling towards him and assuming that I'd been hurt, dropped his shears and ran to meet me. When I told him what I'd just witnessed, he held me tight until I ran out of tears. 'War is a horrible thing, darling,' Daddy said quietly 'I'm afraid it'll get much worse before the end, and you'll just have to learn to be brave.'

'Well going to Finishing School isn't exactly going to win the war,' I said crossly.

'You're still very young, so just do what your mother wants for now; finish your education and enjoy yourself while you can, and then you can become a nurse or do whatever war work you want.'

'Will the war still be going on in a year's time?' I asked him.

'It could go on even longer than that,' my father replied sadly. 'The Germans have far more resources than we have and although we've won a temporary reprieve, we must be ready to face whatever they throw at us next.'

That night I rang Jane to see if it would be possible for her to come and spend a few days in Woking with me before I had to go to my Finishing School at the beginning of September, but she told me that her mother wasn't at all well, so she felt she couldn't leave the house.

'It looks as if we'll have to wait until Christmas to see each other then,' I said.

'Well, make sure you write to me then, you silly cow, at least once a week and tell me all about your snobby friends at Finishing School,' Jane giggled before hanging up.

The next day my mother and I took the train to Victoria station where we had arranged to meet the school matron, who would be escorting me and some of the other girls, to Eastbourne. After my mother had said a tearful farewell, I was introduced to some of the other girls, who didn't seem to be snobby at all, not even the very aristocratic looking girl in our group, who I was told was a Russian princess.

I was thankful that I had persuaded my mother to allow me to use one of the old worn out suitcases rather than borrow her best new leather one, as having old things, which were often a bit shabby, was considered the 'norm' for the class of girl that went to a Finishing School, whereas having new things was considered very nouveau riche. I thought that most of my new schoolmates would most probably have old luggage too and I was right, one even had a ghastly old case with broken clasps tied together with cord, but I did notice that it had a coronet stamped on its leather lid.

My Finishing School was a Queen Anne-period Manor house that Signora had rented in a small village about five miles outside Eastbourne. When we arrived, I was told that I would be sharing a room with a girl called Cherry. It didn't take long before I discovered that she was incredibly untidy and left everything either on the floor or on my bed.

We were supposed to be ready for breakfast by eight sharp, but Cherry never got out of bed until the last minute, and often turned up with only one stocking on, but it didn't seem to matter to Signora, as she rarely appeared before ten herself, and as there were no prefects or bossy mistresses at this school there was a very relaxed atmosphere.

The first lesson that Signora gave us was Italian, a subject that very few of us girls knew anything about. We all spoke a little French and German though, as it had been compulsory at all our previous schools. Our French teacher was an elderly woman who had recently retired, while an equally old Austrian refugee taught us German and also gave us piano lessons.

'Next term,' Signora warned us, 'I will speak to you in French or Italian depending on how I feel, so you'd better hurry up and become fluent in both languages.'

Fortunately I found Italian quite easy to learn, as it was such a pretty language and I didn't find the pronunciation strange, which was a big help. Signora would give us a lesson on famous Italian artists and sculptors and would thumb through a book of beautiful photographs to find pictures to illustrate what she had been talking about.

'Such a shame you 'gals' have to be here in England and not at my home in Florence,' Signora would sigh, 'If you were there you could see it all for yourselves and be able to 'breathe in' the art.'

Signora insisted that we make our own beds, and twice a week, dust the furniture. She also insisted that we clear the dining room table after each meal. How else, she explained, could we teach our own staff to do it properly after the war?

Signora insisted lunch was a silent meal, saying that fifteen girls talking at the same time while eating was not her 'cup of tea'. To ensure our silence she played classical music on the radiogram, which at the same time was a good way of teaching us to recognise different composers. Fortunately her taste in music was very similar to mine; she'd play French and Italian music most of the time, but occasionally if the mood took her, she would play a whole symphony by an English composer, such as Vaughan Williams or Elgar.

In the evenings after dinner we would often talk about the dreaded house parties that we would be expected to attend the following year, as part of our 'coming out' season. This light hearted 'chit chat' helped us blot out the reality of war until it was time for the nine o'clock evening news. We would then all listen to the radio and hear about the latest horrors that were going on in the war.

One day I received a letter from my mother telling me that a bomb had fallen in the garden next to Jane's house in St John's Wood. Thankfully nobody had been killed, as they had all taken shelter, but the water pipes had burst, the gas mains were damaged and the electricity was cut off, so now our cousins had rented a small house in the country near Ascot until the damage could be repaired. She included their new address, so I wrote a letter to Jane straight away to tell her how relieved I was to hear that she and her family were alive and asked her to write and tell me all about the awful experience that they must have gone through. I then told her how my life was slightly less scary than hers and that I was now being taught how to make soufflés and how to curtesy without falling over, which I hoped might make her laugh.

On one particularly rainy afternoon, I decided to teach some of the girls how to play Animal Snap, which involved making loud animal noises that made us all laugh in a most unseemly and unladylike manner. When Signora came into the room to see what could possibly be causing such a din, she asked whether we might consider spending our time doing something a bit more useful, like practising our languages, so we then played Animal Snap in French, German and Italian, which made more noise than ever!

Seeing that we enjoyed card games so much, Signora decided to employ Mr Strong, a retired professional Bridge player, to teach us all how to play the game. For the first month we all found the game very difficult to learn but gradually we improved and soon began to enjoy it. To my surprise, I discovered I was quite good at Bridge, which I knew would delight my mother and Aunt Beth, as they were both excellent players.

One evening Signora decided it was time to give us a pep talk on how well bred girls should and should not behave towards the opposite sex. On no account should a 'nice girl' ever allow a member of the opposite sex to touch her body in an intimate way before marriage. What she meant by 'intimate' was of course discussed in great detail by some of the girls later after lights out. Two of the older girls seemed to know a great deal about the subject, but they were not prepared to tell us younger girls quite how or where they gained this forbidden knowledge.

I wrote to Jane the following evening and told her about what the girls had discussed the night before, 'One of them told me that 'a man's willy no longer looks like a chipolata but grows into a huge German sausage!' I didn't believe a word of course.

The following day we were given the opportunity to go riding at a nearby stables, which I was very excited about, as I hadn't had a chance to ride a horse for ages. But before any of us were allowed out of the sawdust ring, the retired Captain who owned the horses and stables, made each of us girls prove that she could ride well enough to venture out into the lanes that led to the woods and fields. He really put us through our paces and in the end only five of us were good enough to continue. He told us that we could come twice a week if we wanted, which I was thrilled about as I enjoyed riding so much even though I hadn't ridden for over a year.

'Who taught you to ride Miss Arden?' the Captain asked me, 'You're a natural.'

'Thank you sir. My father did. He was in the Royal Horse Artillery during the last war,' I explained.

The following week the Captain told us that he was looking after a friend's Arab pony and had promised that he would only allow experienced riders to ride it, so I was flattered when he said that I could take it for a gallop along the cliff top overlooking the sea. All went well until suddenly something must have upset the horse and without any warning, he bolted. The only reason that I didn't fall off was because I had shortened the stirrup leathers a couple of notches before we had set out, which enabled me to be able to grip tighter with my knees. I also remembered the advice I had been given by my father, which was if a horse bolts let him have his head and he will then naturally slow down on his own. However, as this horse showed no signs of slowing down I wondered whether different rules applied to Arab horses.

Suddenly, a white fence appeared before me, blocking the way ahead. On the other side of it was a sheer drop to the beach below the cliffs. How on earth was I going to get this horse to stop in time? The only thing that I could think of was to talk to him in a calm voice and pat his neck gently.

'I think that's quite enough for one day, don't you?' I said out loud and to my surprise and relief the pony immediately responded and slowed down to a canter and then a trot.

'Couldn't have ridden the bastard better myself!' the Captain yelled, as he pulled his horse up next to mine. High praise indeed, especially from an ex-cavalry officer.

When I got back that evening, I decided to have a bath, one of the three baths per week we were allowed because of the fuel rationing. For the rest of the time we did regular strip washes. As I soaked in the lovely hot water, I started to sing 'Oh for the Wings of a Dove' until one of the girls knocked on the door and told me to 'stop warbling and get a move on', as it was her turn to have a bath.

Our singing teacher, Mrs Stern, had chosen a rather strange selection of music for us to learn: Ave Maria by Gounod, some Hebridean songs and a few arias from Italian operas. She was a superb pianist and sometimes I would ask her to play the piano just so that I could sit and listen to her.

One day when I arrived for a lesson, there was a rather tall and distinguished looking gentleman with Mrs Stern. She told me that he wanted to hear me sing. He sat quietly in the corner of the room while she got me to sing for her in Italian and then in French. When I finished singing, the man said, 'You're a lucky girl. You have a large range from mezzo-soprano to soprano. After the war, I suggest you get your voice trained.' I thanked him and then after he left the room, I asked my teacher who the man was, but she just tapped her nose conspiratorially and gave me a mischievous smile. When I told the other girls what had happened later that evening, one of them thought he must have been someone famous and another said that perhaps he was her secret lover. How exciting! I couldn't wait to tell Jane all about it.

When we broke up for the holidays, I was happy to discover that my cousins were going to spend Christmas with us, but when they arrived I was sad to see how pale and thin Aunt Edith had become. My mother told me that she was dying so we all had to make a special effort to make this Christmas as happy as possible.

The few days that we spent together the Christmas of 1940 seemed a bit unreal; there just wasn't the same carefree spirit as the previous years. No one mentioned Aunt Edith's illness and yet everyone could hear her coughing. My mother told us that we'd better not put on our usual play this year, as it would be too noisy for Aunt Edith so we played card games as quietly as we could instead.

It had been an awful year with Western Europe falling to the Germans, and thousands of British servicemen had been killed and wounded. Many had also been captured. The good news was that there seemed to be a break in the bombing over Christmas but we were all too aware that this respite might only last a few days.

The lull came to an abrupt end on the evening of the 29th December when St Paul's Cathedral got struck by a number of bombs. Luckily the one incendiary bomb that hit the dome, fell outwards rather than inwards, or the damage could have been much worse.

When the time came for my cousins to leave, I felt desperately sad knowing that I might never see Aunt Edith again.

CHAPTER 3

1941

At the end of the first week of 1941, I decided to go to London to spend some time with Aunt Beth. Unbeknown to me, she had arranged for her nephew, Marcus, to join us for supper one evening while I was there. When I opened the front door I hardly recognised my cousin, as he had grown a lot since I had last seen him three years ago and was no longer the little boy I once knew. He was obviously just as surprised to see that I was no longer a schoolgirl and was becoming a woman. Marcus was going to qualify as a doctor soon and sounded very grown up to me. Once we had caught up on everything we had been doing since we had last set eyes on each other he laughed and said, 'You do know why Aunt Beth's invited me round don't you Mary? Its' because your mother is already looking for people to escort you to the Coming-out Balls, and she thinks I would make a respectable chaperone.'

I made it clear that I thought it was all a waste of time and that I'd much rather be nursing wounded soldiers. He was pleased that I wanted to work in the same profession as him but warned me that it wouldn't be easy. 'It's all very well changing dressings and wiping a sweating brow or two, but when it's broken bones and blood, or missing limbs, it's not the same thing at all. I've seen some horrific injuries from all the bombings recently. Are you sure that you really want to be a nurse? It's going to be damn hard work and very bloody.'

His question made me stop and think. I wasn't so sure anymore.

'Anyway, you still have plenty of time to think about what you want to do,' and then he added, 'In the meantime you can invite me to your coming out parties, as there'll be lots of free dinners and weekend house parties, which I wouldn't get a chance to go to unless I was your escort!'

We spent a happy evening catching up on old times and it was like having an extra brother to talk to, and better in some ways as I felt that I could talk to Marcus about things that I never would have with Peter and William.

A week later, I was back at the Manor for the new term. The temperature had dropped below zero. The news announcer warned that one of the coldest winters on record was predicted, and he was right. We woke up the following morning to see that all the trees were now encased in ice, and hanging from each branch and every twig was a stiff white icicle. They looked breathtakingly beautiful but I was quite happy to appreciate them from indoors.

All the pipes had frozen solid, and unfortunately because most of the plumbers had been called up to serve their country, the pipes remained frozen for days. Signora announced at breakfast that 'Instead of afternoon walks, I'd like you all to wrap up warmly, go into the woods with sacks, and collect fallen twigs and branches so that we can keep the fires going, which will help our coal ration last longer.' These afternoon collections became known as 'Twigging'.

The ground was so hard that there was no question of doing anymore riding, as it would be far too dangerous for the horses, and the roads were so slippery, that there was no prospect of driving into Eastbourne for singing lessons either, so Signora decided to take advantage of her girls being held captive indoors and gave us one to one lessons on how to use a typewriter, and how to do shorthand so that we would be able to join one of the ministries, where these skills would be required. A number of us said we would prefer to join the WRNS or even the WAAFS, and two of the girls said that they would prefer to become VADs. My roommate, Cherry, said she would like to become a FANY, as a lot of her sister's friends had already joined and were meeting some gorgeous men! This of course set us all off giggling, but only after Signora had left the room.

In the first week of the Easter holidays, after kissing all her family goodnight, Aunt Edith fell asleep and never woke up. Bridget, Jane and their brother Tim came to stay with us for a few days after the funeral. It was a very sad time. My father wrote to Signora to tell her about the death of his sister and asked her if she would accept Jane at the school, after she'd passed her School Certificate. Signora agreed to think about it.

Once Jane and her siblings had gone back to London, life for my family carried on as usual. My mother was still doing her bit for the war effort, driving an ambulance five days a week, and my father was travelling up to London to the War office every day.

The sound of German bombers flying overhead at night made sleep almost impossible. We would all listen solemnly to the wireless at nine o'clock each night to hear the latest news about the casualties from the air raids, aircraft that had been shot down, ships that had been sunk with all hands on board, and the loss of our troops in North Africa. I was finding it hard to keep my spirits up, after listening to so much horrific news night after night, so my mother took me to one side and gave me some good advice, 'The best thing to do my dear, is to keep busy,' so that is exactly what I did for the rest of the holidays.

I worked several hours a week at the Woking Cottage Hospital, carrying trays and learning how to make beds with neat hospital corners, and when the nurses were busy I was entrusted with changing dressings. Matron had told the other nurses that I was not to empty bedpans, which I was very grateful for as it would have meant wiping the men's bottoms, which I didn't fancy doing one bit, but that I could take a bottle to a man and empty it when required, but apart from being excused bedpan duty, I worked every bit as hard as all the trained nurses. When I wasn't working, I spent my time off either looking after my brother William, playing tennis, going for bike rides or helping Kay with her baby son, Richard, who I would take for walks in his pram to give her a break. Then one evening, Andrew suddenly turned up at out house out of the blue.

'Its horribly quiet at the Derwents, as the boys are all away,' Andrew remarked, 'so I was wondering if you felt like going to the flicks with me tonight, my treat?'

The film was a Whodunit and neither of us guessed who the villain was, which made us laugh and say what useless detectives we would make. On the way home Andrew told me that he hadn't been sleeping very well.

'Does being a Pathfinder worry you?' I asked, thinking that might be the reason he was having problems.

'To be honest, it's been Goddamn terrifying these last few months,' he admitted.

'The thing is that when you get caught in the Germans' searchlights you're blinded for a few moments and as it takes time for your eyes to adapt back to the dark again, you're very vulnerable and that's the time you are in the most danger.'

'Couldn't someone else do it instead of you, after you've done this turn?' I asked hopefully.

'There's a limit on the length of time we're expected to do this work, but if I funk it too soon, some other poor chap will have to take my place, and I don't think that's fair,' Andrew explained. 'But I'll have a month's leave in September, thank God.'

'Good, well it will be my turn to treat you to the flicks next time,' I promised, as he kissed my cheek goodbye.

But I wasn't able to keep my promise, as two nights later, Andrew's plane, according to Mrs Derwent who phoned my mother with the terrible news, was caught in the enemy's searchlights and blown to pieces.

I was so shocked I couldn't speak. My mother took my hand in hers and told me that I must try to hold on to the thought that Andrew had been doing what he had wanted to do: to serve his country and help win the war.

I whispered over and over again, 'It can't be true. There must have been a mistake. He can't be dead. I was only talking to him the day before yesterday.' I put my hand up to my cheek: 'I can still feel where he kissed me goodbye.'

The following day, my mother and I went round to the Derwents house, and let ourselves in, as we usually did. We found Mr Derwent sitting alone in the drawing room. His eyes were red rimmed from crying. All I could do was to put my arms around him and give him a hug.

'Will there be some sort of funeral?' my mother asked.

'I am not sure,' Mr Derwent replied. 'His parents are in Singapore somewhere. I'm doing my best to contact them but it's not easy. This has really been the boy's home on and off over the last few years, and to be honest he's more like one of our sons than he's ever been to his own parents,' he confided, his voice breaking.

I couldn't bear it any more. I ran out of the Derwent's house, back through the gap in the fence and up the garden to the air raid shelter. I sat there on the steps and sobbed.

About an hour later, Peter appeared looking very worried and said that he'd been hunting for me for ages. He was quite distressed to find me weeping so miserably and did his best to make me feel better.

There wasn't a funeral for Andrew in the end, as there was no body to bury and his parents were unable to come back because of the war. However, the Derwents arranged a private memorial service for their family only.

A few days later Signora rang my mother to tell her that she had had to relocate the school, as she'd been informed that as the Germans were now using long-range guns to fire across the English Channel, so the south coast was no longer safe enough for us. She said that she had already found the perfect house in Northamptonshire, near Oundle, and that it was called 'The Hall'. She also agreed that Jane could come and join me there, but not until the autumn.

When I arrived at The Hall for the summer term, there were a few new girls who all seemed very friendly. Apart from continuing all our usual lessons we were also taught how to skin a rabbit, pluck a hen and degut fish, all quite disgusting tasks that made one or two of the girls retch. Making sponge cakes and soufflés was a lot more fun.

One day, I noticed a letter on the hall table addressed to me but I didn't recognize the handwriting. When I opened the envelope and started to read it I realised with surprise that it was from Henry. He had written to tell me that he was now temporarily based near Oundle not far from my Finishing School, so if I saw any planes flying over The Hall, it would most probably be his squadron, so if I was outside when they came over, I was to wave like mad, and he might see me. If he did, he would waggle his wings, and then I would know which plane he was in.

Sure enough, a few days later when we were 'Twigging' in the woods once again, we suddenly heard the sound of several planes approaching. I shouted to my friends to come and wave at the planes with me. The planes, which I could see were Spitfires, flew very low over The Hall and then disappeared out of view. I thought we had missed them but then the planes reappeared, but this time seemed to be heading straight towards us.

'It's Henry, It's Henry!' I screamed, waving with both hands and nearly falling backwards in the process. One of the girls then mimicked me, which made all the other girls laugh and soon there were five young girls all screaming at the sky 'It's Henry, It's Henry!'

To my delight, one of the planes separated from the others and waggled its wings before then quickly re-joining the others. It really was Henry, and he had seen me. I was so happy that I burst into tears. One of the girls said that she had been so frightened by how low they had flown that she'd nearly wet herself. I thought that this was so funny that later that evening I wrote to Henry to tell him. He wrote back a week later to tell me that he had got one of the ground crew to paint a pair of knickers on the side of his Spitfire! Naughty Henry!

On Saturday 10th May, Westminster Abbey, the Houses of Parliament and the British Museum were all damaged after London was bombed very heavily, and there were many casualties. It was the worst night of The Blitz, so far and I was very worried about Jane and her family but knew that my parents would let me know if anything awful had happened to them or to Aunt Beth.

My mother wrote to me a few days later to reassure me that everyone was all right and that I should concentrate on my studies. As I was writing back to my parents, Signora came into the room and told us that she had decided that it would be a good idea for her gals to host a fund-raising party at the school, to which she would invite local dignitaries, our parents, and possibly some sixth-form students and their parents from Oundle School.

'We'll put on a dancing display and set up some stalls,' Signora announced. 'And I want all of you to think up other ways to entertain the guests. Maybe we could even do a Morse code demonstration?'

The week before the big event, Signora came to watch our dance rehearsal. We had made our own costumes out of some slightly transparent material, which we thought made us look like very glamorous Greek nymphs, but Signora told us that she could see our white knickers through the material, and suggested that to rectify that problem perhaps we could wear 'little slips' instead, which would match the colour of our dresses. She told us that she would get the local seamstress to make them for us, which she did, but took the word 'little' too literally, delivering slips that were barely decent! But we wore them anyway, and they caught many a stray male eye, far more than our white knickers would ever have done. Signora was delighted when we received an encore and, I think, had been pleasantly surprised at how good our dancing was. The stalls were a great success too: with customers buying up all our bottled fruits, jams and cakes, knitted articles and other donated goods. Signora was delighted by the funds that had been raised. A week later we broke up for the summer holidays.

My brother, Peter, was at home and told me that he had just got off the phone with Henry, who had mentioned that his cousin was staying in his house in London, recovering from a nasty leg wound. Apparently he worked for Intelligence and was supposed to be overseas somewhere, and not in England, which is why I had to keep it secret and not say a word to anyone. I thought that if its supposed to be a secret surely Peter shouldn't be telling me about it, so why was he? I then found out.

'Henry needs your help, Mary,' Peter continued, 'He will explain the situation to us when we arrive. The thing is, he needs someone with a bit of nursing experience to take care of his cousin, warming up the meals that his cook will prepare beforehand, and Henry thought you might be willing to do both.'

I was amazed that Henry had thought of me and immediately agreed to help. Peter then explained that Henry's cousin would be transferred to Henry's father's home in the country to convalesce, but not until the end of the week, as he was in too much pain to be moved at the moment. Apparently there would be an army nurse who would come daily to do dressings and administer medicine, but it might be necessary for me to change bandages now and again, if the wound seeped too badly.

'We won't be on our own very much, Mary,' my brother assured me, 'Henry says that his sister, Lavinia, will pop in most afternoons, and that he'll do his best to help out by keeping his cousin amused in the evenings, when he isn't on flying duty.'

My mother was a bit taken aback, when Peter told her that he and I had been invited up to London to stay with one of his chums, Hamish, and attend some concerts with him at the National Gallery. It was a lie of course, but one that my brother thought my parents would believe. In fact, she not only believed him but also thought it was a good idea, in principle anyway. She then fired him with questions such as, 'Will there be another woman in the house where you are going to stay?' and 'Will you stay with your sister all the time, and if you can't, who will look after her?' Peter reassured her, and I had to admit that his string of lies was really quite masterful. He then told her that we would be visiting Aunt Beth several times during the week too, and so my mother finally agreed to let me go with him.

When we arrived at Waterloo station, Peter bought a copy of the evening paper, so that we could check the programme for the lunchtime concerts at the National Gallery, which would enable us to convince our mother that we had attended them. We then took a taxi to Redcliffe Gardens to see Aunt Beth's new flat, and when we arrived I handed her the eggs and flowers that my mother had asked me to give her. We didn't stay very long, but promised to come back the following day.

'It's essential to see quite a lot of Aunt Beth to make an alibi,' Peter reminded me, as we hailed another taxi to take us to Henry's father's house near Grosvenor Square.

As we approached the house we were both still laughing at Aunt Beth's request for us to try and find her a 'spiv,' whom she explained was a street-vendor that sold knickers-elastic, cottons and other haberdashery, illegally on the streets. If we saw one, she pleaded, would we please buy anything that might be of use for sewing, 'Look near Barker's in Kensington, or near Harrods,' she suggested, 'as they usually stand around the street corners near there, out of sight of the police.'

'It's bad enough that our mother barters the stuff we grow in the garden to get extra sugar and stuff,' Peter chuckled, 'without Aunt Beth asking us to break the law by buying things on the black market. We'll have a look tomorrow, though, before we book the concert tickets and see what we can find.'

Henry had told Peter that his father's batman, Mr Tom, would be in the house between three-thirty and five that afternoon, so we weren't surprised to find the elderly man waiting to let us in.

Mr Tom reiterated how grateful all the family were that we'd agreed to come, and told us that he'd do his best to help us all he could. Peter then asked Mr Tom how Henry's cousin was doing.

'The Colonel will do better now that you are here I am sure,' Mr Tom replied.

I hadn't realised that my patient was a Colonel and wondered whether I should call him Sir. Mr Tom carried my case up to Lavinia's bedroom and asked how our journey had been, 'You and Lady Lavinia will be sharing, Miss Mary, but her Ladyship is seldom at home these days, as she has her own flat now,' he informed me.

'Now let me show you the Colonel's bathroom, Miss Mary,' he said kindly.

We walked along the landing to the Colonel's bathroom, and as we entered, Mr Tom pointed to a pee-bottle, that was half-covered with a towel, next to a bedpan.

'Leave everything personal to me, except in an emergency,' he said and then turning to Peter asked, 'perhaps if the Colonel needs help in the night you will do the honours.?' Peter nodded and said that of course he would.

As soon as Mr Tom had left I went to meet the Colonel. As soon as I opened the door to his room I recognised the smell of infected flesh at once. Determined not be put off, I entered with a cheerful smile: I'd come to help, and help I would, so I strode forward with my hand outstretched: 'Hello Colonel, I'm Mary Arden, Henry's friend, and I'm very glad to meet you.'

'And I'm bloody glad to see you too my girl!' he said smiling. 'Excuse my French, but its damn boring sitting here all day with no one to talk to.'

I guessed that the Colonel must be a similar age to my father, and immediately felt at ease with him. He smiled and beckoned to me to come nearer, 'Thank you for coming; now do tell me something about yourself.'

I told him a little about my family and how we had known Henry since he was a boy and then offered to make him a cup of tea, 'Tea?' he said in disgust and shook his head saying, 'No thank you my dear, its gut-rotting stuff, but I'll love you forever if you can find where that damn boy, Henry, has hidden his whisky bottle.'

Trying not to laugh and putting on my primmest nurse's face, I then told him firmly 'You shouldn't drink whisky while taking pain killers, it's one of the first things I learned when training as a nurse!'

'To hell with that young lady,' he replied 'if you want to play Florence Nightingale then you need to learn that at least half a glass of whisky does far more good for a suffering patient than any amount of pain killers.' He smiled at me again, a rather naughty smile this time, and said that as I'd told him to call me Mary I must call him George, as saying Colonel every time I spoke to him was far too formal when handing him his piss-bottle, 'Which I need badly now, by the way,' he added.

Having seen to George's needs, I now checked the nurse's chart at the bottom of the bed, which had a note at the end that made me grin; 'only two drams of whisky with water a day,' it read. I fetched a fresh glass of water and gave it to my patient with two painkillers. The Colonel winced as he moved.

'I guessed it must hurt,' I said sympathetically, 'Let me get you some tea and then I'll put on a clean dressing that should ease the pain. All the soldiers in the hospital where I help out say that a clean dressing makes all the difference. It will hurt a bit when I take the old dressing off, but I'll try my very best to be gentle, and if you're good, I'll give you a glass of whisky later.' George smiled and blew me a kiss. He really was very charming

I found a spare pillow in the airing cupboard and put on a clean pillowcase and then went back into George's room to put it behind his head. I wasn't happy about his position, and felt instinctively that I must try to sit him up a little more to prevent his lungs from filling with fluid. The Colonel was a tall man, over six foot I thought, and realising that he would be pretty heavy by the look of him, I decided that I'd better wait for Henry to arrive so that he and Peter could lift him between them.

When I went downstairs I found Peter in the drawing room surrounded by three different piles of records, which he'd got out ready to play. He was delighted with them all saying that they were excellent recordings. I asked him if he'd carry the tea tray upstairs for me, as it looked too heavy for me.

'Of course,' he replied, 'that's what I'm here for. You're the nurse and I'm the kitchen maid!' We both laughed. It was good to have my brother with me.

I went to the larder and poked about in the various cake tins hoping to find some biscuits to have with our tea. What I found instead was a delicious-looking sponge cake with jam in the middle and a sprinkling of icing sugar on the top. I went back into the kitchen, wondering whether I should try to find some fine bone-china teacups, or just use the cups and saucers in the kitchen cupboard. 'Better use the kitchen stuff,' I mumbled to myself, 'I'm bound to break something if it's precious.'

Peter helped me take the trays upstairs to the Colonel's room. Pain or no pain, George managed to wolf down a very large slice of Mrs Flower's cake and drink two cups of tea with three spoons of sugar in each one. The Colonel obviously had a sweet tooth, I thought. After tea I told George it was time to change his dressing.

'Nurse usually gives me an injection first,' he said, 'I suppose you couldn't do that too?' I shook my head and said that I hadn't done that yet and if I attempted it I'd probably get the needle stuck in his bum!

Forgetting his wounded leg for a moment, George nearly fell out of bed as he was laughing so much. Then he fell back with a groan, his leg was obviously very sore.

'Would you mind if I played the piano quietly while you see to George's wounds?' my brother asked, 'If I hear him bellowing in pain, I'll put the loud pedal down and then the neighbours won't hear,' he joked.

Mr Tom had pointed out an old bucket by the back door, which he said I could put the soiled dressings in, so I went down to get it and then noticed a pile of newspapers beside it. I brought up the bucket and several sheets of the paper, and then went back into the bathroom and scrubbed my hands once more, doing my best to do everything that I'd been taught to avoid spreading infection. I then collected a pile of bath towels, filled a washbowl with hot water and some disinfectant in case the old dressing had stuck to the wound and I needed to soak it off, and then carefully folded the sheet back from George's feet and laid it over his stomach. The smell that met me almost made me retch, but somehow I managed not to.

'Would it be alright to have that whisky now?' poor George begged, as he clutched at the bedclothes in dreaded anticipation of what I was about to do. I went into the hall and leant over the banisters to call out, 'Peter, will you rummage about in the sideboard to see if you can find a bottle of whisky please?' and then added, 'oh and a jug of water too.'

'Bring the damn whisky and to hell with the water!' George called out loudly. When the whisky finally arrived George drank it down in one gulp before I had a chance to add any water to it.

The dressing was stuck, so I gently dribbled a bit of water over the wound until I was able to remove it without doing too much damage. The wound needed cleaning, which I thought I should leave to the army nurse to do, as all I'd been told to do was to change the dressing and put on a clean bandage, but I hoped she'd give him a morphine injection before she started.

With the clean lint in place, I then began to bandage from the foot up. The bandaging done, the Colonel begged to have another whisky. I handed the bottle to him and before I could stop him, he'd poured most of what was left into his glass.

'Well, it was almost empty,' he said wickedly, 'You did that dressing better than the army nurse.'

At that moment, I heard footsteps on the landing, and thinking it was Peter, called out that I wouldn't be a minute. But it was Henry's voice that called back 'It's me,' and my heart pounded with joy.

'Phew!' Henry said as he walked into the room, 'What a stink! His leg smells worse than his farts!' I didn't know whether to be shocked or to laugh. George retorted, 'And your socks smell of sweat and horse shit.'

I left the two men to swop insults and laughter and went downstairs to see what we could have for supper. About ten minutes later, Henry joined me in the kitchen and I asked him whether he would prefer fish pie or cottage pie.

'Let's have the fish pie this evening because by tomorrow it could smell as bad as my cousin's leg!'

'I was trying to do my best not to notice the smell, but now I'm not sure that I will be able to eat anything after what you've just said!'

'Thank you for coming Mary,' Henry then said sincerely. I then asked him how the flying was going. He looked very serious for a moment and then said quietly, 'Frightening. I have to fly very low to drop off and pick up my passengers in France,' Suddenly a bellowing voice from above broke the spell: 'More whisky nurse!'

While Henry went to look for another whisky bottle, I busied myself in the kitchen, reading very carefully the notes on how long and at what temperature to cook the fish pie. Then I managed to find a saucepan for the peas and a Pyrex dish in the larder with halved tomatoes already arranged in the bottom with little knobs of butter on the top and an instruction: 'a quarter of an hour on the bottom shelf'.

'Easy-peasy!' I muttered to myself.

After supper Peter offered to do the washing-up, but when he got to the saucepans, Henry insisted that Peter left them soaking overnight in the sink for Mrs Flower to do in the morning. 'Enough is enough,' he said cheerfully.

When the army nurse arrived later that evening she was pleasantly surprised to see her patient looking comfortable and sitting upright, but not amused when George blew kisses to her and appeared to be a little drunk. She raised an eyebrow and looked at me. I just shrugged. I'd done my best.

Later that evening when Henry was upstairs talking to George, I found out from Peter that the Colonel had been involved in a covert operation blowing up bridges and trains in France, and had caught a bullet in his leg while being chased by a group of German soldiers. The Resistance fighters had looked after him, but it had been several days before he'd been able to fly back to England.

When Henry came down and joined us in the drawing room, Peter decided to go upstairs to have a bath, and suddenly we were alone, 'Thank you for all your help Mary,' he said, and then lent forward and gently kissed me on my lips, placing a hand over my breast for a brief moment. I trembled, as he then pulled me closer and started to kiss my neck. He then quickly pulled away and said in a serious tone, 'Don't worry if I don't turn up for a couple of days, it just depends on the weather; it's my turn to be on duty, you see?' And then he was gone.

I came back down to earth with bump as I heard George bellow, 'Mary, I need my bottle – now!'

After I'd settled the Colonel down for the night, I went to bed and started to read the book that I had brought with me, but I didn't read a word, all I could think about was how nice it had been to feel Henry's soft lips on my neck.

When Peter came in to say goodnight, he said, 'Tomorrow we'll go to our first concert. Goodnight Mary, see you in the morning.'

By the time I was bathed and dressed the following morning, Mrs Flower, Henry's cook, was already in the kitchen preparing breakfast for the Colonel. I noticed that she had laid a table in the small breakfast room, which I hadn't even known was there before then. I thanked Mrs Flower for preparing our evening meal and for leaving the helpful notes.

'What did you put in the fish pie?' I asked, 'It was delicious.'

'When anyone stays at the family home in London, his Lordship sends a fresh salmon, when it's in season that is, and he always puts in a bit extra for me to take home – a trout or a pheasant – to help out with the rations. He's a lovely man, just like his son,' she said smiling.

Just as Peter and I were about to leave for the National Gallery concert, Lavinia, turned up. I was surprised at how unlike her brother she was, and guessed she must take after their French mother. She was exceptionally attractive with an elegant figure, dark hair and blue eyes. After greeting one another, Lavinia told us what a 'couple of bricks' we were for coming to the rescue at the last minute.

My brother and I spent the next two days, going to concerts, dropping in on Aunt Beth, and looking after the Colonel. We had our routine down to a tee.

When Henry eventually came back from his latest mission, I noticed that he looked extremely strained and tired, but decided to say nothing, except to suggest that he should lie down on his bed and have a rest while I cooked dinner for us all.

He agreed and I watched him as he walked slowly up the stairs. Guessing that he'd need at least an hour, I delayed cooking the evening meal, and went upstairs to check on my patient, who was dozing. I then had a quick peek into the half-closed door of Henry's bedroom and saw that he was sleeping like a baby too, his jacket and trousers thrown onto a chair and his shirt on the floor.

I then heard George call out, 'What's for dinner tonight, Mary? I'm starving!' so I walked into his room and said, 'That's a good sign you must really be getting better. I'm cooking pork chops tonight.'

'With apple sauce and gravy I hope?'

'The apple sauce is no problem, as apples aren't rationed, but as for gravy—' I thought for a moment and then said jokingly, 'I wonder if Sir Henry has anything as common as Bisto in his cupboard?'

'He has, believe it or not!' Henry said as he came into the room, 'Actually Sir Henry loves his Bisto, but Mrs Flower disapproves of using artificial ingredients. Why don't I come down and help you make it?'

We found the Bisto and a pan and then stood at the stove together giggling like school children making the gravy, adding the juices from the pan the chops had been cooked in, just as I'd been taught at my Finishing School.

After supper, Peter went straight to bed and Henry offered to help me with the dishes. As I stood at the sink, he stood close behind me and started to outline my figure with his hands, so I told him to behave himself or he'd have to do all the washing-up himself. But instead, he kissed first one ear, and then the other, which felt like a bolt of lightning going through my body.

'Goodnight Goldilocks!' he said with a radiant smile and then took himself off to bed. After he'd left, it took me a good five minutes to pull myself together, and I felt so flustered that I washed-up everything all over again.

The following morning, the Colonel was picked up very early by the people he must have been working with. I hugged George goodbye at the back door. He thanked me profusely for all that I'd done for him, and then whispered, 'You're very fond of Henry, aren't you?' When I nodded he said, 'I'm very glad about that.' Then he kissed me on both cheeks and hobbled towards the car.

When Peter and I got back to Woking later that evening, my parents wanted to know all about our visit. I was aware that I had to be very careful, and not let the cat out of the bag, by mentioning anything connected with the Colonel. Peter described the concerts we'd been to, and I told Mummy about taking Aunt Beth to a matinee and about the 'spiv' I'd bought haberdashery from at the corner of Hans Crescent. She was happy to know that we had fun in London, and to my relief, didn't ask any more questions.

After we'd been back home for a week or so, I began to wonder whether it had all been a dream, until one morning a letter arrived, addressed to me. It was from Lavinia, inviting me to have lunch with her at her club in London.

'Who is Lady Lavinia Neville?' my mother asked, having obviously not connected the name Neville with Henry. Not knowing quite how to answer, I was grateful that Peter was there; he butted in quickly, 'Oh Henry popped in at Hamish's one evening and introduced Mary to his sister, Lavinia.'

'Yes that's right Mummy,' I continued, 'And we got on so well; she said that if I was to be in London any time soon, she'd give me some advice about how to behave when I'm presented at court.'

My mother accepted Lavinia's invitation on my behalf and even insisted on lending me one of her handbags, and then told me that if I went I would have to wear a hat.

Not wanting me to arrive at the club with dusty shoes, she had given me enough money for a taxi from the station to the club, but as we approached Berkeley Square, I felt myself becoming increasingly nervous, as I'd never been to a London club before. I hoped that I wouldn't make an embarrassing mistake, such as spilling something down my dress or some other equally gauche faux pas.

Lavinia was waiting just inside the club reception hall to meet me and greeted me with a kiss on my cheek. She then introduced me to her fiancé, Major Crown McFarlane, whom I thought was rather handsome.

'Call me Arthur please,' he said, smiling.

I noticed that Lavinia wasn't wearing a hat because she was in uniform, one I'd never seen before, although it was khaki and obviously had something to do with one of the women's services.

When we went through to the dining room, I looked at the menu but couldn't decide what to choose and wondered whether we were going to have three courses or two. To avoid making a decision and guessing that Arthur, like Henry, was a member of the club, I asked him if he would order for me.

The food was excellent, and I became much more relaxed, as I sipped the lovely white wine, that I thought went with the second course of chicken in a tomato and onion sauce.

Arthur and Lavinia talked about the latest Neville family news – much of which was very amusing – and said how difficult it was proving to make plans for their wedding, 'We're both so busy,' Lavinia said taking her fiancé's hand across the table, 'I would like a proper white wedding, if possible, but that requires calling the bans, and if Arthur is suddenly sent overseas we might have to get a special licence instead. Have you met anyone yet that you would like to marry?' Lavinia asked casually.

'No!' I said rather too quickly and immediately started blushing, turning my head away for a moment to hide my embarrassment. I could not believe my eyes when they fell upon the figure of Henry standing in the doorway, scanning the dining room for our table, and when he spotted me, he grinned from ear to ear and started to walk towards us.

The look of joy on my still blushing face must have given away my real feelings for her brother immediately, and when I turned back to look at Lavinia, she smiled at me knowingly and squeezed my hand.

'Hello gorgeous!' he said to me as he pulled one of my curls, before bending down to kiss his sister and shake hands with Arthur, 'Ah, good, I see you're about to serve the pudding, I'll have everything on the menu. I'm starving!'

For nearly an hour, I listened with interest to Arthur, Henry and Lavinia discussing plans for the following week. Lavinia then looked at her watch, 'Gosh, it's half-past two, we must go. We are both expected back at the War Office before three. What do you two plan to do this afternoon?' she asked, looking first at me and then at Henry.

Henry replied that as he had the afternoon free, perhaps I'd like to go for a walk in Green Park, and he'd then take me to tea at the Ritz. I thought to myself, that is exactly what I would love to do too.

Lavinia gave me a big hug as she left and said how lovely it was to be getting to know me better. She said that we must keep in touch and when I was next staying with my aunt in London, we must meet up again.

While Henry and I were walking through the park, I asked him to tell me something about his childhood, so he told me how he used to spend a lot of time with his mother in France during the holidays, and how much he missed her. He went silent for a while so I said, 'We don't have to go to the Ritz Henry. We could just keep walking.'

'And talking,' he said looking at me with a smile.

'Yes, that would be nice,' I replied.

Henry bent down and began to pick daisies, which he then threaded into a chain while we walked… and talked, and when it was big enough he put it on my head.

'There, my little princess,' he said, 'you're as fresh as this daisy chain, and one day I hope to—.'

I never did hear what he had hoped to do for me, or give me, because just at that very second, an air-raid siren wailed; and it was deafeningly loud.

Henry quickly grabbed my hand and we ran towards Green Park tube station to take shelter underground. Weaving amongst the other people hurrying for shelter, Henry found us a safe place against a wall on the lower level, and then stood facing me to protect me with his body, leaning his hands against the wall so that the crowd wouldn't crush me. As the area filled up with more and more people, Henry was pushed even closer to me, but I didn't mind, and laid my cheek against the jacket of his uniform.

A resounding crash made the tube station shake, and I was really scared but then I felt Henry's reassuring lips on my forehead and I felt quite safe.

When the All Clear siren sounded there was a mad rush for the stairs, 'We'll wait until everyone else leaves before we move,' Henry said, grinning down at me with a mischievous smile. 'It's rather nice standing like this, isn't it little one?' and then looking at his watch he exclaimed, 'Goodness, it's nearly five; we must have been down here for nearly an hour! I've got to get back to my squadron, and you my pretty young lass must get back home, so we will have to make a date for tea at the Ritz another time.'

Henry guided me up to the entrance and we both stood for a moment taking deep breaths of fresh air. We could hear the sound of a nearby fire engine bell, and then two ambulances with their emergency lights on and sirens blaring, passed us at a speed.

'Thank God it wasn't us,' Henry said quietly. Then suddenly seeing a taxi, he put his fingers to his mouth and whistled for it to stop. Looking down at me he chuckled, 'See how common I can be? But don't tell my father, he'd have a fit.'

'I can't tell your father about your bad behaviour,' I grinned, as he sat down next to me in the taxi 'because I don't know where he lives.'

'Really?' Henry asked, looking surprised. 'I thought you must have heard that my family lives in a dusty castle.'

'A real castle? Like in a fairy tale?' I asked naively.

'No a real castle like not in a fairy tale but in real life!' he laughed.

'Stop teasing me, I don't believe you,' I told him, but he assured me that it was true.

'I promise I'll take you there when I have a longer leave.'

We took the taxi to Waterloo and when we arrived at the station, Henry escorted me to my platform and then apologised, saying that he was sorry but he must leave me now otherwise he would be late for his briefing. He removed his cap, bent down, and gave me a kiss on my lips.

'Goodbye Goldilocks,' he whispered in my ear and then he saluted me, turned around, and disappeared into the crowd.

For the next few days, all I seemed capable of doing was wandering about the house in an absent-minded way with a dreamy look in my eyes.

'You have a soppy look on your face. Are you all right Mary?' William asked me one day, which made me laugh and make an effort to pull myself together.

About a week before William was due to go back to school, we were both asked if we would clean out the hen house, as everybody else was busy. It was a disgusting job that we both hated doing, but it had to be done. I changed into what William called my 'chicken shit' trousers, which although they had been washed since I had last had to do this nasty job, still looked stained and shabby.

William and I were halfway through cleaning out the henhouse, scooping all the old straw and sawdust into buckets, when I suddenly heard Henry's voice calling my name. I almost jumped out of my skin, but when I turned around there was nobody there. I told myself that it must just have been wishful thinking because I so badly wanted him to be there.

We'd almost completed the job, when once again I heard Henry's voice calling my name, but this time the voice came from the direction of the rose garden, a few yards away from the chicken run.

'Henry's here!' I said excitedly. 'I'll just go and fetch him.'

William looked at me strangely and asked, 'How do you know he's here?'

'He just called my name, didn't you hear him?'

'No,' William replied, 'You're just making it up so you don't have to carry these disgusting pails of poo to the compost heap.'

'I'm not,' I insisted. 'I promise you, I did hear him call me, I'm going to go and look for him.'

I hurried down towards the air raid shelter bank, but there was no sign of Henry anywhere. I decided I'd better go through the hole in the hedge to see if he had gone back to the Derwent's house. I expected to see Henry's MG in the drive, but it wasn't there.

As I reached the front door I slowed down and opened it very quietly. I could hear sobs coming from inside the house and as I turned the handle, the sobs grew louder. When I went in, I saw Mrs Derwent in tears.

'Oh Aunt Nora, is it one of the boys?' I asked now starting to cry too.

She shook her head, and then in an almost inaudible voice, she whispered, 'No Mary, it's Henry. He's missing, presumed dead.'

I wanted to scream but all I could manage was, 'It's not possible, I just heard him calling me,' But when Edward and Robert came into the room and I saw the grief-stricken look on their faces I knew that it must be true and my knees gave way and the room began to whirl around me.

They carried me into the sitting room, laid me on the sofa and wrapped a rug around me. Edward, now openly crying too, put his arms around me and rocked me as if I was a baby. After a few minutes, I became aware that I should try and pull myself together, all the Derwent family, had known Henry since he was eight, and their anguish must have been ten times worse than mine.

'Oh Aunt Nora,' I cried, 'I know he loved you all dearly. He told me often that he loved coming here.'

'You've got to be brave Mary, just as we have to be,' Edward insisted. 'This kind of thing happens in war, especially with the sort of work Henry was doing. I'm very proud of him; he was a very brave man. But what made you come here just now? No one else knows that Henry is missing yet except us.'

'I thought I heard him calling me; in fact I was sure he did, twice. That's why I came here.'

Robert then put his hand on my shoulder and said kindly, 'It must have been your imagination.'

'If he is missing in action, could there be a chance he is still alive?' I asked desperately.

'We'll have to wait for two or three days, and hopefully one of the radio operators will be in contact with London and be able to explain what happened, but it sounds as though his plane was destroyed on the ground while he was picking up some of our chaps.'

Then Edward looked deep into my eyes and told me gently, 'I know it sounds awful to say this, but if he has been captured, he would be better off dead than a prisoner of the Germans as he'll be treated as a spy.' Then he put his head in his hands and wept.

Robert said, 'Henry told us that they had all been issued with cyanide, and if forced to, he would have to swallow his pill.'

'You mean commit suicide!' I gasped.

Seeing my horror, Robert quickly tried to reassure me, 'Not to save himself but to stop him from betraying the lives of others under torture. That isn't suicide, that's giving up your life for your friends.'

The next minute, all of us were clinging on to each other, trying desperately to give each other the courage to face the truth.

My legs felt like lead, as I walked home, forcing one leg to move in front of the other. When I reached our garden I climbed up the bank to the air-raid shelter, went inside and shut the door, and then sobbed as if my heart would break.

William, meanwhile, had got fed up thinking I'd just decided not to return to finish the job, because I was enjoying myself with Henry at the Derwent's. In fact, he'd become so angry that he was on his way to the hole in the hedge to come and get me, but when he'd passed the air raid shelter, he'd heard sobs coming from inside. When he opened the door and saw me lying on one of the bunks with my knees curled up to my chin sobbing uncontrollably, he ran to the house to fetch our mother.

'What is it my little one?' my mother asked me while stroking my hair, as she had done when I was little and had hurt myself. I told her that Henry was missing in action, presumed dead.

She told me to come with her and once we were back in our house, she called the family doctor and asked him if he could come and give me something to make me sleep. When the doctor arrived, he sat with me until the drug he'd administered had done its job. I slept right through until the morning, and woke to the sight of Agnes pulling my curtains. When she turned around to look at me, I could see tears running down her cheeks. 'You loved him, didn't you?' she whispered. 'I saw it on your face when you came home last week. He'll take that with him, dear, and be blessed.'

Later that morning I went to find somewhere quiet, where I could be on my own and think for a while. Just as I was about to sit on the bench in the rose garden, I heard a fluttering sound, and looking up, I saw a flock of white doves. It made me think of Henry's squadron flying over the Hall. I watched them disappear over the Derwent's house and then turn around and fly back over our house. It was almost as though they were flying in the shape of an arrow. I had heard of doves flying in flocks before but never in formation. I wondered why they were doing it today of all days. I so wanted this to be a sign from Henry that he wasn't suffering, but deep down I knew that this was just wishful thinking.

A single dove then landed on the edge of the birdbath and it had something white in its beak. I crept very slowly towards it, hoping that I wouldn't frighten it away, but when the dove saw me, it flew off, dropping whatever it had been holding into the birdbath. I peered into the bowl to see what it had dropped, and to my amazement, there was a solitary daisy floating on the water.

I stared at the daisy in disbelief and then lifted it out, holding it in my opened palm. I was convinced that Henry was trying to send me a message to say goodbye and I burst into tears. I knew then that Henry must be dead and that I would never see him again. I took the daisy carefully back to the house and then placed it in my diary between the blotting paper next to the daisy chain that Henry had given me in Green Park, and whispered, 'I will never forget you Henry'.

CHAPTER 4

1941-42

It took me a long time, to get over Henry's death, and to stop thinking about him all the time. To help my grieving process, I made sure that I filled each day and worked even harder at the Cottage hospital than ever before, looking after wounded soldiers and scrubbing hospital floors during the week, and then travelling to London at the weekends to buy new clothes for the 'coming out' season, which now held little interest for me. Seeing my reflection in a shop mirror one day, all dressed up in a very expensive evening gown, I suddenly felt very ashamed, especially after seeing all the damage that had been caused by the bombing, and the idea of attending cocktail parties and dances now felt totally repugnant to me.

After supper that evening, I told my father what was on my mind, and that I didn't want to go back to do my last term at Finishing School or be presented at court. He said nothing for a moment, and then got up from his chair and kissed me on the top of my head, saying that he knew exactly how I felt, and that he was proud of me for feeling the way I did. But then he explained to me that there was a practical side that I had to consider too, as if I didn't go back next term, he would still have to pay the expensive school fees, as there was a term's notice in the agreement, so it would mean him losing a lot of money. He then said that another thing I had to consider was how terribly disappointed it would make my mother. In the end, I felt that I really had no choice but to return to my Finishing School for one more term, which was very frustrating, as I had now set my heart on doing some proper war work.

I was still in this frame of mind when I received a call from Miss Bowden, one of the YMCA helpers, who I had assisted at the station during the Dunkirk evacuation. She told me that she had been asked to take her refreshments' van to a few isolated outposts, where some of the Ack-Ack gun emplacements were situated, near Guildford, and that she really needed some help and as I had been so useful before, could I help her out again for a few days.

'It'll only be serving tea and buns to about ten men,' she explained, 'so it won't be hard work, and I was wondering if you would consider singing a few songs before we leave, dear, to cheer them up, and perhaps the boys might join in too? I could easily put my gramophone and a few records in the back of the van.'

I then mentioned our recent school fete and how some of my school friends and I had danced in the open-air with balloons, and how well our performance had been received.

'That sounds marvellous! Would you be willing to do the same thing for the troops here? Miss Bowden asked, 'Poor boys, it must be terribly boring for them in these isolated outposts, and it would cheer them up no end, I'm sure, dear. I have a large selection of records. What type of music would be appropriate for your dance?'

'Do you have any of Debussy's music?'

'I have *Clair de Lune*,' Miss Bowden said happily. 'Would that be suitable for a balloon dance?'

The following day, Miss Bowden picked me up in her van and we drove to one of the outposts, not far from Guildford, and while the dozen or so men drank their tea and ate their buns, she handed out free pens, paper and razors to them from a box that she had brought with her. While she did that, I examined the grass around the Ack-Ack posts. I noticed that there were quite a lot of thistles and stones, so decided that I would have to wear my dancing slippers rather than dance barefoot as I preferred. When it was time for my dance, I asked Miss Bowden where I could change into my costume and she told me to do it in the back of the van. As I got dressed, I imagined that she had a vision of me skipping about with a balloon in a pretty cotton dress, so she would be in for a shock when she saw my Greek-style dress and matching slip!

When I came out of the van she took one look at me and said, 'Oh, that does look pretty, but won't you get terribly cold?'

As soon as the music started, I began to dance and the young soldiers sat on the ground watching my every move. Every now and then, I felt a breeze waft around my legs, which blew the light material of my dress well above my knees. It felt lovely and cool, so I continued dancing not realising the effect I was having on my male audience. When the music ended there was a chorus of wolf-whistles and loud applause and shouts of 'encore!' and 'do it again luv!'

Miss Bowden quickly suggested that we should have a singsong, which we did for the next half hour and I must admit that the men all had very hearty voices and appeared much happier than when we had first arrived. As I looked at the men's smiling faces, I remembered that it was the duty of the YMCA to bring comfort to the troops and thought that we had certainly done that today. In fact comfort, and joy!

The next day we went to the Purbright practice gun range, and when we arrived there were far more men there than Miss Bowden had anticipated, including a couple of subalterns, who she told me had no right to be there.

'Word must have got out!' she said, appearing rather put out, 'I just hope we've got enough milk and buns for this lot,' she muttered as I helped her make the tea. But she need not have worried, as whatever the van lacked in supplies, the small kitchen in one of the army huts seemed ready and happy to provide.

Before we set off the following day, Miss Bowden told me that she'd better put two extra bottles of milk in the van, so that if there were more men than expected at the next outpost, we would be able to cope. It was just as well that she had, as when we arrived, there were over thirty men waiting for us, 'This is most strange,' she said. 'I was assured that there'd only be about ten men at each outpost.'

We dutifully served the tea and buns and Miss Bowden distributed the free goods, and then it was time for me to dance, which went just as well as before and received the same wolf whistles and applause at the end.

It was Lady Albright who eventually put a stop to the impromptu entertainment; Colonel Travers, who was in charge of all the troops at the outposts, had got wind of our 'tea run' and telephoned her to thank her very much for so thoughtfully sending Miss Bowden's refreshments' van, but then asked her if she was aware that a half-naked nymph was flittering across the fields entertaining his troops and emptying nearly all of the more isolated gun posts? And furthermore, did she realise that this was leaving the field telephones unmanned, and that should a call come through warning of an air raid heaven only knows what would happen, as no one was available to man the stations.

Lady Albright, unsurprisingly, was very concerned. That very evening she made a point of telephoning Miss Bowden to ask her why her young helper was dancing in the fields at all. Singsongs were fine she said, but whose idea had it been to skip about scantily clad with a balloon? Did she realise how inappropriate this was? Miss Bowden said that I had offered to do it, and added quickly that the men had really enjoyed it, 'You should have seen their smiles, Lady Albright, I've never seen so many happy faces; they must have enjoyed it, Mary was asked to do three encores!'

It was soon time to go back to Finishing School, and although I was still annoyed at having to go back, at least, Jane would be with me now. I had already talked to her about what we did each day and told her the names of all the girls, so when she did finally arrive she didn't feel like a new girl for long, and soon made friends with the other girls. Although we shared a bedroom and chatted most nights until we went to sleep, we didn't live in each other's pockets. Jane was in different classes to me, so we mainly met up at meal times.

Signora suggested that this term it would be a good idea if we learned how to use the sewing machine, as she wanted us to try something a little more complicated than black-out curtains, which all of us had made already. I eventually managed to make myself a satin petticoat – although by the time it was finished, I'd grown another size up and it was too small for me – and the sewing teacher showed me how to put in a zip at the side so that it would fit. I was very proud of my zip petticoat, but had to admit that I was most probably better at knitting.

I was immensely proud of the little jacket and leggings that I'd knitted for Kay's son in pretty turquoise wool. I then decided to knit my father a pair of socks for Christmas. I'd unpicked one of the socks twice, but it still turned out slightly longer than the other, which I hoped he wouldn't notice. Jane's knitting efforts resulted in the longest and most colourful scarf that I had ever seen, as she had used everyone else's leftover balls of wool to make it. Signora called it 'Joseph's scarf of many colours!'

We were then all asked to make bed covers for the local children's orphanage, not from knitted squares, but out of scraps of material. I wrote to Aunt Beth to ask her advice on colour schemes, what type of materials to use, and whether she'd be so kind as to look out for any old blankets or clothes in her local second-hand shop for me. I had no spare clothing coupons to buy new material, and knowing that all the coupons would be needed next year for my coming out clothes, Aunt Beth wrote back with the brilliant idea of looking for old cardigans and jumpers, where the elbows had gone through but the backs of the garments were still as good as new.

The waistcoat I'd made from some coffee-coloured material Aunt Beth had given me, and onto which I embroidered flowers, was quite a success, at least superficially, so long as you didn't look at the underside. It had quite neat blanket stitches around the edges on the outside, but inside, it was a terrible tangle of knots, threads and different coloured wool, which no one saw. Even Signora turned a blind eye to its failures when we exhibited our efforts at the end of the term. As she said goodbye to me, she told me that she appreciated that I'd done my best. Having not wanted to come back at the beginning of term, I was now sad to leave and wept as I hugged her for the last time.

Nothing could have prepared us for what we saw when we arrived in London. We had all been talking excitedly about what we were going to do in the holidays, but as the train slowly pulled into Kings Cross station, a guard ran along the platform and told us to remain in our seats until a porter came to escort us.

When he finally came to get us he said, 'Last night a huge bomb demolished a block of flats nearby. It's a miracle the station 'ain't been closed, but some 'ow we 'as to keep goin'. Can't give in to those ruddy Germans can we?'

We decided to share a taxi to Jane's house and then I could ring my parents to let them know what had happened and that I'd be getting a later train back to Woking than planned. Once we were in the taxi and on our way to St John's Wood, we could see that the streets around the station were badly damaged; we drove past bombed-out buildings and burst water mains that gushed like rivers down the streets; and there were firemen and air-raid wardens everywhere. When we eventually arrived at Jane's house, and explained what had happened her father paid the taxi driver and then said that he'd ring my parents for me to explain why I'd been delayed.

Over the next two weeks, with my cousin Marcus as my chaperone, we attended three country house parties, all of which were in freezing cold homes, two rather smart cocktail parties and my first Ball. It felt very strange, almost as if everyone was pretending the war wasn't happening. But it wasn't that people didn't care, it was just that 'Carrying On' had now become a British virtue.

It was getting more and more difficult to find different outfits for me to wear for all the 'coming out' functions I was attending, as clothing coupons were so precious, so Aunt Beth suggested that we buy second-hand clothes from a couple of actresses, who lived in the flat above hers. I was a bit surprised at the selection when I saw what was on offer, because the girls' unwanted clothes were actually old costumes that they no longer needed at the theatre, so it looked as though my only choices would be to attend my next Ball as a fairy queen or an ugly sister!

'Don't worry Mary!' Aunt Beth said seeing the look on my face, 'the next time you come to stay with me they will look very different.'

A week later I went to stay with her again and when she showed me what she had been able to do with the old costumes I could hardly believe my eyes at the transformation.

'Aunt Beth, you are a genius!' I exclaimed, giving her a big hug. 'How on earth have you managed to change those old fancy dress clothes into such beautiful gowns?'

'I used my magic wand!' she giggled waving a needle and thread at me, 'go and try them on, so that I can make the final alterations to make sure they fit you properly.'

As Aunt Beth started to stick pins all over the material, and in me, she described how she'd managed to redesign the garments, turning some of the worn cloth inside out, so it looked as good as new, and had then added some new trimmings and buttons, 'which of course, are all my own 'exclusive' designs!'

She had not only made me four new dresses, but had also dyed two pairs of evening shoes to match. Now that I had a whole new wardrobe, I realised that I was actually starting to enjoy 'coming out', and for the first time I began to feel quite grown up. This was partly due to my recently acquired habit of smoking. My first attempt with a cigarette had resulted in a coughing fit, followed by a few hours of feeling that I might be sick at any minute. But determined to fit in with the older crowd, I managed to overcome my initial adverse reaction to nicotine and persevered.

When I told my father that I had taken up smoking, he gave me a small ladies' silver cigarette case to use, saying that it might look a bit more sophisticated than my cardboard packet of fags!

I couldn't wait to show it off, so at the next cocktail party I casually took it out of my handbag, flipped open the case, and slowly removed a cigarette, placing it between my lips, like I'd seen the film stars do. My new rather over-confident behaviour then vanished in a puff of smoke, or rather the lack of one, because I had forgotten to bring any matches. Suddenly, a very handsome young guard's officer appeared at my side and asked if he could light my cigarette for me.

'Thank you, I forgot to bring my matches,' I said as he produced a lighter and lit my cigarette for me.

'Sorry, I'm not very sophisticated,' I confessed. 'To be honest, I have only just started smoking.'

'In that case, it sounds as if I am here just in time to offer my services as your advisor and protector for the evening: Captain Michael Kensingham at your service,' he declared gallantly.

I smiled, amused by his warm manner. He then proceeded to offer me some very useful tips, 'A lady should never light her own cigarette in public, smoke in the street, or at the dinner table.'

I thought that this was very funny, and immediately felt comfortable being with this lovely man.

'Who was that?' Marcus asked me, after Michael had left to talk to some of his friends.

'Don't worry Marcus, I am still missing Henry terribly, so the thought of being any more than just a friend with that man or anyone else for that matter, is just not on my mind.'

When it was time to leave, Michael came over to say goodbye, so I introduced him to Marcus and within a minute the two of them were chatting away like old friends.

A week later a parcel arrived for me, and inside I found a small jade cigarette holder and a packet of exotic black and gold Balkan Sobrani cigarettes. There was also a note that read, 'I enjoyed meeting you and hope that these small gifts will make you feel a bit more sophisticated! Warmest regards, Michael.'

I could hardly wait to try one of the strange looking cigarettes, so later that evening after dinner in the drawing room with my parents, I took out one of the Sobranis from the silver case my father had given me, and after placing it in my jade holder, lit it. The room was immediately engulfed with strange smelling smoke and I started coughing uncontrollably – these cigarettes were much stronger than any I had ever smoked before. My parents looked up at me, and then at each other and then burst out laughing.

A week later, Marcus and I attended another ball, and after we had been there for about an hour I spotted a rather striking looking man wearing a smart uniform, whose face looked familiar but I couldn't place him. I thought that he looked like a pirate, or at least like the ones I had seen in Pantomimes, like Captain Hook. I then noticed that he was looking at me with a slightly amused smile on his face. He then turned to Marcus, who was standing near him, whispered something in his ear, and after my cousin had whispered something back to him, they both looked straight at me and laughed. What on earth could they find so funny? Marcus and Captain Hook then started walking straight towards me.

'You remember Charles Edham, don't you, Mary?' Marcus said. 'He was the one that taught us both to sail when we were on holiday in Norfolk.'

So that's why his face had looked so familiar. It was hardly surprising that I didn't recognise him now, as it had been so many years since I had last seen him, but now happy memories of sailing on the Broads came flooding back and I remembered how fond I had been of him when I was a little girl.

'Hello, Mary,' Charles said looking deep into my eyes. 'I have been looking forward to seeing you again.'

I suddenly found myself tongue-tied. The way he was looking at me made me feel weak at the knees.

'Have you got your dance card with you?' Charles asked me. I nodded and took the card out of my evening bag.

'Good, well put me down for the supper dance and the last dance,' he insisted, before giving me one last smile and moving on to join some of his friends.

'Well that was kind of him,' Marcus said, 'after all those are the two most important dances of the evening.'

It wasn't until I wrote Charles' name on my dance card that I realised that I hadn't said one word to him yet. He must have thought me very rude, or hopefully just very shy.

'What did you think of Charles?' Marcus asked breaking my trance.

'I think he looks like a pirate,' I whispered in reply.

Marcus looked at me as if he couldn't believe his ears, and then laughed out loud, 'I don't believe it! Charles Edham is the best-looking man in the room, most of the girls here are openly drooling over him, and my dear cousin thinks he looks like a pirate, that's priceless!'

It was another hour before I had my first dance with Charles and I was surprised at how good he was, so when it was over I complimented him on his footwork.

'Are you saying that I'm not too bad for someone as ancient as me?' he said laughing and then asked, 'How old are you now, Mary?'

'None of your Bee's Wax!' I replied laughing back, 'what about you?'

'A hundred and one,' Charles answered, grinning, but thought that he must be about eight years older than me.

He then told me that as his regiment was on duty in London at the moment, he wondered if we could meet up with one another while I was in town for the Season. I said yes as long as he was willing to escort me to a dance or two if Marcus wasn't available and I needed a partner.

'Of course I would love to escort you, Mary,' Charles replied gallantly, 'but first of all let's go to see a film or a play together one evening.'

'I'd love to do that,' I replied, and then asked, 'Did you ever meet my Aunt Beth?'

Charles nodded, 'Yes,' he replied, 'I did. She taught me how to play golf!'

'I will give you her address and telephone number, as I am staying with her, so that way we can keep in touch.'

'That would be fun,' Charles said and then excused himself, as he went off to dance with one of the other girls who had his name on her dance card. I felt a pang of jealousy, which was ridiculous but I now wanted him all to myself.

Three dances later, the supper dance was called. It was a slow waltz and I felt Charles's arms close tightly around me. Although I had danced with many other young men, at the various parties and Balls that I had attended over the past few weeks, I had never allowed them to hold me as close as Charles was now doing. I felt myself responding to him in a way that I hadn't thought possible since Henry had died, and although I still missed him very much, I realised that perhaps it was time to let him go and allow someone else into my heart.

When the dance was over, we all flowed out to help ourselves to the buffet supper set out in the conservatory and dining room.

'Hungry?' Charles asked.

'Starving' I replied, grinning, 'especially after all that dancing.'

A grand buffet such as the one set out that evening was a real treat and something that, probably, few of us had enjoyed since war had been declared. I greedily helped myself to whatever I thought looked appetising, which was almost everything, and put one of each on my plate and then some on Charles's plate.

For half an hour, Charles and I sat at a table chatting and enjoying the delicious savoury food, but when the puddings were served, he only took a plate of rather boring vanilla ice-cream, while I chose a plate of extremely rich and creamy chocolate éclairs and some meringues. Charles, realising his mistake immediately, started helping himself from my plate.

'Hey, get your own!' I exclaimed.

'I am!' he replied, and so not to be outdone, I helped myself to some of his ice cream, which made us both giggle like school children. Marcus then joined us and said, 'You two seem to be getting on well,' Yes, we are I realised happily.

As the night progressed, the light in the ballroom was getting dimmer and dimmer. I knew that some of the men liked to take advantage of the darkness to steal a kiss or two from their dance partners, and I suddenly felt a surge of panic. But I need not have worried, because instead of trying to kiss me when the last dance was over, Charles pushed me gently away and said, 'I think that I am either too tall or you are too short for us to be able to kiss one another without one of us falling over and making a spectacle of ourselves!'

To my surprise, I was rather disappointed, and blurted out, 'Perhaps I could stand on a chair?'

'That sounds like a splendid idea' Charles responded, laughing, 'but maybe we should save that experiment for another time when there are no spectators around?'

Suddenly everyone started clapping. The Ball was now over and it was time for the guests to leave. Marcus and I said goodbye to Charles and we took a taxi back to Aunt Beth's. I smiled the whole way home.

That Christmas I decided to spend more time with my little brother William, as it was just going to be the two of us at home this year. After Peter had finished his studies at Cambridge, he had been head-hunted and was now training as an Intelligence Officer.

I decided to make home-made Christmas presents this year, and William told me he planned to 'renovate' a few old things as his gifts, which was typically practical of him. And rationing was now more important than ever. My mother told me that we were very lucky to have our own hens, as everyone else could only buy three eggs a month. Having a big vegetable patch was also a blessing, so when it was William or my turn to dig up potatoes or cabbages we never complained.

Earlier that month, the Japanese had bombed Pearl Harbour, which as awful as it must have been, now meant that the Americans were with us, and there was a feeling that the war had turned. My father told us that he thought the Allied forces would win eventually, but at great cost, which was an awful thought.

Christmas Day was the quietest we had had for many years, but we managed to have an enjoyable day. William and I had made paper-chains and hung them around the house and we had collected enough holly to not only deck our halls but the neighbours as well. In the evening, I called Jane and we spoke for over an hour about all the parties I had attended. I could tell that she was a bit envious.

On Boxing Day I went over to Kay's and spent time playing with Richard, while she did the ironing. As she was now pregnant with her second child, she appreciated any help I could give her. As her husband Jack was away helping putting out fires wherever he and his team were needed, she didn't see him as much as she liked, so I tried to spend as much time as I could spare with her. I was also helping out in the hospital most days, which was such a contrast to all the elegant parties I had recently been going to.

On the morning of my birthday, Agnes called me to the phone and whispered, 'There's a Lord Edham on the phone for you Miss Mary.'

For a moment I had to think who Lord Edham was, and then realised it must be Charles. I had forgotten that he had a title.

'Happy Birthday Mary!' he exclaimed.

'How did you know?' I asked him.

'When I rang Marcus for your parents number, he told me,' he explained.

He told me that he had spent Christmas with his parents in Gloucestershire and then asked me if I would like to come up for a few days after New Year, to meet his family and go riding with him. I said that I would love to, but that I would have to ask my parents permission.

When my father came home that evening, I asked him if I could take Charles up on his offer. My mother was a bit concerned, as she knew that Charles was quite a bit older than me, but my father came up with a good idea and said that he would ring Uncle Arthur and Aunt Felicity, our other cousins who lived in Gloucestershire, to ask them if they would be willing to put me up for a few days, as they lived quite near Charles's family estate and knew them very well. After he put the phone down, he said that they were happy to have me for as long as I wanted, so I rang Charles back to let him know I was going to come. He sounded very pleased.

When I arrived at Cheltenham Spa station, I wondered if I'd recognise my Uncle and Aunt, as I hadn't seen them since I was a little girl. They had two sons who were roughly the same age as Charles, but I knew they had both been called up, one in the Army, the other in the Navy, so I wouldn't get to see them this time.

However, my Uncle or Aunt were not there to meet me but had sent their elderly chauffeur, Briggs to collect me. When we arrived at the house, he dropped me at the front door and a very young maid greeted me; and as she bobbed a curtsey she said, 'Lady Felicity is waiting for you in the small drawing room, Miss Mary.'

I was very glad to see a log fire burning brightly in the fireplace in the hall; at least the old house felt warm, remembering how bitterly cold some of the old houses had been that I'd stayed in for long weekends during the season.

The minute I saw Uncle Arthur, I recognised his warm smile and happy memories came flooding back. He opened his arms and gave me a big hug, while Aunt Felicity just stood and stared at me. 'My goodness how you've grown.'

'I hope so, I was only ten when I last saw you both!' I said.

After we'd had some tea, Aunt Felicity explained that their former Nanny, who they now called Nurse, would help me choose the most suitable clothes to wear each day as they no longer had a ladies maid.

'And if any of your shoes seemed to have gone missing,' Uncle Arthur chipped in, 'don't worry, it will just mean that Nurse has given them to Briggs to clean. She's got a thing about clean shoes; I've even started wearing house slippers in desperation, so that I know that I've got something to put on my feet at the end of the day!'

My aunt then said she'd show me to my room, and as she did so explained that only Nurse and I would be using the hot water in the nursery bathroom. 'You can take a bath any time, dear, except, if you don't mind, in the afternoons when Nurse prefers to take hers.'

I met Nurse later that evening and she invited me to sit down by her fire so that we could get acquainted. She explained that a bell in her room was connected between the nurseries, so if I required anything at all in the night I only had to ring and she would hear me.

'Tell me dear, who sees to your hair in the evening when you are at home?' she asked.

'Oh, I do it myself,' I replied.

'And who cleans the house dear?' Nurse asked, sounding most concerned, 'Surely not your mother!'

I explained that Pansy came in daily to clean the house for us, but that I also helped with the household chores as much as possible.

'That's kind of you to help your mother, I approve of that, especially in these difficult times. It's possible that Lady Felicity may be glad of your help too, perhaps you could help her arrange the flowers while you are here?'

'I'd be happy to,' I told her.

When I went back to my room I noticed that my hot water bottle, which I had left on my bed, was now missing. I hoped that the maid had taken it down to the kitchen to fill later.

Feeling grubby from my train journey I decided to have a bath, but when I saw how big it was, I realised that the regulation two inches at the bottom would hardly cover my toes and feared that I'd freeze to death! There's a limit to being patriotic, I thought, as I defied the regulation and ran it until it was half full.

I had no idea what I should wear for dinner that evening and was about to open the wardrobe to make a choice when there was a knock on the door. Nurse bustled into my room and handed me a long-legged pair of woollen drawers, 'Lady Felicity suggests that you wear these under your skirt, as it's draughty in the dining room, and then you'll be playing Bridge after dinner in the boudoir, which is even colder,' she warned me.

I smiled and thanked Nurse politely, but once she'd left the room, I stuffed them under a cushion: 'My gym knickers are bad enough, but these really are the end!' I muttered, but later that evening after dinner and feeling half frozen to death, I excused myself to go and tidy my hair and ran upstairs to my room to retrieve the long drawers from underneath the cushion and pulled them on, before going back downstairs to play Bridge with my cousins, the vicar, his wife and a local spinster known as 'Miss Betty', who'd also been invited.

We played a number of hands and everyone seemed to take it very seriously. The vicar's wife was deaf and didn't always hear what was being called, which meant that we all had to shout; while the old spinster who had looked like a shy lamb during dinner now played Bridge like a fierce lion; and without mercy. I played reasonably well that evening and was grateful to Signora for insisting that her gals were taught to play Bridge by an expert, otherwise 'Miss Betty' would have had her claws in me too.

I slept like a baby that night and was woken at eight o'clock by the housemaid with a tray of tea and two dry biscuits. She seemed quite nervous at first, but after I had thanked her for the tea and told her what a treat it was, she relaxed a bit and told me her name was Rose.

'Oh, Miss Mary, I nearly forgot. Nurse gave me a message for you: you should dress in your riding clothes this morning as Sir Arthur is planning to take you riding after breakfast.'

When I went down for breakfast I found Uncle Arthur reading his newspaper, 'Help yourself m' dear.'

Fried eggs, grilled tomatoes and my favourite – fried bread – nothing that required food coupons. Bliss!

Nervous about interrupting the silence but needing to ask something after my second piece of toast and marmalade, I cleared my throat and said, 'Excuse me Uncle Arthur, but do you wish me to wear a hard hat this morning?'

'Good Lord, no, my dear, we only wear those when hunting.'

After breakfast, I went out into the yard where the groom was waiting for me. He had two horses saddled: a grey Welsh pony, and a lovely looking bay, but on seeing how small I was, the groom suggested kindly that I should ride the Welsh pony that morning and see how I managed to keep up with the others.

'If you'd just canter round the field, Miss Mary; you might find Morag a little slow, but she's good at the gates,' he suggested. 'The bay – now he can be very naughty!'

I let him tighten the girths before I mounted, and then cantered Morag around the field; she was comfortable but awfully boring. Better safe than sorry though, I thought. Perhaps once I'd got to know the paths and rides I'd be allowed to take out the bay; he certainly looked like a beautiful horse and I longed to get on his back.

'You'll need to kick Morag on as you leave Miss Mary, but there'll be no bother from her on the way home, as she knows there'll be a feed waiting for her,' the groom told me, smiling.

I was glad that I'd put on a warm polo-necked jersey under my riding jacket that morning despite the bright sunshine. An hour later, Uncle Arthur and I were riding down the lanes chatting happily together about horses, and as we reached a narrow part of the bridleway he said that he'd better lead the way, 'mind your head on the overhanging branches,' he warned as his mount broke into a trot.

About ten minutes later we came to a gate leading out into open fields, and I found that Morag and I were being left behind somewhat, but Uncle Arthur had kindly waited for me before opening the gate. Then, pointing to some woods in the near distance, he explained there was a gap between the two fields that led to them.

'Close the gate behind you,' he said jovially, as he galloped off.

Morag behaved beautifully and didn't back away as I closed the gate, 'I think I'll call you Lady Morag,' I whispered in her ear laughing, 'because you've behaved like one.' but she obviously wasn't listening, as suddenly she took off as fast as her little legs would carry her to catch up with the big black stallion that Uncle Arthur was riding.

Thankfully, I managed to stay on Morag's back and arrived at Uncle Arthur's side flushed with the excitement of the gallop. As I pulled up, I was surprised to see a group of other riders join us from another field.

Uncle Arthur beamed, as he introduced me to his friends. I just smiled and nodded, thinking I'd never remember their names, deciding, therefore, that it would be a good idea to give them all nicknames so that at least I'd know who was who: 'Miss Mole' had a mole on her chin and was riding a chestnut horse. 'Lady Side-Bottom' was riding 'side saddle' like a Victorian Lady on a lovely grey mare. Then there was a gentlemen farmer, whom I named 'Farmer Jolly' because he looked like a Toby jug someone had given my father some years before. There was also a young man on a horse bigger even than Uncle Arthur's who had put his hand to his hat to greet me while staring at me in a rather strange way.

I was just wondering what to call him, when I heard him say, 'Spiffing morning, don't you know,' and so he became, 'Sir Spiffing'. I thought it was a bit like riding with characters from the Bertie Wooster books.

We all rode together for a while and then suddenly we were galloping across a field towards a very high hedge. I was fearful that Morag would be too small to jump it, and tried to pull her towards the gate where one or two of the ladies were waiting, but she had ideas of her own. I closed my eyes and squeezed my knees even tighter against her sides, praying: 'Please God, don't let me go head over heels and shame Uncle Arthur by falling off if Morag suddenly stops. Amen.'

I opened my eyes again and was relieved that Morag and I had safely jumped over the hedge, but then when I realised that everyone else had galloped on ahead, a slight sense of panic began to take hold: I had no idea where I was or where Uncle Arthur's house was, but just then, 'Sir Spiffing' appeared at my side and explained that one had to turn sharp right down a lane.

'Follow me,' he said kindly.

When we got back to the stable yard I left Morag with the stable boy and hurried back to the house to wash my hands and tidy my hair before lunch, but when I couldn't find anything to brush or comb my hair with I looked at myself in the mirror and thought 'What the Hell, its only horsey people, they won't mind if I look a bit of a mess.'

A few minutes later, eating my lunch and feeling very happy and relaxed I noticed that 'Sir Spiffing' had spied me and was coming towards me with a glass in his hand, but before he could reach me, I heard a deep voice shout out 'Mary!' and when I looked behind me there was Charles standing right in front of me.

'Did you get caught in a hurricane on the way here?' he laughed pointing at my hair, but then realising that I wasn't laughing along with him, made a complete mess of his own hair and said, 'That's funny, me too!' and then I did laugh.

The following morning I was given the chance to ride the bay, which I was very happy about, and as I mounted, I saw Charles trotting towards us on his beautiful grey horse. He looked every bit like the country squire, and as we rode through nearby villages, it was obvious that all the locals accepted him as the future Earl. Men touched their caps and the women bobbed a curtsey to him. I liked the way that he acknowledged each of them in a friendly way and knew them all by name.

After we had taken the horses back to the stables, Charles told me that his parents were expecting us both for lunch, but assured me that it would be very informal, so to wear 'something comfortable'. I took him at his word and while he spoke to my Uncle and Aunt, I got changed into what I thought was appropriate for lunch, and then he drove me to his family home. On the way, he said that his father, Anthony Lord Walbrooke Earl of Netherly, was one of the kindest, gentlest people I'd ever be likely to meet, and that they had a family nickname for him: Brookie. However, I should address him as Lord Walbrooke until told otherwise, and that I should call his mother, Lady Celia.

As we rode up the long drive, I got my first glimpse of the Walbrooke's lovely old house. It was about twice the size of my parent's home.

Lady Celia met us at the door, looking every bit the Lady of the Manor in a smart skirt, twin-set and pearls, as she guided us into the drawing room where we found her husband, a tall, dark-haired man, with a few flecks of grey here and there on the temples. He wore a military moustache that was also grey.

We had a lovely lunch together, which was very informal, as Charles had promised, and I found his parents easy to talk to, which made me warm to them immediately. After lunch Lady Celia told me that she'd like to show me one or two very rare books in their library, and as we wended our way to the other side of the house, I noticed that she was hobbling a bit. I enquired if she'd hurt her foot, 'Not foot, my dear, feet!' she exclaimed, 'I'm standing on them for much longer these days than ever before, as I have to do so much around the house now that most of the servants have been called up and they get damn sore!'

'Why don't you buy a pair of smart velvet slippers?' I suggested 'that's what my mother wears in the evenings now. They don't look like bedroom slippers at all and they're very comfortable apparently.'

'I have to go shopping tomorrow in Cheltenham, so I'll see if I can find a pair, as they sound like just what I need.'

When it was time to go Lord Walbrooke took both my hands in his and said, 'Next time we meet my dear, please call me Brookie, everyone does.'

Charles drove me back to my uncle's house and when we were nearly there he turned to me and said, 'I have so enjoyed seeing you again after all this time; may I drive you to the station tomorrow morning? It'll save your Aunt and Uncle some petrol.'

'That would be lovely, thank you,' I replied.

As I packed the following morning, I felt a little sad that my stay had been so swift, as I had really enjoyed my visit and wondered how long it would be before I had the chance to see everyone again. Before I left, I made a point of tipping each of the staff personally, and gave Rose a little bit extra for being so attentive to me. I gave Nurse a big hug and then went into the drawing room to say thank you to my Uncle and Aunt for having me to stay. Charles had already arrived and as I kissed Aunt Felicity goodbye, Charles kindly carried my suitcase to his car.

When we arrived at the station, he insisted on carrying my luggage all the way to the train. I couldn't help but laugh quietly to myself, as he walked towards a first-class carriage and opened the door for me. He was obviously under the impression that I was travelling first-class, and appeared to be a bit nonplussed when I informed him that I only had a third-class ticket. I explained that I felt safer being in a crowded carriage full of friendly people than I did on my own in a first-class carriage.

Charles made sure that I was comfortable and then gently kissed me goodbye on my cheek, holding me by the top of my arms in a respectful half embrace, 'I'm going to miss you, Mary, let's try to meet up again soon.'

He then closed the carriage door and as I leaned out of the open window to wave goodbye to him, he said with a cheeky grin, 'At last! I do believe we are now the same height, so it would be much easier to kiss you now, if that would be alright?'

I nodded so he lent towards me and very gently kissed me on my lips. I managed to stay upright until I had waved him out of sight and then went weak at the knees again.

The next morning, when nobody was listening I rang Jane, who was still at home on school holidays, and told her about my visit to Gloucestershire and all about Charles.

'Has he got grey hair, he sounds terribly old?' she teased.

'Certainly not, he has gorgeous dark hair and he's very good looking,' I replied indignantly. She then told me how she would miss me next term but was grateful that at least I had been there for her first term to show her the ropes.

Over the next few weeks I travelled up and down from Woking to London to be with Aunt Beth and go to all the parties, and balls that I had been invited to. Marcus told me that he was rather enjoying being my chaperone, and I noticed that he was putting on a little weight, which was most probably due to all the free food he was guzzling.

Charles rang me at Aunt Beth's one evening and invited us both out for a meal at a rather expensive restaurant, which was a treat for us all. The following week Aunt Beth said she would cook a meal for us at her flat, which was just as good. After several more dinners at restaurants and at her flat, Aunt Beth began making excuses, saying that she was busy and couldn't join us, and told me that as long as I didn't tell my mother, it was all right with her if I wanted to go out with Charles without her as a chaperone; as she trusted Charles to behave as the perfect gentleman that she knew he was. But she did insist that I was back by ten.

The next time we met up Charles suggested that we walk through the park, as it was such a fine spring evening, and as we approached the gates, he asked me whether I'd like to have supper with him back at his house rather than go to a restaurant, 'I'm a marvel with a tin of baked beans, and a dab-hand at hot-buttered toast, best in the regiment,' he boasted so I agreed, but as we walked towards his father's mews house, the air-raid siren sounded.

'Damn and hell,' Charles said taking my hand and urging me to run, 'the quicker we take cover the better,' he shouted over the wail, but as neither of us knew where the nearest public shelter was in this neighbourhood, Charles suggested that we took shelter under the steps that led down to the basement area of one of the large Georgian houses nearby. As I stood against the wall, he put his arms around me protectively and then we waited there for the air raid to finish. Suddenly there was a loud crunch, followed by a boom, and then the whole street shook.

An eerie silence followed, as Charles and I stood motionless in each other's arms, 'We'd better stay put for a bit, the wardens will come along and tell us when we can move.' We waited for another five minutes but no one came and then Charles told me to stay where I was while he went to find a taxi.

'Promise me you won't move Mary, because if you do, I won't know where to find you,' Charles ordered.

'Yes Sir,' I said saluting him, giggling with the relief that nothing awful had happened to us.

Charles bent down and after kissing me passionately on the lips, said gently, 'I mean it. Don't leave this spot.'

I was so stunned by his kiss that I couldn't have moved anyway.

Suddenly I heard the throb-throb-throb of an engine overhead, and realised that it must be a doodlebug. I listened carefully, terrified, because I knew that while the engine was still throbbing I was safe, but when the engine stopped the bomb would immediately fall out of the sky and whoever was underneath it had very little chance of survival. To my horror, the engine stopped.

I squatted down under the stairs and braced myself for the explosion. A terrific bang was followed by the sound of breaking glass, and then a strange blast lifted me off my feet and sent me flying halfway up the basement steps. I tried to stand up, but my legs were shaking so badly that they gave way beneath me; I tried again a few minutes later, this time managing to pull myself up the stairs and into the small garden at the front of the house, where

I was able to hold onto a tree to steady myself. I looked down at my feet and saw that I was now wearing only one shoe and that I no longer had my handbag with me. I carefully went back down the steps to the basement where I found my bag but there was no sign of my missing shoe.

A chilling thought then struck me: where was Charles? Had he been killed in the explosion? I couldn't bear it if he had, as I had become very fond of him, no more than fond I suddenly realised. It was at that very moment that I knew I had fallen in love with Charles.

'Oh Charles, please don't be dead,' I called out.

Suddenly I felt a hand on my shoulder and a gruff voice said, 'Are you all right Miss?' It was an air raid warden, who asked me why I wasn't in a shelter, so I explained what had happened and asked him if he'd seen a tall, dark man in guard's uniform on the road. 'He was going towards a taxi rank somewhere,' I said, my voice trembling, and desperately trying to hold back my tears.

The air raid warden shook his head, and said that he hadn't seen a soul since the siren went. He then noticed that I was wearing only one shoe and that my legs were bleeding, 'You'll need those cuts cleaning up, Miss,' he said gently putting his arm around my shoulder, 'You'd best come with me, Miss.'

I stood there rooted to the spot and explained how I'd promised Charles that I'd stay where I was until he returned.

'Okay, Miss, I'll come back in half an hour, and if the gentleman hasn't arrived then, we'll get in touch with your family and get you home.'

While I waited for Charles, I tried to take my mind off what might have happened to him by hunting for my missing shoe. There was glass everywhere, and I had to tread very carefully, so that I didn't cut my bare foot. After about ten minutes of fruitless searching I decided to take off my remaining shoe and go out onto the street to wait.

'Oh Charles, where the hell are you?' I shouted.

'I'm right here!' a voice replied. I turned around and to my delight there was Charles stepping out of a taxi.

'I thought you were dead,' I sobbed, running into his arms.

Charles whispered, 'I thought something terrible must have happened to you too; first a bomb and then a doodlebug in the same area, we're both jolly lucky to still be alive.'

I clung to him, crying like a baby, and then Charles put his finger under my chin to make me look up at his face, 'There is something I need to ask you.'

For a moment I thought Charles was about to propose to me in the middle of the road, but instead, he just grinned and asked, 'Do you still fancy beans on toast for supper?'

I hit him playfully with my remaining shoe, 'That sounds wonderful.'

He picked me up with ease and carried me to the taxi and placed me carefully in the back seat before climbing in and sitting next to me. When we got to his house he carried me indoors and placed me on a chair in his drawing room, while he went back outside to pay the driver.

As soon as he was back inside, he pulled all the blackout curtains and put the lights on. Then seeing that I had blood running down my legs, he came closer to inspect them. I had tiny pieces of glass sticking out of my stockings, so he suggested that I go upstairs and wash my legs in the bathroom.

As I got up, I handed him my remaining shoe and said, 'Such a pity that was my favourite pair.'

I went upstairs to the bathroom, turned on the taps, and while the water was running, I took off my stockings and sat on the edge of the bath to rinse the dirt and blood off my legs. I then suddenly felt a sharp stab in my left breast, and when I looked down, I saw that the top of my blouse was covered in blood. I slowly undid my buttons and noticed that there was something sticking through my brassiere, and it appeared to be embedded in my flesh.

Just then there was a soft knock on the bathroom door, 'Are you alright Mary, or do you want some help?' Charles asked.

'Yes, actually I think I do Charles,' I said as he walked in, 'I seem to have something sharp sticking out of my,... my chest.'

'Now, Mary, please don't be shy and take off your blouse, so that I can have a closer look,' he said now looking very concerned.

Charles then gently pulled aside my brassiere, and looked quite alarmed when he saw that I had a shard of glass sticking out of my chest, 'Mary, I think it's too dangerous for me to try and pull it out in case I do more damage. We need to get you to a doctor so that it can be removed and cleaned properly.'

'Why don't we call Marcus?' I suggested. 'He lives nearby, so that would save us having to go to the hospital.'

Charles phoned Marcus straight away, who said that he'd come as soon as he could find a taxi.

When he got there, Marcus strode straight into the bathroom and without wasting a moment said, 'Right let's take a look at you then.'

He gently touched the shard of glass sticking in my chest and as he waggled it, the shard glistened under the ceiling light, and I could see that I was still bleeding.

'Charles, can you go and boil a kettle please, so that I can sterilise a pair of tweezers?' Marcus asked and then turned to me and said, 'Don't worry, Mary, I don't think it's too deep and I should be able to remove it fairly easily. Let's get you downstairs, though, while the kettle's boiling, so that I don't need to tackle it with one foot in the bath and the other in the lavatory!'

I giggled. Good old Marcus, his calm manner had immediately made me feel more relaxed, and I thought what a great doctor he will make when he is fully qualified. He then helped me down the stairs and we joined Charles in the kitchen, just as the kettle boiled.

'You'll have to remove your brassiere, Mary, so that I can clean up the wound and stitch you up,' Marcus said to me.

Charles, ever the gentleman, turned his head away, while I removed my brassiere. Meanwhile, Marcus just got on with it, tut-tutting every now and again, and calling to Charles for a clean towel each time he drew blood. After some time and persistence Marcus finally managed to remove the thin shard of glass cleanly with the tweezers.

As he put in some stitches, Marcus told me that I had been very lucky because if the glass had gone into my breast an inch higher up, it could have severed an artery.

I suddenly began to feel rather sick and said that perhaps I should go home now. Charles rang for a taxi and insisted on coming too, so that he could explain to Aunt Beth what had happened. Marcus decided that he had better come with us as well.

Aunt Beth was horrified when she saw me with my blouse all covered in blood, but after Marcus assured her that I was going to be fine, she started to relax and then he promised her that he would take me to the hospital in the morning, just to make sure that all my cuts were thoroughly clean.

Aunt Beth thanked them both profusely for getting me home safely to her.

Marcus brushed it off, 'Oh, that's alright Aunt Beth, don't mention it; I needed to practice stitches anyway!'

'Thank you, Marcus,' I said giving him a big hug. Then I said goodnight to Charles and told him, 'You'll have to make me beans on toast another day!'

The following morning, Marcus kept his promise and took me to see a doctor at the hospital, who told him that he had done a great job and that the wound was healing already, 'Good stitches, by the way!'

Charles turned up later that afternoon with two enormous bunches of flowers, 'Oh… and I found this one up a tree in the garden next to the house where we took shelter,' he said handing me my missing shoe. I couldn't believe that he had taken the time to go back and look for it. Yes I definitely had fallen in love with this charming man, I thought to myself.

'Mary, I want to say something to you, while we are alone,' Charles whispered, kneeling in front of me, 'You must have realised by now how I feel about you, and my darling girl I would like to make you my wife very soon.'

'Oh, Charles,' I sighed, thinking how very romantic this all was and then I suddenly sat bolt upright, 'But I can't! I am only just eighteen, and I don't think my father will allow it.'

'I had better go and ask him then,' Charles said laughing.

I returned home to Woking the following morning, and as Aunt Beth had already telephoned my mother to explain what had happened to me, she was anxiously waiting for me at the station, and as I got off the train, she hugged me tight and said, 'Thank God you are alive.'

When we arrived home she examined my wounds and said how pleased she was to see that they were already healing and not as serious as she had feared. And then she said smiling at me, 'Now Mary, tell me everything.'

'What do you mean, Mummy?' I asked her.

'I mean Charles Edham!' she laughed, 'I think that he must be a bit more than just a friend, from what Aunt Beth has told me,' she then added, 'And I understand that he wants to speak to your father. How do you feel about that?'

'Well, yes, he did mention something along those lines, but I told him I couldn't possibly get married yet, as I was sure my father would never allow it,' I told her.

My mother took my hand in hers and sat down beside me. She then asked me question after question about Charles, who he was, what regiment he was in, where he lived and so on and after the interrogation was over she gave me a nod of approval.

'I think you will make a perfect country squire's wife, Mary,' she said smiling.

'But do you think Daddy will give Charles permission to marry me?' I asked her.

'I will make sure that he does,' my mother replied. Then she thought for a moment and added, 'But I think he will agree anyway, because otherwise all the things that you have learned at Finishing School – not to mention those expensive fees – will have been wasted – and you know your father – he hates waste!'

Two days later, my father received a letter from Charles asking him if they could meet up in London, when my father was next at the War Office. The two men met for lunch at my father's club later that week.

When my father returned from London, he told my mother that he was very impressed with how mature Charles was, and that he had invited him down to Woking for the weekend, so that she could meet him too.

When Charles arrived, Agnes met him at the front door to let him in, and as she took his coat she asked politely, 'Should I call you Your Lordship?'

'Certainly not!' I overhead him reply, as I walked down the hall, 'I would much prefer that you call me Major Edham, as I had to work jolly hard to become a Major, whereas my other title is just the one I was born with, which really has nothing to do with me!' he said laughing. Agnes then turned in my direction and gave me a huge smile.

I took Charles into the drawing room to join my parents and after the introductions had been made, my mother and I left the men to talk. As soon as were in the hallway, my mother looked at me lovingly and said, 'I think he will do very nicely for you, my dear.'

My father was equally happy thank goodness and I wished I could introduce Charles to my brothers too, but as they were both away that weekend, that would have to wait. However, after lunch I took Charles to meet Kay, Jack and little Richard at their house.

Kay greeted us warmly the moment we arrived and showed us into the sunroom where her son was playing on the floor. Charles starting talking to Jack about how I had mentioned he was a fire fighter and told him how much he respected the fire fighting teams, as he would be absolutely terrified if he had to put out fires and rescue people from bombed-out dangerous buildings. I could see Jack's pride swell before my eyes.

Charles then asked Kay to tell him stories of what I was like as a small girl when she was my governess, and she made us all laugh with one or two recollections. When it was time to leave, Kay told Charles that she was very fond of me and that we were more like sisters, to which Charles had replied, 'In that case I hope you will accept me as another brother.'

As we walked home Charles took my hand in his and said how good I was with little Richard, asking me if I wanted children of my own.

'Dozens, but not yet,' I replied.

'That's a relief!' he said, and we both laughed.

That evening, as I listened to Charles and my father discuss the war, I realised once again that I had a tendency to worry about my own sadness and losses and seldom faced up to the anguish and sorrow that so many others all over the world were going through. When later that evening I confessed this to my mother, she told me that I wasn't the only one that thought like that.

The next day, my father gave his permission for Charles to marry me on the condition that he waited until after the Queen Charlotte's Ball before announcing our engagement formally. Over lunch we discussed where the wedding should be held, and Charles said that he was certain his parents would expect him to marry at Saint Margaret's in Westminster, but then said that it was the bride's prerogative to choose the venue, so it was up to me.

'Wouldn't a big church like that be very expensive?' I asked.

Charles looked at my father and they both grinned. 'I'm very glad that my future wife minds the pennies so carefully!' Charles teased.

'It runs in the family!' my father replied.

CHAPTER 5

1942

The night before the Queen Charlotte's Ball, Aunt Beth invited me to stay with her, so that we could spend the day of the Ball making absolutely sure that my dress fitted me perfectly and then, on the evening of the Ball, she helped me slip into my beautiful white ball gown reminding me, as she did so, that before long she'd be helping me into my wedding dress. She then put the lovely ruby and diamond necklace, that my mother had taken out of the family vault at the bank, around my neck, and arranged some small red flowers in my hair that matched it perfectly.

Marcus was my partner for this special occasion, and when we went down to the waiting taxi, I reminded him to tell the driver to take us to the Dorchester Hotel first, where we were meeting Jane and some other debutantes and their escorts for a drink before going on to the Ball together.

When we got to the Dorchester, Jane introduced me to her escort, who was the brother of one of her best friends at the Hall. Most of the others girls in our party that night were also from our Finishing School. Queen Charlotte's Ball was being held at Grosvenor House, and the moment we arrived there, all the girls went to the cloakroom to tidy their hair. It was all terribly grand and exciting and both Jane and I were suitably awestruck, as we finally entered the huge room, which was lit by candles, and chandeliers that hung, glittering, from the ceiling.

When we joined the rest of our party at our table, I noticed that Belinda, a friend from Finishing School, was looking admiringly at Marcus. She came up to me and whispered in my ear, 'Who's the tall fair boy you're with?'

I whispered back, 'He's my cousin, Marcus.'

'My partner for tonight is also my cousin, perhaps we could swop?' she asked cheekily.

'What's he like?' I asked her.

'Oh Tommy's an absolute scream! You'll get on well with him,' she assured me. When Marcus joined us at the table, he pointed to a row of rather serious looking women sitting nearby and said, 'You girls had better be on your best behaviour tonight, as those women over there are watching you.'

Belinda and I looked at the women and remembered how we had been warned that there would be some middle-aged dowagers present tonight to chaperone us 'gals'.

After dinner, all the girls took turns dancing with each of the young men seated at the table. And when it was Marcus's turn to dance with me, he told me that Belinda's cousin, Tommy, had invited us to an exclusive nightclub after the Ball was over, but as he was only allowed to take two guests, we wouldn't be able to take Jane with us. I told him not to worry, as I knew that her father was picking her up later after the Ball anyway.

Suddenly a drum roll announced that it was time for all the debutants to collect together ready to curtsey to a young Duchess who, as part of the Royal Family, was standing in for the King and Queen, as they no longer attended these events because of the war. The Duchess was standing next to the hugest cake I had ever seen, covered with white icing and decorated with hundreds of pink sugar-flowers. The cake was so enormous and the Duchess so tiny in comparison, that I thought she looked a bit like an ornament that should have been on top of it, so when it was my turn to curtsey, I had to concentrate on not getting the giggles. Thankfully, I made an elegant enough curtsey not to shame my family, and now my mother would be able to tell all her friends that her daughter had officially 'Come Out'.

When the Ball was finally over, Marcus, Belinda, Tommy and I took a taxi together to the nightclub, and on the way Belinda confided that she had never been to a nightclub before. I told her that I hadn't either, so we were both very excited.

When we arrived, Tommy showed his membership card to the man at the door, who recognised him at once and said, 'Good to see you M' Lord' and let us all in.

'Where is the dance floor, Marcus?' I whispered, as we descended the stairs into a small dark interior, 'There isn't room to swing a cat in here.'

'People don't dance at night clubs, Mary,' he laughed, 'they smooch.' I wasn't quite sure what smooching was, so he explained to me that smooching consisted of holding one's partner very close and kissing them almost continuously, while shuffling around slowly on the dance floor in the dark.

I could tell that Marcus was keen on the idea of smooching with Belinda, but I wasn't interested in Tommy in a romantic way, and to my relief he obviously wasn't interested in me either, so we just danced closely together and talked.

Later that evening there was a floorshow followed by a sing-song where everyone sang some rather rude songs, which went over my head, but reduced all the men to shouts of mirth like silly school boys. Two hours later I felt very tired and was quite relieved when the boys agreed that it was time to go home.

It was after two in the morning before our taxi came to halt outside Aunt Beth's flat. Marcus asked the taxi driver to wait for him, while he made sure I was able to get into the flat, and then once I was safely inside he went home.

'Tell me all about it,' Aunt Beth insisted, as she came out of her bedroom pulling on her dressing gown.

'I will,' I replied, 'but first, I must soak my feet in a bowl of hot water, as they're killing me. I have been dancing non-stop all night.'

I must have looked a funny sight with my beautiful white Ball gown now pulled up to my knees and both my feet soaking in the washing-up bowl. I did my best to describe the Ball to her, and to remember all the names of the other people that had been there, but Aunt Beth was far more interested in what the other girls were wearing, and how my dress had compared to theirs. I told her that many of the girls had complimented me on my dress and asked me who my dressmaker was, as it looked 'unbelievably expensive', so I had said that I couldn't tell them, as I had promised to keep her name a secret. Aunt Beth roared with laughter, as she had created my dress from two different second-hand wedding dresses, which had cost her less than ten pounds.

I returned to Woking the following afternoon and an hour later Charles telephoned to ask me how the Ball went and to tell me that he was about to go on a reconnaissance trip in Exeter to ensure that the city would be safe for the King's visit, which was due to take place later in the year.

'As soon as I get back to London, will you come back to town and join me?' he asked, 'I am really missing you darling.'

'How much?' I joked.

'My arms ache to hold you!' he teased.

'That sounds like the sort of soppy thing I used to write for the soldiers in their letters to their sweethearts,' I giggled.

'Well maybe I am not saying it properly but I will try to come up with something a bit more romantic when I am alone with you again,' he promised.

'So when will that be?'

'The day after tomorrow,' he told me. 'So why don't you see if you can stay at Aunt Beth's for a few nights again, and then, as soon as I'm free, I will call you.'

'That sounds like a good plan,' I replied, 'I look forward to it.'

'That's settled then, see you very soon my darling girl,' Charles said before he rang off.

I promptly rang Aunt Beth and asked if she would put me up yet again and she was delighted to hear that I would be seeing Charles again.

When my mother arrived home, I told her about my plans, and she asked me if I would take some fresh eggs with me to give to Aunt Beth and that she would also give me some pork sausages and a few extra rashers of bacon, which she had persuaded her butcher to sell to her that morning.

I arrived at Aunt Beth's flat the following evening, and she gratefully took the extra rations, 'This is a real treat, let's save them for when Charles comes to supper and then we can eat the lot together!'

Later that evening, Aunt Beth announced that she had a surprise for me, 'My brother John has offered to hold a luncheon party for you and Charles at the Savoy when you officially announce your engagement, and he wants you both to invite whoever you like.' She also told me that she'd found a very pretty dress that would be perfect for me to wear at the party, and that she would take me to see it in the morning so that I could try it on.

The following morning, I heard the newspaper flop through the letterbox onto the floor, but as I was in no hurry to get up, I stayed in bed and went back to sleep. When I woke up again about an hour later, I was surprised to see both Aunt Beth and Marcus standing at the foot of my bed. They were both as white as sheets and were looking at me in a very strange way. Aunt Beth was crying.

'What is it?' I asked them. 'What's happened?'

When neither of them answered me straightaway, I immediately knew that something was terribly wrong.

'What's happened?' I repeated.

'Exeter has been bombed,' Marcus said.

'Oh, no, that's where Charles is. Has he been hurt?' I asked fearfully.

'Yes he has, Mary,' Marcus said, and then sat down on the bed and took my hand in his. 'It's the worst kind of news, I'm afraid.'

Aunt Beth then burst into tears and ran out of the room.

'No, please no!' I screamed.

'I am sorry, Mary, but it's in the papers this morning,' Marcus said.

He then told me that when Aunt Beth had picked up her newspaper this morning and read the headline 'Hero killed whilst rescuing bomb victims in Exeter', she had immediately thought of Charles and when she finished reading the full story, her worst fears had been confirmed. Charles was dead. She had then phoned Marcus and told him to drop everything and to come over to her flat at once.

When Aunt Beth came back into my bedroom, she hugged me tightly, and started rocking me in her arms. I then heard a strange howling sound, like a wolf in the night, and it was a few minutes before I realised that the sound was coming from me.

Marcus then explained that Charles had been killed while trying to rescue a family who had been trapped in their house after a bombing raid. He had managed to save a young child, but when he went back in to look for any other survivors, the building had suddenly collapsed and everyone inside had been killed.

'He was a real hero, Mary,' Marcus said, as he injected something into my arm, which made me fall straight to sleep.

When I regained consciousness, I could see my father's tear-stained face looking down at me. I remembered that something terrible had happened, but couldn't quite remember what, and I felt very disorientated. My father quietly told me to get out of bed, and as I tried to stand up I felt my legs give way, a bit like a puppet with no strings, but my father helped me stay upright. Someone wrapped a blanket around me, and then I saw Marcus was now by my side. He guided me down the stairs, out of the building and then into the back seat of my father's car. I felt a sharp prick in my arm and then must have gone back to sleep.

When I next woke up, I was in my own bed at home, in Woking. My mother was standing by the bed, and when she saw that I was awake, she put her arms around me, which made me start to cry, and once the tears started, I wondered if they would ever stop.

Charles's funeral service was held a week later in their family village church, in Gloucestershire, but I was still in too much of a state of shock to feel well enough to attend. My mother told me that she had spoken to Charles' parents on the phone to offer our condolences and that they had told her there would be a memorial service for the rest of their family and Charles's friends the following week.

'We have all been invited.'

'I can't go,' I told her, hugging myself tightly for protection.

'Not even for Charles?' my mother asked, 'I think he would want you to be there to help his parents get through this awful tragedy. Try to think about how they are feeling right now, darling. I know its not easy but you are going to have to try to pull yourself together quickly and put on a brave face.'

I don't remember much about the memorial service, as it all seemed so unreal. Charles' mother approached me after the service was over and put her arms around me, 'Thank you for making Charles so happy,' which made me burst into tears.

When Charles' father came over to join us, he looked ten years older than when I'd last seen him, and after we had hugged each other I told him that I would come and see them again soon, 'Please do Mary,' Lord Walbrooke said, 'and know that you will always be part of our family and welcome anytime.'

As we left to go home, I vowed that I would come back to visit Charles's grave one day, but didn't know when that would be. Life felt so uncertain. I was frightened to make any plans for the future, because it seemed to me that every time I tried to, something terrible happened.

After a few weeks of alternating between sadness, self-pity and anger, I finally began to recover and decided it was time to get on with my life, so told my mother that I was ready to go back to doing my bit to help the war.

'I'm very glad to hear that darling, as you still have your life to live,' she said.

'But I don't just want to empty bedpans and change dressings, I want to do something that will really make a difference,' I told her.

'Well then I think that I might have had a good idea.'

'What?' I replied without showing much interest.

'I am going to give Archibald McIndoe a call,' my mother said, 'you remember 'Uncle Archie' don't you Mary? He's that charming man we met with his family on holiday in France before the war, and since then he's set up a specialist unit at the Queen Victoria Cottage Hospital in East Grinstead to re-build the faces of pilots who have been badly burnt, so I want to ask him whether you could work there and train, as a voluntary aid detachment nurse.'

I perked up immediately. I had forgotten all about 'Uncle Archie', but now remembered telling him, that when I grew up I wanted to work as one of his nurses.

Later that evening I overheard my mother talking to him on the phone, arranging a date for me to visit him. When she got off the phone she told me that 'Uncle Archie', had asked her to warn me that most of his patients were very badly disfigured, so it was important that I try not to show any reaction when I saw them, as that could do more harm than good. Apparently he was attempting to give these poor men 'new faces', but the reality was that they would never look normal again.

When I arrived at the Cottage Hospital, I nearly told the sister who greeted me that I had come to see 'Uncle Archie', but fortunately stopped myself in time, and instead said that I had a meeting with Archibald McIndoe. She took me to his office, and told me to wait there until he was free to see me. I gratefully accepted her offer of a cup of coffee and sat down, while the nurse went to fetch it. While I waited, I thumbed through one of the magazines and to my surprise suddenly saw a photograph of myself staring back, which must have been taken at the Queen Charlotte's Ball. It was so unexpected to see a photograph of myself that I burst out laughing, just as Archie McIndoe opened the door and walked into his office.

'Uncle Archie!' I cried out, jumping up and leaping into his arms, still laughing.

'Dear me! Is that really you Mary? If I hadn't known you were coming to see me I wouldn't have recognised you. Last time I saw you, you were still a schoolgirl.'

He then took my hands in his and looking directly into my eyes, said how sorry he was to hear about my recent loss, which my mother must have told him about, and then he told me how delighted he was that I still wanted to help him.

'I know you must feel that your plans for the future have been turned upside down Mary, but when you see my poor boys, you'll realise that they must feel even worse than you do, because the impact of their disfiguring injuries has made them very depressed and believe that they have no future at all,' he said seriously.

I asked him how their families coped with such a situation, and Uncle Archie replied that, sadly, very often, some of them found it impossible to come to terms with the situation. 'I've seen wives and sweethearts shun the boys, unable to face the rest of their lives looking at someone they no longer recognized. It is utterly cruel, and yet quite understandable,' he sighed.

He then warned me that I would see some horrifically disfigured faces, when he took me round the wards, and that some of the men's hands looked like claws.

'The worst thing about their hands is that they are unable to feed themselves because they cannot hold a knife and fork any longer, and find it humiliating to be fed like babies. I've seen some of them put up with unbearable pain very bravely, and then weep when someone offers to help them have a drink of water. My job is not only to rebuild their burnt faces and hands, but also to give them the courage to carry on, so if you feel that you really wish to work here, you will have to do the same.'

Uncle Archie then explained that the scale of his work was so large that it meant that he needed to find people who didn't mind taking on more than just one role, so if I was to do any nursing for him, that wouldn't be all he wanted me to do.

'It will all be rather different here, Mary,' he warned.

We then left his office and went through to a room where he told me that his 'guinea pigs' were recuperating. When I looked a bit shocked by his remark, he explained that some time ago one of his patients, who was being wheeled into surgery for the umpteenth time, had shouted out as a joke, 'We're nothing but a plastic surgeon's guinea pigs!' and the nickname had stuck.

Most of his patients were pilots, who had been caught in the inferno of a crashed plane, often trapped in the cockpit, as the fuel tank exploded with them still inside. Archie told me that some time ago he had noticed that many of the airmen who had ditched into the sea, had appeared to be in less pain and in better shape than those who had crashed on land, so he quickly realised that the salt water must have benefited them in some way. It had also made it easier for him to graft on new skin, so he had then come up with the idea of giving all his patients saline baths, which would give them the same benefit as being in the ocean. After a few experiments, mainly with the water temperature, the saline baths had now become common practice.

Uncle Archie went on to tell me how he used skin from one part of the body, as a graft to repair another. The men had to be very brave, and cope with having an arm attached to their face while the graft was taking. When we finally went into one of the wards, I was shocked to see such terrible disfigurements, far worse than I could have imagined, but did my best to look at the men square in the face, as instructed but it was one of the hardest things I had ever had to do.

Archie told me that getting the men used to showing their faces in public, was a real challenge but something they would have to get used to doing, if they were to ever have any chance of a 'normal' life, so he had gone into East Grinstead and had a word with the local publicans, about the work he was doing and asked them all for their help and support. He had pleaded with them to talk to his boys and make them feel welcome in the pubs, so that they felt like they were being treated as 'normal people' and he even asked the locals to take them into their homes. Fortunately many people showed kindness to McIndoe's 'guinea pigs', and opened their houses to the wounded airmen.

Uncle Archie then surprised me by telling me that he not only allowed the men to drink beer with their meals in the hospital but that he also arranged regular outings to the local pubs. I couldn't believe it!

'The chaps were used to going out for a drink and flirting with girls before this damn war,' he said smiling, 'and scarred or unscarred, boys still enjoy looking at a pretty face like yours Mary!'

As he said this, I noticed that some of the men were looking at me, so I smiled back at them thinking that if I was kind and joked along with them perhaps they might start feeling better about themselves. I think it must have worked, as it didn't take long before a couple of them began flirting with me.

I marvelled at how courageous these men were to even attempt to 'carry on as usual', as though nothing had happened to them. I was full of respect for them.

I couldn't help but smile, when one of the pilots complained that his moustache wouldn't grow anymore, so Uncle Archie offered to graft on a new one for him, but using his pubic hair, which made all the men laugh. Then he asked one of the other men whether he'd decided on whether to have a snub nose or a big long one, telling him to hurry up and make up his mind as his decision would affect the amount of skin he'd need to take from his backside.

Despite the very good-natured banter and humorous remarks, the reality that most of the skin for the grafts came from one, or both, of the individual's inside legs or arms could not be ignored.

Uncle Archie seemed to be pleased that I was taking it all in my stride, and excused himself saying that he had work to do. 'I'll send one of my nurses to show you round the recovery ward before lunch, Mary, after which I'll be free again for a while.'

When the nurse arrived to take me on my tour, she suggested that I leave my jacket in the office, explaining that as many of the men had to lie naked to help their burns heal, all the wards were well heated. Noticing my look of concern and embarrassment, the nurse smiled and said that they did try to cover them up whenever possible to respect their modesty.

When she took me into the recovery ward, I smiled at one of the patients whose bed I was passing, but he didn't smile back. It took me a while to realise that he couldn't smile back, because he no longer had any lips to smile with.

As the nurse led me from bed to bed, I found it was difficult not to express shock on my face, when I saw a patient with an arm attached to his face, or a strange-shaped nose that looked more like an elephant's trunk. I began to understand how the wives and girlfriends of these men must have felt when they first saw the men that they had once found so attractive, as they were now. I blew my nose in an attempt to cover the fact that I was crying, and then asked the nurse whether I could go outside for a while.

We went outside into the garden and sat down next to each other on a bench, which I noticed had been donated by a grateful relative of a former patient.

'Don't worry,' the nurse said kindly, 'I get upset too, especially when a patient arrives with his body so badly charred that you wonder how he can still be alive. If Mr McIndoe takes you into one of the intensive care wards and you feel faint, you must tell him at once, he'll understand. He's one of the most compassionate men I've ever known. It's an honour to work for him.'

The nurse then asked me how it was that I knew Mr McIndoe, so I explained how my family had met his while we were on holiday in France, and how my parents had kept up the friendship over the years. 'It's been a few years since I last saw him,' I continued, 'and I was hoping that I can train to be one of the nurses here.'

'I hope you don't mind me saying so,' the nurse said, 'but to be honest with you, its very hard work here and physically challenging, so I think you might be a bit too frail and I can't really see you lifting one of those heavy boys onto a bedpan. Can you?'

'No, perhaps you are right,' I agreed, 'But I could still do dressings and things like that, and I'm very good at scrubbing floors, carrying trays and sterilising instruments.'

'I am sure you are, but I don't think it would be appropriate for a friend of Mr McIndoe's to be seen scrubbing floors!' She then looked at her watch, and asked me what I was doing for lunch, 'Would you like to have lunch with the young RAF pilots in their mess? I think it would be very good for their morale if you could.'

When we went into the mess, I could see a group of young men sitting at the tables; some of them had one of their arms grafted to their face. I wondered whether I would be able to get through lunch without making it obvious that I was horrified by their appearance. Then I wondered how I would have coped if Charles hadn't died but had been terribly burned like this, would I have still loved him? Of course I would, but would I have been able to look at him in the same way and wanted him to kiss me? He would be the same person after all, just a disfigured version of the man I was in love with. I wasn't sure that I wanted to hear the answer to that question right now, so instead I took a deep breath and went to sit down next to a group of men that were drinking beer together.

'Good morning, my name is Mary,' I said putting on my best smile.

The men then all introduced themselves and within minutes they were offering to buy me a gin and lime, a glass of wine, or a beer. I managed to politely turn down the alcohol but added that I wouldn't say no to a fizzy drink.

'I wouldn't say no to you!' one of the men chuckled, and then another man whose eyes were covered by a bandage asked, 'Why, is she pretty?'

The first man then told him, 'Well I will describe her for you Jack: she is about six foot tall, has a huge tummy and she's completely bald!'

They all laughed, but Jack had the last laugh when he said, 'I think you must be looking in the mirror Freddy!'

One of the other men then called out loudly, 'Nurse come and hold my hand,' and another quipped back 'But you haven't got a hand anymore you fool, it's grafted to your bum!'

'How can you tell?' one of the others joked. 'They both look the same!'

As we ate lunch together, I started to feel more relaxed in the company of these men, who I thought were more like schoolboys than grown men, and I couldn't help but admire them. I then noticed that Uncle Archie was standing in the doorway watching me, and smiling.

After lunch was over, Uncle Archie took me to see some of the more seriously injured patients, and as I accompanied him from bed to bed, I was aware that he was keeping a careful eye on me to ensure that I wasn't about to faint, or burst into tears.

When we got back to his office, he said, 'Now Mary, you've seen a little of what the nurses have to do here every day. Do you think you're up to it?'

I replied that I didn't think I'd be much help doing the heavy work like bathing and lifting, but that I was more than willing to learn how to change dressings and accompany patients for saline baths, which I knew many of the patients had to bathe in for long periods of time to heal their wounds.

'The trouble is that you can't pick and choose the work you do here,' Uncle Archie said and then he told me that he'd been observing me to assess my reaction to his patients, and also to see what the boys' reaction would be to me and while many of the men were only teasing and having a bit of fun, there were one or two that he'd noticed looking at me with longing in their eyes. He then went on to describe that recently the hospital had identified a problem with some of the patients falling in love with the younger nurses. Some of these nurses had boyfriends, and when they told the lovesick patients that they were already taken, the men didn't believe them and thought that they were lying because of their disfigurements.

'These kind of incidents have been affecting the men's mental wellbeing, so I am now considering recruiting older nurses, with more experience, rather than younger prettier nurses, like you,' he explained and then continued, 'Can you imagine how these young men might respond if you were asked to sponge them down in very personal places?'

I blushed but Uncle Archie continued, 'Yes exactly! And that would embarrass you and it wouldn't be fair on the boys either.' He sat back and said, 'I am sorry Mary, but sadly, I am going to have to turn you down.'

Then after a moment's pause he said, 'Perhaps instead of working here, where there is sadness and despair and, sadly, death very often, have you thought about working in a completely different area of war work, such as one of the Armed Services?'

I laughed and replied, 'What, like, join the Navy and see the world?'

Uncle Archie smiled and said, 'Why not? I've heard that the Wrens are very well respected and a very suitable Service for a girl like you, and I think you'd look delightful in a Wren's uniform and three cornered hat!'

'I'll talk to my parents about it,' I assured him.

On the journey home, I told my mother everything that I had seen at the hospital that day, and how it had affected me. 'I thought I could cope when I saw the first few patients, but when Uncle Archie took me to the admissions ward and I saw the state of the men that had just been brought in, I almost fainted. Some of them were so badly burnt that they looked like over-cooked sausages on a campfire. How they survived I can't imagine, and I suppose some of them won't. I don't think I could cope being a nurse in that sort of hospital after all, Mummy. I'm sorry.'

My mother just put her hand on my knee and we continued the rest of the way home in silence.

I felt a little ashamed that I had given in so easily, but also knew my limitations and that I just didn't have what it takes to be able to nurse those poor men day after day. Perhaps nursing wasn't my vocation after all and I should consider Uncle Archie's idea of joining the Wrens more seriously. I'd think about it.

After dinner that evening, I asked my father whether he could find out what qualifications I would need to join the Wrens. He promised me that he'd find out, as soon as he had a spare moment at the office.

The next day I went to see Kay, who was now eight months pregnant with her second child, to ask her what she thought about the idea of me joining the Wrens.

'I think it would be an adventure!' she said, while preparing Richard's lunch. 'You'd have the opportunity to do something different, meet new people and maybe see more of England too.'

I felt encouraged by her enthusiasm and was just starting to get excited about the idea of becoming a Wren, when she said, 'Mary I know I am not your governess anymore, but I feel that I should give you some advice as your friend.'

I looked at her without saying anything, wondering what she had to say.

'You have had a very sheltered life up until now, and been very privileged too, but when you leave home, which in my opinion, by the way, it is about time you did, you will have to learn to make your own decisions and stand on your own two feet. It won't be easy for you, but somehow you must make your own way in life now, and not come running home every time things go wrong for you.'

I didn't know what to say, so said nothing and just nodded.

On the way home, I thought about what Kay had said and decided that the time had come to stop 'talking' about doing something more worthy for the war effort and to actually do it.

The next day I applied to join the Wrens, and received a letter back two days later inviting me to come to London, to see whether I was a suitable candidate, and the envelope also contained some forms I had to fill in.

Looking carefully down the list of categories that were open for Wrens, it seemed that all the interesting sounding jobs, like plane spotting, were for Officers only, and then I saw that you had to be over twenty-one to request a commission, so I went through the list to see what other jobs were available. I could be a typist, I thought, but I would have to learn to type much faster than I could at present and learn shorthand too, so that didn't sound much fun; I could be a driver, but then I would have to learn to drive, which I was happy to do but that would take time, and what would I do if I failed my test? And then something a bit more interesting caught my attention: 'Girls wanted as Boat Crew'.

I thought that my mother would be happy about the idea of me being 'Boat Crew', as long as I wasn't expected to sleep on a yacht with any men I hadn't been formally introduced to!

'I doubt that it will be on a yacht, my dear,' my father laughed, 'it's more likely that you would be part of a crew on something more like a lifeboat, or a liberty boat,' he explained, hiding a smile.

The next morning I posted the forms back, and then put it out of my mind, as it was William's half term and I'd promised to take him to the cinema that afternoon. When we arrived, the usual Pathe News was showing before the main film began. I watched transfixed when a news item about the Wrens appeared, showing some of the girls marching up and down on parade. I noticed that nearly all the girls were wearing an ugly pudding-basin hat, which was similar to the one I'd worn at school. However, two of the Wrens looked very smart, and wore a well-fitting coat and a three-corner Nelson-style hat, so I decided that if I were accepted into the Wrens, I would wear the Nelson-style hat, as is so much more fetching, and if I tilted it on one side it might even look quite fashionable!

On the way home, William, who was top of his class in Maths at school, explained that if I were accepted into the Wrens, my pay would be less than a pound a week.

'Your wage,' he pointed out persuasively 'will be less than what Mummy pays Pansy. It'll be like slave labour, so the sooner you become an Officer the better.'

I told William that I wasn't joining up for the money, but that I was doing it to be useful and to help win the war.

'Well you can't be much help if you are broke and go into debt,' William said seriously, 'I think you should ask Daddy to teach you how to look after your money.'

The next morning, before my father went to London, I asked him if he would teach me some basic bookkeeping, which he said he'd be happy to do but that it would be a good idea if we also went to his bank one day later in the week, so that he could get the Head clerk to explain a few things to me, such as how the interest rates affected my accounts.

When we went to the bank, my father had a chat with the manager, who was an old friend of his, and I was left in a small room with the Head Clerk, who opened a folder and handed me a piece of paper.

'Gosh,' I exclaimed, when I saw the amount I had sitting in my account. 'I have nearly twenty pounds. That's oodles of money!'

The Head Clerk patiently pointed out that the reason I had 'oodles of money', was because my father had recently put the money into my account, and I hadn't drawn anything out of it yet.

'No doubt, until now, your parents have taken the responsibility of paying for everything for you,' he explained. 'However, if you are considering leaving home and becoming more independent, you need to understand that it isn't wise to spend more than you have.'

The Head Clerk then tried to explain interest rates to me, but seeing that he was fighting a losing battle, soon gave up and just handed me a cheque book, that had my name printed on it, telling me that all I had to do was write down the amount of money I needed, and then sign and date it correctly. Easy Peasy, I thought.

When I got home, there was another letter waiting for me, which informed me that I was requested to present myself at 11.00 hours in two days time for an interview in London. It gave the details of an address that I didn't recognise and said that during this interview consideration would be given as to whether or not I was suitable to join the Wrens. I showed the letter to my mother, who after reading it for herself, noticed that I would also be required to have a medical examination.

'Make sure you wear clean under-things, darling, as you may need to strip down to them, and wash your hair and clean your nails,' she added, 'you need to give a good first impression.'

'Yes Mummy.'

'Oh, and remember to dust off your shoes before you go in for the interview,' my mother added.

So on the day, my father accompanied me to London, to make sure I got to the right place for my interview.

'Now don't be nervous, darling, just sit up straight and answer all the questions you're asked politely and as best you can. Oh, and just one more thing, Mary, don't smile at any of the male naval officers, or chat to them unless they talk to you first, things are a bit different in the Services.'

'Why is that Daddy?' I asked.

'Discipline, darling,' he replied. 'I'm afraid you'll get a lot of that if you become a Wren.'

When I got to the address I had been given, I went up some stairs and was met by a rather bossy woman at the reception area who asked me my name, and then handed me a gown and told me to strip to my knickers. What already? I thought, but did as she had instructed.

To my relief, I was then taken to see a female doctor, who asked me some very personal questions, such as did I have all my own teeth, which infectious diseases had I had, when was the date of my last period and had I had sexual relations recently? I presumed that she meant sex but wasn't completely sure, so just said 'No' hoping that was the right answer.

The doctor then said, 'Have you ever had VD?'

'I'm awfully sorry doctor,' I replied, 'but I don't understand the question, is VD a bit like chicken pox?'

'No, not really,' she said smiling at me, 'I'll just put No.'

I'd had chicken pox when I was younger and had been covered with itchy spots all over my body, not an inch of me was free of them. I knew that you couldn't get chicken pox twice, but maybe VD was different. I'd call Jane later, perhaps she would know.

The doctor asked me to slip down the straps of my brassiere.

'I just want to make sure that you don't have any strange lumps or bumps,' she explained.

She then asked me to lie down on the couch and open my legs, explaining that she needed to check that my pelvis was in line. In line with what I wondered? Instead of asking me to remove my knickers, she gently pulled them to one side, which I found most embarrassing.

'Are you still intact?' the doctor then asked me.

I had no idea what she meant and told her so. She then explained that she needed to confirm whether I was still a virgin or not, to which I replied that I most definitely was. She then asked me whether I'd ever had a steady boyfriend, to which I replied that I had, but that he'd recently been killed.

'Oh dear, I'm so sorry to hear that, please forgive me, but I have to ask these awkward questions,' the doctor said kindly. 'And I'm afraid that I still have to examine you anyway, as part of your medical.'

I was glad when it was all over, and couldn't wait to tell Jane about this weird examination of my most intimate places. I knew she would make some rude remarks about it and we'd end up giggling like schoolgirls again.

The doctor then stood up, smiled and said, 'I expect you're anxious to know my initial thoughts on your health. And although I believe you're a bit too thin, I'm going to give you a clean bill of health. When you join the Wrens, you will be marching up and down a lot, so I'd like you to try and eat a little more to build up your strength.'

I got dressed and then went to wait in the reception area for the next stage of my interview. Eventually, when my name was called, I was directed to another room, where I was met by a First Officer and told to discuss the three category choices I'd put down on my form, so that she could work out where I would fit in best.

I tried desperately to remember what I'd originally written down on the forms: yes, I'd passed School Certificate; no, I hadn't stayed on at school to do Matriculations; yes, I had been a Girl Guide; yes, I had attended a Finishing School, where I'd learned to speak three languages fluently, turn out a room, bake delicious soufflés, skin rabbits and a lot of other domestic science, as well as touch-typing.

'At a pinch, I suppose you could supervise the other girls who do all the cleaning,' the First Officer said and then seeing my face fall explained, 'The problem is that although all the things you've learned would be very useful in civilian life, they aren't going to be very helpful if you're to join the Wrens. Tell me, Miss Arden, why do you wish to be a Wren?'

'Because I want to do full-time war work, and now that I have 'Come Out' that's all I want to do.'

"Come Out'? Of what?' the uncomprehending First Officer asked, a bit taken aback.

I couldn't help but giggle, 'Oh, you know, as a debutante.'

'Oh I see,' the First Officer said.

'But I have also been helping out in our local hospital when I can,' I added.

The First Officer looked at me in disbelief and then asked to see my hands, which were still a little red and sore, so the First Officer asked me why that was.

'Oh, that's because we have to use a great deal of disinfectant at the hospital, you see,' I explained.

She looked surprised and asked, 'Don't they supply you with rubber gloves?'

'We used to be provided with them,' I replied, 'but due to the shortages, our hospital has run out at the moment.'

The First Officer paused for a moment, 'You put down that your first choice was to join as a Boat Crew,' she continued looking down at my form. 'But I wonder whether you realise that this is extremely hard, often very cold work. You would be crewing on the liberty boats that take naval personnel from ship to shore in all weathers. You would also be expected to secure the boats to the quay with thick rope. Can you tie any nautical knots by the way?'

'Oh yes,' I beamed, 'I learned to tie knots when sailing dinghies and, recently, I've been practising using my dressing gown cord, as well as the thick string our gardener uses to tie up the bamboo poles for the peas and beans.'

The First Officer looked at me for a moment, and then said: 'I don't think you'd be strong enough to work on the boats.' She then checked my form and went on, 'I see that your second choice is as a Driver, well, have you passed your test?'

'No, not yet but I've had several lessons; I know what to do and will soon learn,' I replied.

I watched the First Officer as she noted down on my form that 'Driver' was a possibility; then she looked back up at me, and asked 'What about your shorthand and typing?'

'I type at about forty-five words per minute and use my own version of shorthand, but I'm willing to learn whatever shorthand is used in the Navy, if that would help.' I then added, 'I don't mind being taught anything new so long as it's useful.'

The First Officer smiled at me and said she thought it would be worthwhile if I spent a probationary two weeks at HMS Vernon in Portsmouth to see if any of my choices were possible, and if not, other choices of work would be suggested to me. She then warned me that as I would be joining the Wrens as a Rating, I would have to sleep in a Nissen Hut on a dormitory bunk.

'Oh, I don't mind sleeping in a room that I have to share with other people,' I said brightly. 'We slept in dormitories at boarding school, it was fun, and we had midnight feasts. I expect the Wrens will be much the same!'

'The discipline in the Wrens,' the First Officer said firmly, 'does not allow midnight feasts; and you will have to get used to calling all Women Officers in the Wrens 'Ma'am', and all the Male Officers 'Sir', and you will be expected to salute all senior personnel while out of doors, and speak to them only when spoken to first.'

'Oh, I'll soon learn,' I said happily. I wasn't in the least worried about the protocol or the discipline.

'You may go now,' she said. 'Expect to receive a letter in a week or two telling you if you've been successful with your application or not. Then you will be given a date to attend training, unless you change your mind in the interim of course.'

'Thanks awfully for giving me your time,' I said standing up and putting out my hand to say goodbye.

The First Officer took my hand in hers hesitantly, and said, 'When, or I should say, if you join the Wrens, you will not be shaking hands with Officers; you will have to stand to attention and salute.'

'Oh,' I said, slightly embarrassed, 'I've a lot to learn, haven't I?'

I left the interview delighted that I hadn't been turned down out of hand and that at least I might get the chance to do two weeks initial training.

I'll make myself so useful they will be begging me to stay on, I thought, as I gaily skipped down the stairs, coming to an abrupt halt, as I realised I'd bumped squarely into a very tall, good-looking middle aged man dressed in naval uniform. I noticed that his jacket was decorated with gold braid up to his armpits, and that strange, gold dressing-gown cord interwove with a multitude of different coloured ribbons on his chest.

I apologised for not looking where I was going and explained that I was preoccupied because I'd just come out of my interview to become a Wren. Then suddenly remembering what the First Officer had just said, I smiled at him and said, 'If I become a Wren I'll have to call you Sir, won't I?'

'Eh, well, yes,' he replied, grinning. 'As I am an Admiral, I think that would be quite a good idea!'

Gesturing at his ribbons I asked, 'Excuse me, but can I ask you whether you sewed on all those ribbons yourself, or did your wife sew them on for you?'

'As a matter of fact young lady, I was very fortunate: the jacket arrived at my home with them all already sewn on,' he replied, looking at me with amusement.

'I hate sewing on badges,' I said chattily. 'We had to do it ourselves when I was a Girl Guide and I always pricked my fingers, I'm so glad that you didn't have to do it yourself.'

'Which category are you applying for young lady?' the Admiral asked.

'Boat Crew,' I replied, beaming, 'maybe one day I'll collect you and take you to your ship.'

The Admiral smiled, 'I don't get the opportunity to go on many ships these days' he said a bit sadly. 'I have to work in my office most of the time.'

'Oh well, if I'm not accepted as Boat Crew, maybe I could learn to be your secretary and make myself useful,' I offered brightly, and then put out my hand to shake his, 'I must go now or I'll be late. Goodbye.'

'Goodbye to you too,' he said taking my hand. 'By the way, what is your name young lady?'

'Mary Arden, Sir' I replied, 'but hopefully soon it will be Wren Arden.'

CHAPTER 6

1942

Nearly a month went by before a letter finally arrived to tell me that I'd been accepted for two weeks probation at HMS Vernon in Portsmouth, during which my suitability to be a Wren would be assessed. The letter explained that there was no guarantee that I would be offered any of the listed categories that I'd chosen, or that I would be accepted at the end of the course. I would have to wear civilian clothes to start with and then if I passed the probationary period I would have to get a uniform at the stores, which would include the ugly pudding-basin hat, like the one that I'd seen on Pathe News at the cinema.

On the day of my departure my parents took me to the station and as I said my goodbyes, my mother said, 'Now, darling, promise me that if you are not enjoying yourself you will come straight back home!'

My father offered to exchange my third-class railway warrant for a first-class ticket, but I insisted that I must get used to travelling third-class from now on.

'See you soon,' I said, as I stepped into the carriage. I put my suitcase and overnight bag on the rack above my seat and then as I sat down I heard a woman say, 'You goin' to Portsmouth too?'

'Yes, I am,' I replied and then added, 'I am hoping to become a Wren.'

'Likewise,' she said.

'My name's Mary Arden, what's yours?'

'Elsie Clark,' she replied, putting her sticky hand into mine. She then asked me how old I was, so I told her that I was now eighteen, and she said that she was twenty-five.

I started to feel a bit hungry, so took out the packet of sandwiches that our new cook, Mrs Green had made for me to take for the journey, and offered one to Elsie, 'Marmite and tomato or egg and cress?'

'You got 'ens then?' Elsie asked accepting an egg and cress sandwich, 'You must 'ave if you can spare eggs for sandwiches. Where d'ya keep 'em then? You got 'n allotment?'

'No,' I replied, 'we keep them in our garden actually, but well away from the house, so as not to attract rats!'

Elsie looked me up and down and asked, 'Where d'yer live then, in a big 'ouse with its own garden?'

'Yes I do,' I replied, 'where do you live?'

'Down the docks,' she replied

'Do you mean on the Thames? That must be lovely, overlooking the river,' I replied.

'Not when bleedin' bombs is fallin' all night it's not,' she said quietly, and then I suddenly realised which docks she was referring to, and shuddered.

''Ere Mary, when you 'ad your medical what did you 'ave, a man or a lady doctor?'

'A woman thank goodness,' I replied, 'otherwise I'd have died of embarrassment.'

'I 'ad to put up with a man peerin' up me privates,' Elsie whispered.

'Elsie!' I said shocked, 'Surely not, he must have just been examining your pelvis like my doctor did?'

'If that's what you think Mary Arden, you'll believe any think!' Elsie said.

When she saw that I was deadly serious, she smiled and said, 'You talk jus' like the Queen, Gawd bless 'er; 'ere, you ain't a relation of hers or some fing are ya?'

I giggled and replied that of course I wasn't. I then pulled out my silver cigarette case and offered her one of my cigarettes. She almost exploded with giggles at the sight of it: 'Gaw blimey, you can't go carrying that about, Mary, for Gawd's sake, put it away!'

'Why ever not?' I asked, taken aback.

'Cos it'll get bleedin' nicked, that's why,' Elsie assured me, 'it'll get pinched before you've even unpacked yer things.'

'But surely I will be able to trust the other girls at the base?' I said incredulously, 'I mean it is part of the Royal Navy after all!'

'Gawd, you go' a lot to learn.' Elsie sighed shaking her head in disbelief. I was feeling a bit worried now.

A few minutes later Elsie pointed at the sandwich bag and asked, 'If you don't want that last sandwich, can I 'ave it?'

'Of course, Elsie,' I said handing her the remaining sandwich.

'Did yer Mum make these for yer?' she asked.

I answered without thinking, 'No, our cook made them for me.'

Elsie snorted with laughter, and then realising that I was being completely serious, took my hand in hers and said, 'I 'ope you won't take offence or nuffink, but you are going to 'ave to be careful wot you say and not let on to the uvver girls that your Mum 'as a cook, an' that you got a big garden and all that; and you'll 'ave to stop sayin' 'actually' and 'thanks awfully,' 'cos you sound like a bleedin' toff and the uvvers might think you think you're better then them.'

'I'll try,' I replied, 'but I'm so used to saying those sorts of things that they just slip out.'

'Well then, put a zip on yer mouf,' Elsie told me. 'You'll get on all right wiv the officers, but they ain't the ones in charge of us. The ones called Petty Officers tell us what to do, and if they don't like you, they'll make life 'ell for you,' Elsie warned. 'So mind what yer say!'

Just then the train slowed down and we pulled into a station. I looked out of the window and saw a middle-aged woman struggling with a heavy suitcase along the platform. When she came into our carriage she looked at Elsie with a rather superior air and asked her to put her suitcase on the rack for her.

'I'm not your bleedin' servant, do it yerself,' Elsie said, rudely.

There was obviously no way that my new friend was going to wait on the woman, so she now put her suitcase onto the seat and sat next to it. After a few moments, Elsie, having now examined the woman's luggage label and seen that she was going to the same destination as we were, exclaimed, 'You bin called up then?'

'No, I volunteered,' the woman replied haughtily. 'I thought it was my duty to serve as a Wren' she explained, 'I'm a highly trained secretary and feel wasted as a civilian, so I have offered my services to the Navy.'

'Lucky them!' Elsie said cheekily, winking at me.

When we arrived in Portsmouth we hurriedly got our luggage and scrambled out of the carriage. Two young sailors checked our papers and helped us climb into the back of an open lorry, and then tossed our cases in with us.

'Thanks awfully,' I said. Elsie gave me an exasperated look, but fortunately, the sailor had been too busy staring at my legs to notice the way I spoke.

In the back of the lorry there were two boards on each side, which acted as seats. Several sailors were already sitting down but when they saw Elsie and me they willingly squashed up to make room for us. There was a strong smell of sweat, and I thought that one or two of the sailors could probably do with a good wash.

There must have been several potholes in the tarmac, probably the result of a bombing raid, so as the lorry drove over them, it lurched and the sailor sitting next to me put his arm around me to stop me falling off my seat. I smiled gratefully up at him and thanked him for being so kind and he told me in a broad Scottish accent that it would be his pleasure any time. The other sailors made whistling noises and asked Elsie if she would like some steadying hands too.

'Not bleedin' likely,' she replied.

When we arrived at HMS Vernon, the sailors helped us down from the lorry and then gave us our cases. 'Meet us down the pub if you're feeling lonely later,' one of them said to Elsie.

'I'll think about it,' she replied casually to the sailor.

Elsie then told me that I'd have to manage on my own from now on, as she had to go and cook the meals for the Officers.

'Meet me at seven down the Wren's NAAFI,' she suggested. I had no time to reply either yes or no before she hurried off, and I was left standing on my own.

There were dozens of Nissen huts and I wondered which one I would be sleeping in. I picked up my case and overnight bag, and began to walk through the gates. A large man in uniform stopped me and asked for my pass.

'I'm new,' I said meekly, 'so I don't have a pass yet. How do I get one please?'

The man asked me my name and then checked his list. He handed me a temporary pass and then warned me that I would have to show it every time I went in and out of the barracks. I asked him where the billeting office was and he pointed to one of the many brick buildings near the parade ground.

After finding the right office, I was then ushered into a small room where a woman in naval uniform was sitting at a desk reading a file. It felt a bit like being back at school, as I stood to attention and waited for her to finish reading the file before she looked up and spoke to me. After a minute or two she looked up and asked me my name, and checking it against her list, she then instructed me to go to Hut 12.

It took me quite a while to find Hut 12 but when I eventually got there I used the key I'd been given to open the door of the hut, and then peered inside. There were six beds, two of which I presumed were unclaimed, as they weren't made up. Each bed had a window behind it, none of which were open. I dumped my cases on one of the beds and as the room was a bit stuffy, I flung the window behind it wide open. On the bed there was a printed instruction sheet, which told me how and where to 'stow' my things, which made me realise that I would have to get used to using Navy terms from now on.

I looked at my watch. It was four o'clock and I rather fancied a cup of tea, but I'd been told at the billeting office that tea was between six and seven sharp. Funny time to have afternoon tea, I thought, everybody else has it at four, and then I realised they must mean high tea.

As I was putting my personal belongings away in the bedside locker, I sensed someone looking at me, and when I turned around I saw a woman standing in the doorway. She was wearing a navy blue Wren's uniform, which had several brass buttons on it, and she wore a rather grim look on her face. I remembered Elsie telling me that there were women in charge of us, called Petty Officers, and assumed she must be one of them. Before I could say good afternoon, she asked me in an unfriendly tone whether I was Mary Arden.

'Yes, Miss… I'm sorry I don't know your name,' I said.

'I'm not Miss anything,' the woman snapped. 'You refer to me as Petty Officer.'

By now, she was standing by my bed and ordered me to remove my suitcase and to never put it on a clean counterpane again. 'There are plenty of chairs,' she scolded.

There wasn't a chair by my bed, so I went to fetch one from the bed next to mine. The Petty Officer then looked at my shoes under the bed, and enquired if I had some more suitable shoes to wear, as I'd be marching on parade in the morning.

I was about to tell her that the shoes under my bed were my sensible shoes, but I was distracted when she slammed the window behind my bed shut.

'Could you please tell me where to leave my empty suitcase?' I asked politely.

'Ask one of your roommates when they come in,' she snapped. 'I haven't got all day to answer your questions.'

After the Petty Officer had left, I felt tears welling-up in my eyes, and decided then and there that I would nickname this dreadful woman 'Po Face' and hoped that I'd never see her again.

Once I had pulled myself together, I decided to try and find the NAAF1, walk around the parade ground and generally get my bearings. I had no idea what a NAAFI was, but I guessed it must be something like the YMCA where I had served tea to the soldiers, and it was. When I first stepped inside, I saw that there was a counter for serving food and hot drinks at one end, and a shopping area with various things like soap and books for sale at the other. There was a notice saying that it wasn't open until six, so I made a mental note that when I came back later that evening to see Elsie, I would buy myself a Penguin paperback to read to help pass the long evening hours.

I felt a surge of panic when I suddenly remembered that I'd been told by the Billeting Officer to bring my ration card, and any other relevant papers I'd been issued with, to the administrative office once I had unpacked. I'd been so put out by the bad tempered PO that I'd totally forgotten. Thankfully I had put everything of value, including all my important papers, into my gasmask case, so I now ran as quickly as possible to the administrative office, and with a sigh of relief, handed everything in just before it closed.

When I found the 'Wren's Mess', I joined the food queue, and watched carefully what the other girls were doing, so that I could do the same. I picked up a tray and some cutlery and was then handed a plate of mashed potatoes and baked beans. Seeing an empty seat at one of the tables, I asked the girl next to it if she would mind me sitting next to her.

'Help yourself, we sit wherever we can, there's no need to ask,' she replied kindly.

As I began to eat my meal I asked the girl what she thought of the food.

'There is plenty of it, but it all tends to taste of Bisto, custard or a mixture of both!' she quipped and then went on to say that the exception to the rule was on Fridays, when fish and chips was served, which everyone covered with tomato ketchup for a change of flavour.

After our meal was over I wandered back to the NAAFI and was delighted to see Elsie's familiar face, as I'd been feeling a bit like the new girl at school ever since I'd arrived. Poor Elsie looked exhausted, so I asked her why. She explained that the moment she'd reported for duty she'd been told that they were short staffed in the kitchen galley and she'd been asked to muck-in.

'Thrown in at the deep end, I was!' she said, 'I 'aven't even 'ad time to unpack me things 'ave I?'

She was obviously feeling shattered poor thing, but she told me that it should get a bit easier for her by the end of the week, once she began working regular hours. I bought her a cup of coffee and watched, as she piled three sugar lumps into it.

'I need the bleedin' energy,' she explained, when she saw me looking at her, and then asked, 'What are yer roommates like?'

I told her that I hadn't met my roommates yet but that the Nissen hut was very clean.

'Let's have a fag before I go to bed,' Elsie suggested pulling out a packet of Woodbines, and offering me one. I felt uncomfortable taking one of her cigarettes knowing that she was so short of money, so offered her one of my Players instead, which she took gratefully.

'I haven't found anywhere to hide my cigarette case yet, Elsie, but I thought that when I've finished these ones I could put it in my handbag and lock it in my suitcase; I'm worried about carrying it around, after what you told me,' I confided.

'Why not use an ST bag?' Elsie suggested, laughing. 'Put it in one of them and leave it in yer locker, as no one would think of looking in one of those!'

An ST bag was a strong paper bag that was provided in lavatories for soiled sanitary wear, so I thought it was a clever idea and would do as she had suggested.

I then told Elsie about my run-in with 'Po face', and she laughed. 'You got to stand up for yerself Mary and not allow 'em old cows to bully you.'

Elsie then said she was worn out and that it was time she went to bed. 'As soon as I get the hang of the new job, I'll take yer down the pub,' she promised.

We said goodnight and after Elsie had gone, I sat for a while longer and waited until almost everyone had left the NAAFI before going to the telephone kiosk and ringing home. My mother answered my call so quickly that I wondered whether she'd been sitting by the telephone all evening, waiting for me to call her.

I told her that I had arrived safely, that I would be sleeping in a dormitory with four or five other girls, although I hadn't met any of them yet, and then told her all about my first encounter with the bossy Petty Officer. My mother passed the phone to my father, and after a short chat he suggested that I call reverse charges next time, so that we could talk for longer.

When I arrived back at the Nissen hut, four of the other girls were already getting ready for bed, so I introduced myself to them. They all seemed very friendly.

I noticed that Rosie, the girl in the bed next to mine, was putting her gasmask under her knickers in the drawer that we shared, so I asked her why she was doing that.

'We all hide our gas masks under our knickers,' she told me, chuckling, 'as the POs wouldn't dream of touching our personal underclothes and this way there is room in our gas mask cases for makeup, pay-book, fags and everything else we girls need to carry around.'

'Won't you get in trouble if you're caught?' I asked.

'We're not the only ones that do it,' Rosie giggled. 'I know a Steward who cleans for the Officers, and she says they all do exactly the same; shove their gasmasks in their lockers and use their case as a handbag!'

I had a quick wash and decided to get into bed and read my book like the other girls were doing.

'Gosh it's hard,' I said as I climbed into bed, thumping my mattress with my fists.

Rosie suggested that I take the spare blanket from the bed that no one was using and put it over my mattress under the bottom sheet. She said that the girl who'd had my bed before me had done that, and it had made all the difference. I asked her what would happen if someone found out about what I'd done; would there be trouble?

'You pretend you don't know how it got there,' Rosie said, giggling, as she helped me strip the spare bed and remake mine.

'Thanks awfu… thank you very much,' I said, remembering just in time to take Elsie's advice on how I spoke.

Rosie told me that she and Babs, the girl in the bed opposite me, were shorthand typists and were learning speed typing at the government's expense, much to their delight. I told them that if I wasn't accepted as Boat Crew, I might have to do the same. Then a rather good-looking girl came into the hut, and told me her name was Frankie, and that she was also a typist.

The lights suddenly went out, so I thought there must have been a power cut, until one of the girls explained that the lights went out at eleven exactly, every night. 'Bring a torch with you next time,' she yelled across at me, laughing, in the darkness.

About ten minutes later, I heard a window being opened and saw someone climbing through the window. It was Frankie.

'Where's she going?' I whispered to Rosie, who replied, 'She's going out to say goodnight to her boyfriend, but keep your trap shut about it, as it's against the rules.'

'Why couldn't she have said goodnight earlier?' I asked innocently.

'Because the way Frankie likes to say goodnight to her boyfriend is best done in the dark!' Rosie said, and all the other girls sniggered.

I lay down again and thought for a while about what Rosie had said, but it still didn't really make sense to me: why did she need to climb out of the window? Oh well, it's none of my business, I thought, as I shut my eyes and tried to go to sleep.

About an hour later, I was woken up by a sound at the window. I sat up and saw Frankie trying to climb back in, but she was having difficulty, so I got up and helped her.

'Are you going to do this every night?' I asked grumpily.

Frankie sighed and said dreamily, 'If only!'

I clambered back into bed and wondered why she took the risk of getting into trouble just for a kiss goodnight. He must be a very good kisser, I thought, as I drifted back to sleep.

It felt as if I'd only been asleep for five minutes, when I was woken by a loud piercing voice shouting through a loudspeaker, 'Wakey-wakey! Rise and shine!'

I thought that the invasion must have started, so I quickly leapt out of bed, grabbed my dressing gown and hurriedly put on my slippers. No one else moved a muscle, except for Rosie, who pulled her sheet over her head and muttered, 'Go back to bed Mary, that's just the wake up call, we've got another half an hour before we have to get up.'

I looked at my watch and saw that it was only six-thirty, but as I was already up I decided that I might as well go to the shower block before the other girls got up. I had never had a hot shower before, as at home and at school there was always a bath and no shower. At school we were able to lock the door while we washed ourselves for privacy, but now I saw that there was a row of showers with only a shower curtain to pull across. I felt a bit shy about anyone seeing me naked, so when one of the girls pulled back the shower curtain and asked me whether she could borrow my soap, I was very embarrassed.

I need not have felt that way as when I came out of the shower most of my roommates were now up and coming into the shower block half naked to have a strip wash at the basins. The room soon became like a steam bath, as gallons of hot water ran into the drain from the basins. While the other girls were in the showers, I took the opportunity to put my silver cigarette case in the ST bag that I'd taken from the lavatory, as Elsie had suggested. When I was back in our hut, I then tucked the bag into my handbag and locked it into my suitcase, which I then put in the store cupboard with the other girls' luggage.

After breakfast I went for my first training session, which consisted mostly of marching up and down the parade ground. Most of the other new recruits, like me, were wearing cotton skirts and blouses, and having made the decision to wear my gym shoes instead of my sensible leather shoes, I hoped that I wouldn't get any blisters.

The air was warm and the sun was out, and I was used to doing PT at school, so I rather enjoyed the exercise. A male Chief Petty Officer (CPO) was in charge of the drill and seemed determined to transform this gaggle of uncoordinated young women into disciplined naval Wrens. He yelled at us until he was hoarse, and when a few of us went to our left, instead of to our right, which made us giggle, his face grew even redder and he told us not to disgrace the Navy. There was complete silence after that.

At morning break, the NAAFI was packed out with perspiring, panting girls, begging the kind volunteers behind the counter for a drink of water. I had a quick drink and then ran back to the hut to change my blouse. As I was running back towards the parade ground, I was surprised to hear my name being called over the loudspeaker: 'Mary Arden to report, at the double, to the Wren First Officer for category assessment.'

I had no idea where the First Officer's office was, and had to ask someone the way. I ran as fast as I could, arriving pink faced and breathless. There were about twenty other girls there already waiting to be sorted into suitable categories. I was told to leave my gasmask case on the pile by the door with everyone else's. Looking at the pile of cases, I was thankful that my mother had suggested that I stick a red cross onto the outside corner of the flap, as they all looked the same and this would make it easier for me to recognize mine.

Before we were due to go in to see the First Officer we all received instructions, 'You address the Wren Officer as Ma'am, stand to attention until you are told to sit down, and do not speak until spoken to.'

When my turn came, I entered the room feeling slightly nervous, but when I saw that the first Officer was a young and attractive woman with a smile on her face, I promptly forgot all that I had just been told.

Smiling back broadly I said, 'Good morning Ma'am.'

The First Officer looked slightly surprised for a moment, and then told me to sit down. At least I had remembered to call her Ma'am, I thought.

The First Officer told me that she'd received quite a few applications to join as Boat Crew from girls that had been brought up in fishing villages, so I must not be too disappointed if I didn't get a place in this category.

'How old are you?' she asked, 'I know it's down on the form but I'd like you to tell me once again, it will save time.'

'I'm eighteen Ma'am,' I replied.

'I see that you've helped out in Woking Cottage Hospital. What does 'helping out' mean?' she asked.

'I'm trusted with administering dressings and medicines, but I don't mind carrying trays and emptying bedpans if they're short staffed,' I said proudly.

'I must warn you that Boat Crew is a far cry from 'helping out' in a hospital. You won't be sailing dinghies, you know; you'll be helping a liberty boat crew go from ship to shore, and they go out in all weathers throughout the year, and it can be very rough and tough work.'

'Oh, I don't mind when it's rough,' I replied cheerfully, 'That's when one feels really at sea. If I was Boat Crew maybe I could be of use as a translator, as I've noticed that there are many boats in the harbour with flags from all over the world, and we learned about identifying flags when I was a Girl Guide.'

The First Officer made a note and said, 'That's very observant of you.' Then she looked at me and began, 'I'm going to ask you rather a strange question now Arden: how much experience do you have with men?'

When I didn't answer her, she realised that I didn't understand her question, 'What I mean is, are you used to being around men? I see from your application that you were educated at a boarding school just for girls.'

'Oh, I see,' I said, 'Well I have two brothers, and a lot of the time when I was growing up there were other boys in the house, as all our neighbours were boys. So I'm not shy with boys, if that's what you mean.'

The First Officer looked down at her notes, and then at me.

'Would you mind staying up late at night? Because if you work as Boat Crew the hours can be very long and unpredictable; and you will be expected to work all hours of the day and night.'

'Oh yes, Ma'am,' I replied eagerly 'recently, while doing the Season, 'I've been up late dancing half the night.'

The First Officer trying to conceal her laughter, then said, 'I hope you brought suitable clothing to wear on a boat?'

'Yes, Ma'am. I have navy slacks, deck shoes and a warm pullover.'

'If you are accepted in this category, you will be fitted out with oilskins, suitable clothes and underclothes from the stores.'

The First Officer looked at me seriously and then said, 'Arden, I hope you're aware that if you become a Wren you will be what we term 'Other Rank' and you will always have to obey the orders of your Senior Officers, and forget all about your privileged background.'

'Yes, I know that,' I replied cheerfully. 'I must call male Senior Officers 'Sir' and Wren Officers 'Ma'am', and always salute them when out of doors. I read it all in the pamphlet. I don't mind: rules are rules after all, and if it helps us to win the war, I don't mind a jot.'

The First Officer raised her hand to silence me and said, 'Full instructions for your trial for Boat Crew tomorrow morning will be left outside the door of this office at sixteen hundred hours. Collect them in good time, read them carefully, and I advise you to get up early tomorrow morning and ensure you have checked the map that will be attached to your instructions, as you will have to find your own way to the quayside.' Then, as an afterthought, she suggested that it would be a good idea if I ate a cooked breakfast, as she doubted there would be time for lunch when I was on the boat.

'Thanks awfully for warning me,' I said brightly. 'I'll get something from the NAAFI or make myself a sandwich from my breakfast ration.'

The First Officer now laughed openly, and reminded me that if I became a Wren I would not be allowed to talk to other officers in such a familiar manner.

I apologised, and said that I'd do my best. As I left, I felt elated that I was going to have the chance to prove myself suitable as Boat Crew.

The next morning I ate as much as I could for breakfast, and then made myself a couple of marmalade sandwiches. I then returned to my hut to collect my pullover and the natty little scarf that Aunt Beth had given me, and set off full of confidence. In my gasmask case I was carrying a pair of sunglasses to protect my eyes, my marmalade sandwiches, the usual lipstick and a comb.

Although I'd studied the map and instructions the previous evening and again that morning, I still had to ask directions several times, and it took me quite some time to find my way to the quayside. When I finally got there, a naval policeman stopped me at the barrier and asked me why I was wearing civilian clothes on government property without an identity card.

'Oh, I've got my pass,' I explained hastily showing it to him together with my instructions for the day, which thankfully, had been signed by the First Officer, 'I'm having a trial run on a liberty boat today as Boat Crew, and I have to report to CPO Brownlow. Do you know where I can find him please?'

He hesitated, looked at my paperwork and then at me again, and appearing to decide that my papers were in order, pointed to a boat that was moored a short distance from where I was standing, outside the gate. Slowly the barrier began to rise and the naval policeman waved me in, and then called out: 'Good luck!'

I turned back and waved. As I cheerfully strode towards the boat I saw that there were several sailors already on board, and then noticed a man wearing the uniform of a CPO, so I made my way towards him.

'Mary Arden?' the man enquired.

'Yes Chief,' I replied, grinning from ear to ear and handing him my papers.

'I'm CPO Brownlow,' he said, smiling at me. 'If you don't mind me saying so, you are a bit small for Boat Crew. All the other candidates are twice your size with muscles as big as a man's.'

'I am stronger than I look,' I reassured him, but I could see by the way he was looking at me that he didn't think I would be tough enough to be part of his crew.

CPO Brownlow then told me to take a look around the vessel, which I did with great interest. Although I had plenty of sailing experience in various small boats during the summer holidays, I now realised that this would be completely different, and that I hadn't really thought it through enough. However, I was determined to give it a try, and was not going to give up before we had even left the harbour.

CPO Brownlow gave the crew their duties for the day. They had been ordered to pick up some Officers from the quay, and then take them from the shore to their ship. After the Chief had finished talking, he pointed at me and gestured for me to sit near the helm. I watched as two of the young crewmen cast off, and noticed how heavy the ropes were and that they really had to exert themselves to handle them.

'Why are the ropes so thick?' I asked one of the sailors.

'Because the boat is damn heavy Miss!' he replied, 'and you don't want them to break when you are out in rough weather trying to tie up to a Destroyer or a Battleship.'

I felt a bit foolish having asked such an obvious question, and decided that I would keep my mouth shut and just watch from now on.

A very tall sailor, whom the others called 'Shorty', then walked up to the helm. He leaned over to press a button and then the engine roared into life. As he took the tiller he explained that he had to reverse the boat away from the quay before heading out of the harbour. I asked him whether steering a boat was like driving a car, explaining that I'd had some driving lessons recently, and knew a bit about gears. Shorty smiled and then patiently explained that there were some similarities between steering a boat and driving a car, except when reversing, but that you have to be extra careful because the boat has a habit of going to port when you want it to go starboard.

'Oh I know all about port and starboard,' I said proudly.

'I hope you know a bit more than that, Miss, otherwise you are not going to be much use to us as Boat Crew,' he said seriously.

I bit my lip and didn't reply. Shorty, then said kindly, 'Watch everything I do and I will explain what I am doing and why, as we go along, alright?'

'Thank you,' I said gratefully.

An hour later, we had collected three loads of ship-to-shore passengers and I was beginning to understand what was required from a member of a Boat Crew.

When CPO Brownlow came to see how I was doing, Shorty told him that he thought that I was now ready to take over the helm, as long as he was nearby.

'Just in case Miss!' he said smiling at me.

As I began to reverse away from the quay, I came dangerously close to the harbour wall, the result of which was that the entire crew almost ended up on their backsides.

'Sorry,' I called out as I hurriedly corrected the tiller, and then vowed I wouldn't make that mistake again.

I steered the liberty boat on two more trips before lunch without any mishaps, but when I attempted to climb onto the quayside from the boat, it was obvious that my legs weren't long enough and I wouldn't be able to jump that far without falling in the water. Thankfully two Naval Officers, who we were bringing back to shore, very kindly lifted me onto the quay.

'Thanks awfully,' I beamed, 'I never would have managed on my own.'

The crew took themselves off for an hour, leaving Chief Brownlow and me on our own. I offered the Chief one of my marmalade sandwiches and he gave me a cup of tea from his flask in exchange, and then puffed at his pipe.

After lunch we set off again and did two more trips to take various personnel to their ships or bring some back to the harbour. As the afternoon progressed, the wind started to get up and at one point I got very wet; a kind Officer then mopped me down with his handkerchief. By the end of the day, I was really enjoying myself and starting to feel more confident again. When we tied up for the last time that day, the Chief thanked me for my hard work and for sharing my marmalade sandwiches with him. He promised to send in a good report of my day's efforts but said, regretfully, that he didn't think this category was a suitable one for me because I just didn't have the strength required to do the job. Reluctantly, I had to agree with him, and accepted that I would have to apply for a different category. Oh well at least I had a go, I thought.

The following day, I bumped into Elsie who invited me out for the evening with some of her other friends. She told me to put on my party skirt but nothing too smart because we were only going to the pub.

'Don't forget to bring yer purse, as we all go Dutch, an' bring yer own fags unless you don't mind smokin' Woodbines,' she told me, chuckling heartily, 'and don't bring that bleedin' 'silver thing'.'

That evening we went to a very old and picturesque pub called the Blue Dolphin, which looked as if it had been built in Nelson's day. The moment we stepped inside, a cloud of stale cigarette smoke hit us, so I decided that the only way to blot out the smell was to add more to it, and was very glad that I'd brought ample cigarettes to share with Elsie and her friends.

'What's yours' sweetheart?' a cheeky sailor asked me swaggering over to the bar as if he owned the place.

I noticed that he was wearing an anchor on his sleeve and thought he must be a Leading Seaman, but I wasn't sure as I'd only just worked out how to distinguish Commanders from Captains, and Lieutenant Commanders from Sub-Lieutenants, and hadn't expected to be mixing with Other Ranks that evening.

'I'd love a cider please,' I replied handing him a shilling. 'Will that be enough?'

'I 'spect so darling, and if not, I'll get the rest when I come back with your drink.'

Elsie ordered a port and lemon, something my father would have had a fit about had he known, as port to him was like Holy Communion wine and one didn't add lemon to it – ever.

I listened to the men talking to each other about football and their families, and realised just how important these two things were to them. Their lives seemed far less complicated than those of the men who had escorted me to dances during the season, and I soon found myself chatting comfortably with them. As I lit another Woodbine, I wondered what my mother would have thought if she had seen me sitting there smoking the cheapest cigarettes available and talking to young men I hadn't been formally introduced to. I think she would have had a fit!

I now turned to one of the sailors who was showing a photograph to one of his friends and asked him if it was of his girlfriend. The others at the table all burst out laughing, and when I looked the photo I understood why, it was a photo of his pet dog.

After a few beers the talk got a rather bawdy, which made me feel uncomfortable, so I just sat quietly and said nothing hoping that the jokes wouldn't get too rude. We had a couple more drinks and a few packets of crisps and then it was time to leave. As we were leaving the pub, Elsie whispered to me that I shouldn't get upset about the rude jokes, as these sailors were just having a bit of schoolboy fun and wouldn't talk about things 'below the belt' when ladies were present. I felt relieved, but also a bit out of my depth, as I was still so innocent and unworldly in anything connected with sex. I told Elsie that I had a bit of a headache and asked her how she planned to get us back to the barracks, 'Are we getting a lift with your friends?'

'No, they are going in a different direction, but don't worry, there will be lots of transport coming and going, so we'll thumb a lift,' Elsie said.

'Thumb a lift?' I asked. 'What does that mean?'

'Watch and learn, Mary,' Elsie replied.

She then stood in the middle of the road and gestured with her thumb the direction we wanted to go. A jeep slowed down and stopped next to us. When Elsie told the driver that we were trying to get back to HMS Vernon, he told us to hop in and we were on our way. That was my first lesson in how to thumb a lift and I thought if that's all it takes, then I would try it next time for myself.

The lorry dropped us just outside the guardroom gates, where we showed our passes, before going through the gate.

'Thanks for taking me with you Elsie,' I said. 'I had a lovely time and it certainly took my mind off failing to become Boat Crew.'

'That's all right luv, are you 'oping to be a driver now instead then?' she asked.

'I hope so, I'll find out tomorrow.'

'In that case you'd better get yerself orf to bed then. Good night Mary,' she said as she turned and went towards her billet.

'Good night,' I called back as I started walking towards my Nissen hut.

'And good luck!' I heard Elsie call out.

I must have fallen asleep the moment my head hit the pillow that night, as the next thing I heard was, 'Wakey-wakey! Rise and shine!'

That morning I ate my usual cooked breakfast, and just in case it was necessary to miss lunch to attend my interview as a potential driver, I also made a sausage sandwich from the breakfast rations.

Square bashing that morning involved learning how to salute the Navy way, which meant squashing my thumb tightly into the palm of my hand so that only the outside of my four fingers would show before raising it to my forehead. My fellow trainees and I were just getting the hang of it when my name was called over the loudspeaker, asking me to go directly to the transport unit at 14:00 hours.

I rushed back to the billet before lunch and changed into my trousers, and then collected everything I thought I might need for the afternoon and put it in my gasmask case, hiding my gasmask under my knickers like all the other girls did, and saying out loud to myself, 'To hell with it, if I get caught, tough luck!' I was beginning to realise that if I wanted to survive my time in the Wrens I would have to bend the rules like everyone else.

I arrived at the transport unit promptly at two. The Chief Petty Officer of transport looked me up and down with a stern, unsmiling face: 'You're a bit small to drive a lorry,' he observed.

'I'll manage,' I told him cheerfully, 'when I was learning to drive, I put a cushion behind my back and moved the seat forward, and that made all the difference.'

'I am sorry, but the Navy don't provide cushions!' he replied smiling. 'Did you bring one with you?'

'No, Chief.'

He struggled to put the seat as far forward as it would go, saying that this was the smallest transport lorry in the yard, and then told me to get in while he went to find an empty sack, which he then rolled up and placed behind my back. I could only just reach the pedals, because either the seat was too high or my legs were too short.

'Perhaps I could drive a car instead?' I suggested eagerly, 'My brother said that he thought I'd be really quite a good driver given another half-dozen lessons.'

'You could do that, Miss,' the CPO replied, 'but the trouble is, in the Navy, you have to drive a lorry before you're put on cars, unless you're an Officer and already hold a driving licence.'

'Couldn't you make an exception for me?' I begged. 'I really will work hard, I promise.'

The Chief's face broke into a grin as he said, 'Regretfully, rules is rules and it wouldn't be fair to give you privileges that the other girls didn't get as well; anyway, the senior officer Wren wouldn't allow it.'

He then asked me if I'd tried any other category, so I explained that I'd been out the day before as Boat Crew, but that I obviously hadn't passed or I wouldn't have been told to report here.

He then asked to look at my hands, and seeing my well-manicured fingernails shook his head and said, 'I thought I might be able to use you as a mechanic, but seeing your delicate hands, I don't think you'd have the strength to use the tools required for this sort of manual work.'

'Oh dear, it looks like I'll end up having to do typing and shorthand in a stuffy office all day,' I told him sadly.

When I caught up with Elsie later that evening, and told her about my failure earlier in the day, she joked, 'Yer might be the wrong 'eight, but you ain't the wrong shape, I saw how them boys were looking at you last night.'

'Well there isn't a category for models,' I replied, giggling with her. 'So what am I going to do next?'

Just then, I noticed Elsie spooning copious amounts of sugar into her tea, and my mother's request for extra sugar, came to mind, so I took the opportunity to ask Elsie if it was possible for her to get me some sugar from the kitchen, which I would pay for of course.

'Can't 'elp love, sorry,' Elsie replied, 'they watch the store cupboards as if they'd 'idden the bleedin' crown jewels inside, but tell you what, I've seen lots of the girls take their tea ration lumps of sugar and stuff 'em in a bag, and they don't save it to eat it like an 'orse later neither, but they takes what they've collected 'ome to their families on their forty-eights.'

'What are forty-eights, Elsie?' I asked puzzled.

'It's a pass. You know, you gets in the train, goes 'ome and comes back again forty-eight hours la'er,' she explained.

'Of course,' I exclaimed laughing, 'how stupid of me.'

From that day on, I saved the two sugar lumps we were allowed to take at every meal and put them away in a paper bag to save up for my next visit home.

Back at the hut, I found an official note on my bed telling me to report at First Officer Smitherson's office at 09:00 hours the following morning. I presumed that she'd suggest that I do a typing course, or even decide to send me home.

When I arrived at the First Officer's office a little before nine, she confirmed that I hadn't been considered suitable as either Boat Crew or Driver because of my small stature, and then seeing how upset I was, she said kindly, 'I will try to arrange for you to have a typing test tomorrow to see if that would be a more suitable category for you.'

The next morning I returned to the First Officer's office expecting her to send me to another hut to do my typing test, but when she greeted me she said, 'There has been a slight change of plan, and I think I may have found the perfect category for you. It's called a Night Vision Tester.'

My job, which was a fairly new category, would be to teach the young pilots how to use their eyes differently when flying at night. I would have to learn how to use specialised equipment to teach the pilots how to take off and land on their aircraft carriers more safely in the dark. This important category came under the authority of the Special Ophthalmic Unit, attached to HMS Daedalus at Lee-on-Solent in Portsmouth. The person in command of this department was Surgeon Commander Timpston, who had come up with the idea in order to reduce the amount of accidents pilots were having at night.

The First Officer told me that the reason she had been contacted by the Commander was because he was considering the idea of training a younger girl to help with the tests in the hope that the pilots might be more willing to attend this additional training if there was an attractive girl present.

'He needs someone who the pilots will find easy to talk to, someone who's a bit nearer their own age,' the First Officer explained, 'so I think you would be suitable for this new category, but I must warn you that the work will involve sitting in total darkness with six young men at a time while their eyes adapt to the dark. I suspect that some of the boys might play up a bit and flirt with you. Would you feel uncomfortable about that?'

'Not a bit. I am used to boys, and will just treat them all like my big brothers,' I replied.

The First Officer told me that I would have to go for an interview and that she would let me know when and where later. As she dismissed me, she said how pleased she was that there was now a category that was more suited to my capabilities and stature.

'I hope I haven't been too much trouble for you, and thank you for putting me forward for this new position. It sounds much more up my street,' I said happily.

'I think so too,' she replied.

Later that evening, I rang home and reversed the call. My father answered, and I told him as calmly and quietly as I could about the interview I was to have the following day as a Night Vision Tester.

'It's a relief that I've been given this chance as it sounds so much more interesting than just typing,' I told him. 'Keep your fingers crossed for me, Daddy.'

'My darling daughter,' he chuckled, 'you're a very capable young girl although you don't seem to realise that yet. I'm sure that given the chance, and if this is right for you, then you'll be accepted. Try not to chatter too much at your interview though, and make sure the interviewer does most of the talking!'

I felt too nervous to face a cooked breakfast the next morning, so just had a small bowl of cornflakes and a cup of tea before heading off to find the transport that had been allocated to take me to the ferry terminal, where I was supposed to catch the ferry to Gosport.

It was great fun crossing the Solent on the green passenger ferry from Portsmouth. During the crossing I kept my eyes skinned hoping that I'd catch sight of Chief Brownlow's liberty boat, so that I could wave to him, but there were so many boats coming and going that it was hard to tell one from another, so I just waved to them all.

When I arrived at Gosport, I looked around for any naval transport to take me to HMS Daedalus, but all I could see were two official-looking cars, both of which had smartly dressed drivers standing beside them. I was starting to fret, as I didn't want to be late for my interview and I was beginning to wonder whether I ought to try and walk, but thought better of it as I had no idea how far away HMS Daedalus was from the port.

To my relief, I spotted a seaman tying up a boat on the quayside and hurried over to ask him if he knew where I could catch a bus.

'No buses here love,' he replied, shaking his head.

'A taxi perhaps?' I suggested hopefully.

'Have to be ordered ahead of time, Miss, sorry,' he said shaking his head again.

I'll just have to do what Elsie did the other night then, I thought, and thumb a lift from a passing car. The trouble was that there didn't seem to be any passing cars. Just then I saw three young sub-lieutenants coming towards me, and then two navy cars drew up in the yard. The officers immediately hurried towards the first car, which sped off so quickly I didn't have time to ask for a lift. Then I noticed an older man with gold braid on his sleeve walking slowly towards the second car, and without thinking too much about it, I walked quickly towards him and said, 'Excuse me, but I'm ship-wrecked and need help.'

The Captain looked at me and said smiling, 'It sounds like you have missed the naval transport that usually meets the ferry, so can I assume that you are requiring a lift?'

'Well yes Sir, you assume right, as I'm on my way to HMS Daedalus for an interview with Surgeon Commander Timpston, so I don't want to be late,' I told him.

'Hop in, we will make sure you get to your interview on time,' he said kindly.

Once we were both in the car, the Captain ordered the driver to take us to the sick bay on the sea front, and when we arrived he said, 'I shall keep my fingers crossed for you, young lady. Good luck!'

I walked into the Special Ophthalmic Unit and was greeted by a Wren Writer who asked me my name and then told me to follow her upstairs. We walked along a long corridor before she stopped and knocked on a door, with the name Surgeon Commander Timpston on it.

'Enter!' a man's voice boomed out from behind the door. The Wren Writer opened the door and gestured for me to go in.

Surgeon Commander Timpston was sitting behind his desk looking intently at a file with a rather serious expression on his face, but when he looked up and saw me come into his office he gave me a big smile, which made me immediately feel relaxed.

'Good morning Sir,' I said extending my hand before remembering that I wasn't supposed to do that. 'I'm sorry I'm a bit late, but there wasn't any transport. Thankfully I managed to thumb a lift with a kind officer!' I waffled on, forgetting my father's advice about talking too much. 'Wasn't I lucky? Otherwise I might have been late for my interview.'

The Surgeon Commander laughed, obviously seeing the funny side of my predicament. It was good to know that he had a sense of humour. He then stood up and shook my hand briefly before pointing to a chair, indicating for me to sit down.

'I received a letter about you from First Officer Smitherson. She has recommended you to me, and thinks you are well suited for the work here,' he explained. 'She also mentioned that you speak several languages, which would be very useful to us.'

'First Officer Smitherson has been very kind to me Sir, and has been doing her best to find the right category for me,' I replied.

'She and I are not only colleagues but our families are old friends as well,' he continued, 'So I trust her judgement.'

He then explained that the work they were doing there was very serious, and he wanted me to understand the importance of it as it could save lives. If I was accepted, I would not only be training pilots how to use night vision, but also assessing their ability to see in the dark and I would be finding out the reasons why some of the pilots seemed to fail their tests when there was no physical problems with their eyes.

'I need someone who will get on well enough with my boys to sense if the reason for failing their night-vision test goes deeper than just their bad eyesight,' he continued.

'First Officer Smitherson describes you as 'very well put together' and feels that you will be absolutely perfect for what we're looking for. However, I have to tell you that the category of Night Vision Tester does not reflect the importance of the role; it's in the Leading Wren category, which is only one up from the lowest rank. I have been doing my best to get this work upgraded to reflect the responsibility that goes with it, but so far, Night Vision Tester is still considered Other Rank I'm afraid.'

I told him that I understood; I was well under age for a commission anyway, so not being an officer would not worry me one bit.

The Surgeon Commander smiled, 'I'll ask my most experienced Night Vision Tester to explain it all to you in a while but, basically, you will be training pilots how to use their night vision, which requires a different way of seeing than when using one's eyes in daylight. I'm convinced that this training saves pilots' lives, as it prevents them from being blinded when a bright light upsets their darkness adaption.'

I went cold with shock, and asked, 'Would this training help pilots blinded by search lights?'

'Certainly,' the Surgeon Commander replied emphatically.

'Then, Sir, I must do this work!' I said without a moment's hesitation and told him how my dear friend Andrew had lost his life, when he had been caught in the Germans searchlights. When the interview was over he told me to wait outside the office for his senior Night Vision Tester, who arrived shortly afterwards.

'Hello, I'm Lydia Grey,' she said warmly, 'are you the new girl?'

'Oh, I do hope so,' I exclaimed.

I liked Lydia immediately. As I looked around her office, I noticed that there were two typewriters on a long shelf, a cupboard full of forms, a telephone, and two small table lamps. The room was warm and had a carpet on the floor and, oh bliss, a gas fire for the winter months. We walked to the darkroom, so that I could see where the Night Vision Testing took place and then Lydia told me that I could watch her conduct a test after lunch to get an idea of what it was all about.

As we walked to the Wrens' mess, she explained that only four Night Vision Testers had been trained so far and each of them had been posted to different naval air stations after their training. She told me that the individual Senior Surgeon at each air station was responsible for the unit, but that Surgeon Commander Timpston took overall command of the NVT category.

'He is like a father to us, so we have nicknamed him Daddy-T,' she giggled, 'and he protects us from the bossy Wren Petty Officers as well,' Lydia added smiling. 'However,' she continued seriously, 'out of working hours, naturally, we all have to obey naval discipline like all the other Wrens.'

While we ate our meal, Lydia warned me that if I was accepted as part of the Night Vision Testing team it would take several weeks for me to learn how to do the testing, but if I was patient and didn't mind sitting in and watching her for a few days, she was quite sure that I'd learn to manage on my own without too much difficulty.

After lunch we went back to the eye unit, and Lydia led me straight down to the cellar where the Night Vision Tests were carried out. I noticed that the darkroom door had been left wide open, so she explained that this was because they took every opportunity to air the room between tests. Lydia then showed me a hexagonal machine that had six chairs placed all around it.

'When it's switched on, silhouettes show up on all six sides. These vary from images of a plane, a car, a house, an apple or whatever, and they are difficult to see, but we train the men to understand that if they move their eyes sideways, the images become much clearer.'

I thought it sounded quite complicated, but decided to wait until I had seen a test before asking any further questions.

'When the men sit on the chairs, we clip on these short chains to the back of their collars and then to the chairs, but first of all we measure the correct distance they need to be from the machine, so that they are all exactly the same distance away.' She paused for a moment while I took in the information.

'The clips often come undone if the men try to cheat and lean too far forward in order to see the silhouettes better, but I don't make a fuss, and just clip them back on. Don't worry you'll soon be able to feel your way from chair to chair in the darkness to clip them on again; the men seldom try to cheat a second time,' she said with a grin. 'While the men are doing this test we lock the door so that no-one can come in and let in the light, because it takes twenty minutes for the eyes to become adapted to the dark, so if the door is opened and light gets in, we have to start the test all over again, and there just isn't any time to spare, as Testers have to carry out four tests a day.'

'Do you mind being locked in a dark room with six men?' I asked.

'I don't really think about it,' Lydia replied, 'I just get on with the job.'

She then pointed out what she called a panic button, situated just above the main light switch.

'In an emergency, I know I can alert the office upstairs where a spare key is kept, and someone will be down here in seconds,' she laughed. 'But, thankfully, so far, I've never had to use it. What you do have to remember, of course, is to always take the key from the lock inside and hang it on the wall before you start the test, that way, if you do need rescuing, the key will fit in the lock on the other side.'

I thought it sounded very sensible, but couldn't imagine what kind of an emergency a Tester might need rescuing from. Lydia now showed me how the men used Braille boards.

'They're similar to those used by blind people,' she explained. 'As you can see, the metal strips are spaced inches apart, with another strip down the middle, so that the men taking the test can feel with their fingers where each space is, to write down what they think they are seeing on the silhouette machine.

'It's all very straightforward once you know what you are doing,' she continued, 'and we often let the boys have a trial run. You see that there's a pencil attached to a string on each board? One of our jobs first thing in the morning is to make sure that the pencils are sharp and that we have a few spares in this jam jar ready, just in case someone presses too hard and breaks the lead.'

I felt certain that I could do all of this, and I was thankful that there was no height restriction to do the job.

'It will take you a while to learn the words of the lecture that the Testers give the men, as their eyes adapt to the dark and, of course, you must be able to understand it all yourself first!' Lydia chuckled. 'But there's no hurry, it took me several weeks to learn it and I'll give you any help you need.'

Lydia asked me if I had any questions. I told her that I had, but I would wait until after that afternoon's test so that I could see for myself how it all worked. I was relieved that Lydia was a patient teacher, and started to get excited about the prospect of becoming a Tester myself.

Lydia went on, 'One other thing, Mary, you'll have to get used to a bit of schoolboy horseplay, especially when you get to the part of the lecture that explains how essential it is for pilots not to drink any alcohol for at least twenty-four hours before flying at night, because doing so affects their night vision. You should hear some of the moans and groans and swearing!'

Later that afternoon I attended a test with Lydia. We sat in the pitch-dark Test Room with six men, as I listened to Lydia giving them her lecture on how to see in the dark and how to use their eyes differently by using things called Rods and Cells. I wondered whether I would be able to remember it all, as it sounded very complicated. She then began the test with the hexagonal machine, and I tried to recognise the correct shapes made by the silhouettes. I found it quite difficult initially, but when I moved my eyes sideways and looked at them from a different angle, they became much clearer and I began to understand what the test was all about.

The men started muttering curses under their breath as they clumsily held the Braille boards in their hands, trying to write down what they were looking at in the dark. Several of the men leaned forward too far so that their clips pinged off their collars, and I wondered how Lydia managed to clip them back on again without falling flat on her face, or worse still, landing in one of the men's laps.

When the test was over, we all had to wait for a few minutes until our eyes adapted to the light again, and then Lydia told the men to file out of the room and go back upstairs into the daylight. After they'd all left, I helped Lydia tidy up the room before we made our way back up to her office. She then asked me to excuse her, while she went to report to Daddy-T. After a few minutes, she came back to tell me that he now wanted to see me, so I followed her back to Commander Timpston's office and after she left he asked me to sit down.

'I hope you found today interesting Mary?' he asked.

'Oh yes Sir, absolutely fascinating.'

'Good, good,' he said smiling. 'Well Lydia has told me that she thinks you could cope with the job quite well, and as I mentioned before, I trust her judgement completely, so if you would like to become one of my Night Vision Testers, then I'd love to have you on board.'

I wanted to run over and hug him, but fortunately managed to restrain myself and simply say, 'Thank you Sir', and then went to find Lydia to give her a hug instead.

It was obvious that she still had a lot to do that day, so I told her that I had better go before it started getting dark. As I was about to leave Lydia said, 'It could be a month before I see you here again, Mary. At first you'll be sent home and then you'll return to Vernon to be kitted out with your uniform before starting work with us here at Daedalus. Make sure you bring a few civilian clothes with you to change into in the evening. We're not allowed to go out with the naval officers while wearing our uniforms because we are Other Ranks, so we get over the problem by wearing our civvies, which means we don't have to salute them or call them 'Sir'!'

Lydia then gave me a piece of paper, which authorised transport for me back to the ferry at Gosport, and then said, 'Well Mary, welcome aboard, and look forward to seeing you soon.'

It was only when I started making my way downstairs that it dawned on me that I had at last been accepted, and I was now a Wren.

CHAPTER 7

1942

When I got home to Woking, my parents wanted to hear all about what I had been doing for the last two weeks at HMS Vernon. It felt a bit like school holidays again, with me chatting non-stop about the different categories I had tried for. They were thrilled to hear that I had been accepted into the Wrens at last, and my mother started making a list of all the clothes she thought would be suitable for me to take when I returned to start my training.

When I went to see Kay, her son Richard proudly introduced me to his new little sister, who they had decided to call Julie.

'She's so tiny, Kay,' I said in wonderment, 'I hardly dare hold her.'

Kay gently placed Julie in my lap while I told her all about my experiences of the last two weeks. She asked me how long I would be in Woking before having to go back, as she wanted to have the Christening while I was at home, and asked me to be Julie's godmother. I was thrilled.

The Christening was held the following week and was a small celebration with only her nearest relatives and closest friends attending. My mother and I put on our prettiest hats and we all had a happy day filled with laughter. When it was my turn to hold the baby, I was convinced that she smiled at me, but my mother told me later that all young babies do that.

'It's wind!' she said laughing.

When my brother William came back from his cadets' camp, I was amazed at how tall he had grown, and although he looked strong and healthy, I sensed that something was wrong, so later that evening I asked him what was upsetting him.

'With Peter away, God only knows where,' poor William began, 'and with you about to go away too, how will I know where to find you or Peter if anything bad happens to our parents?'

I tried to reassure him by promising to send him my address the moment I knew it.

The next morning, my instructions arrived in the post, telling me to report back to HMS Vernon in two days time; the letter was accompanied by a rail-voucher from Woking to Portsmouth.

On the day of my departure, my father took my suitcase in his car and I stuffed everything else either in my bicycle basket, or strapped it onto the grid over the back wheel. As I pedalled to the station I decided that it would be better to send my luggage in advance, when I was sent to another naval air station in the future.

When the train arrived my father helped me to load my bicycle and suitcase into the Guard's van, and then kissed me goodbye. I told him that I would ring him as often as I could, and he reminded me to reverse the charges.

I was thankful to see that there was a lorry to meet me when I got to Portsmouth, especially as I needed help with my bike and luggage. On arriving at HMS Vernon I was allocated a different Nissen hut to the one I'd slept in before. The mattress on my bed was even harder than the last one had been, if that was possible.

On my first day back, I was told to report to the Sick Bay for my inoculations. The only jab I reacted to was the one for diphtheria, which hurt and caused my arm to swell-up. It also gave me a temperature for the next twenty-four hours.

I collected my Wren's uniform, and didn't mind wearing the rather baggy outfit too much but I hated the hideous pudding basin hat, as it made me look like a schoolgirl. How I envied the officers in their smart three-cornered hats! A few days later when I returned to the naval stores, a friendly male Petty Officer told me not to worry about my hat as a new style had just been ordered for Other Rank Wrens and it was shaped like a sailor's hat. He then showed me how to sew on the HMS Vernon hatband loosely, so that I'd be able to slip it off and replace it with an HMS Daedalus band once I moved there.

The Petty Officer then asked me whether my shoes were comfortable. I smiled and said that they fitted like a glove, which made him laugh, but he knew what I meant.

I would now need to buy an additional suitcase to pack all my uniform in, so I asked whether I might buy one of the nice green canvas suitcases with brown leather at each corner that I could see on the shelf.

'Sorry love, they're only for h'officers,' the Petty Officer explained, pointing out the one for Other Ranks, which was brown and appeared to be made of cardboard, so I turned my nose up at it. He kindly suggested that if I caught the bus outside the gates, it would take me into Portsmouth town centre where I would be able to buy a squashy holdall bag, which might be more my style and perhaps more useful too. He then issued me with some badges to sew on my coats, with anchors on them to show that I was now a Leading Wren.

That afternoon, First Officer Smitherson called me to her office and wished me good luck. She explained that she would receive occasional reports about my progress from Commander Timpston, and that if I was ever in difficulties, I was to go to him for advice.

'Good luck Leading Wren Arden,' she said as I left her office.

The day I arrived at Lee-on-Solent, a driver was waiting to collect me. I explained to him that I was billeted in one of the bungalows belonging to Commander Timpston's unit a short distance from HMS Daedalus, and asked him whether he'd mind me dropping off my belongings first before reporting to the main base.

When we got to the bungalow I found that the curtains were drawn and all the doors were locked. The driver helped me put my luggage into the garden shed before leaving me to make my own way to HMS Daedalus by bicycle.

I now had to check in at the Billeting Office first, and then report to Commander Timpston to tell him that I'd arrived. I reached the main gate, showed my identity papers and cycled on to the Billeting Office, but then a Wren Petty Officer suddenly barked, 'You are wearing the wrong hat-band! You should have the one for HMS Daedalus not Vernon, you stupid girl.'

'But I've only just arrived and I haven't had time to sew it on yet,' I protested.

'Don't answer back. Go and sew one on now and report straight back after you have done that,' the Wren Petty Officer screeched. She was obviously a bully.

'Yes Petty Officer,' I replied meekly and then headed straight to the NAAFI, where I bought a packet of needles and thread. By the time I had sewn on my new hatband I was feeling hungry and my stomach was rumbling, but I was too scared to stop for lunch, so hurried back again to the Billeting Office.

The Wren Petty Officer examined my sewing efforts and with a look of disdain said, 'I suppose that will have to do'. She then confirmed that I'd be billeted in the bungalow about a quarter of a mile from HMS Daedalus, which she said was locked between ten and five. 'You will have to leave your case at your place of work for today.'

I didn't understand why she found it necessary to be quite so harsh, and hoped that the other Wren Petty Officers weren't quite as officious.

I hurried towards the eye unit to report for work, where I hoped that I'd find Lydia, but when I got to her office, it was deserted, so I climbed back onto my bicycle and headed back towards the NAAFI to see if she was there.

When I got there, I saw Lydia about to walk in, so called out to her. It was a relief to see a familiar face again and after I told her about my encounter with the nasty Wren PO, she told me not to worry; and said that they all acted like prison guards.

'You will soon get used to those bossy cows!' she said laughing. 'Petty Officers are a bit like sergeants in the army, and think that they can bark at anyone with lower rank than themselves, but I can assure you that those with officer rank are helpful, and will be much kinder to you. Don't worry too much, and if you have a real problem with any of them, I will take you to see Daddy-T as he protects us from people like that.'

That afternoon I sat in on one of the tests and did my best to understand the lecture Lydia gave the pilots. By five that afternoon my head was swimming, and I began to worry that it could be days before I would be able to understand it, let alone memorise it all.

After high tea, we went straight to the bungalow and Lydia helped me carry my things to the room, which we would be sharing from now on. 'This is your bed and this is your chest of drawers. You can have one side of the wardrobe as well, which I've already cleared for you.'

As I started to unpack, Lydia explained that I would need to make up a small bag of everything that I would require for each day, as the bungalow was out-of-bounds during the day.

'You can leave them in a cupboard at the Wren's cloakroom like I do,' she suggested, 'I always pack a spare shirt in case I spill anything on the one I'm wearing, and a spare pair of stockings in case I get a ladder, and perhaps anything personal that you feel you might need.'

'Thanks,' I said, and continued unpacking my things. When I'd finished we sat together reading in the sitting room. I must have fallen asleep, as I was woken with a start by the sound of someone moving about noisily at the back of the bungalow.

'It's only Joan, one of the Stewards,' Lydia said looking up from her book, 'if you hurry you can go and clean your teeth first before she uses the bathroom.'

I thanked Lydia once again for her help and kindness and, yawning announced that I was going to have an early night.

'Make sure to have your torch by your bed in case there's an air raid during the night. Goodnight Mary.'

I went and brushed my teeth before happily slipping into bed, which felt soft and luxurious compared to the bed in the Nissen hut at Vernon. I sighed to myself: things were not so bad after all; I'd just have to learn to put up with the horrible Wren Petty Officers.

The next morning, Lydia told me that she never ate breakfast and that she'd see me at the NVT office a bit later. I was quite glad to be on my own as it gave me some time to get my bearings before starting work at nine.

When I arrived at the office, Lydia gave me some filing to do and then handed me a copy of the printed lecture and told me to start memorising it. I spent the rest of the day following her around like a shadow, watching everything she did.

My first week at HMS Daedalus seemed to go by very quickly, and I learned all about how our eyes work, both during the day and at night; however, I was quite conscious that I was still not word-perfect on the half-hour lecture and would have to work harder on that. When Lydia told me that it had taken her three weeks to learn it all, so not to get too worried about it, I felt relieved.

By the second week, Lydia trusted me to measure the distance between the hexagonal machine and the men's foreheads and felt that she could leave me in charge of clipping their collars to their chairs, explaining to them why it was necessary. Some of the men made silly remarks and when one of them asked me out for a drink in the evening, I just said with a smile,

'I'd love to some time, but at the moment I'm far too busy to spare the time.'

Lydia then told me I was ready to handle my first solo test session, and fortunately it went without a hitch, so from then on Lydia and I took the tests in turns, both doing one test in the morning and another in the afternoon. At first Lydia checked my typed reports, but after a week or so, she felt confident enough to leave me to it.

I saw very little of Commander Timpston during my first month except to say 'Good Morning Sir' and 'Goodnight Sir', until one of the Wren Writer's asked me if I would be willing to take over her duties as 'Chief Tea and Coffee Maker' for the doctors in the Eye Unit, which included the Commander. I was happy to do this for her as it gave me the opportunity to get to know the medical staff better.

The first time I took Commander Timpston his coffee, he asked me if everything was going well, so I told him that it was, and that I was enjoying working at his unit. He then asked what I did in the evenings, and I told him that I liked reading. He was interested to know what kind of books I read, and raised an eyebrow when I mentioned that I was reading a book about psychology and how the mind works.

When I collected the dirty cups and saucers, I noticed that Daddy-T never ate his biscuits, which didn't surprise me, as they tasted like cardboard and were not very appetising. At the NAAFI that evening I asked one of the volunteer ladies serving behind the counter if there was any chance of buying a packet of chocolate biscuits, and explained that they weren't for me but for the doctors at the eye unit. She smiled and said she would see what she could do.

The next time I went to collect the Commander's coffee tray I noticed that he had eaten both his chocolate biscuits. He looked up with a broad grin on his face and asked me where I had managed to rustle up the new biscuits.

'I've made friends with one of the volunteer ladies in the NAAFI, Sir,' I replied.

'Well done, they really are delicious Mary,' he said. 'By the way, I have some books in my office that you might like to read, they're all about how the human mind works, they are very interesting, and will be useful in your work.'

Within two months I was being entrusted with the Night Vision re-tests that were held on Saturday mornings, as one-to-one sessions, and Lydia told me that she now felt I could manage full time on my own for a couple of weeks, so she was going to take some well-earned leave to go and see her family.

'I'll book in the tests before I go, and only book in three a day instead of four so that you won't get too tired. But, Mary,' she added seriously, 'if one of the men fails his test, you must make sure it's a genuine failure, and not an excuse to be alone with you in the dark!'

I laughed, and assured Lydia that I was learning to tell the difference, 'I sense the ones who really are unable to do the test, as if they're sending out signals for help,' I told her, 'whereas I can pick out the naughty boys that try to flirt with me before they even come through the door, so don't worry, Lydia, but thanks for the warning.'

The following Saturday while Lydia was on leave, I had to do a re-test, and halfway through, I sensed that the young man I was testing was becoming very distressed. He didn't do or say anything in particular, I just knew, so I asked him what was worrying him.

'If I fail this second test my father will never forgive me,' he confessed. 'He has always told me that I am a failure ever since I was little, so if I am grounded and not allowed to fly, he will accuse me of failing on purpose and of being a coward.'

'If you did fail it doesn't make you a coward, it just means you can't see very well in the dark,' I told him truthfully.

There was silence for a moment, and then the pilot let out a deep sigh. 'It's not that I'm afraid of being killed' he said quietly, 'I'm prepared for my death if it comes to it; but I don't want to be responsible for someone else's death, and if I must fly with an Observer and I can't see in the dark when landing at night, I would not only kill myself but him as well.'

'Have you ever thought of becoming an Observer yourself? That way you wouldn't be responsible for flying at night. And with your flying experience you would make an excellent one I'm sure,' I suggested encouragingly.

As he left he thanked me for being so understanding. When I checked his test results against his first test, I noticed that he had done a little better, but had still failed. I wondered whether it was psychological, and whether his fear of his father had affected the outcome.

When I returned to work the following Monday, I wrote a note to Commander Timpston asking him if he could please spare a minute or two to speak to me, as I needed his advice about the young pilot's fear.

'He definitely isn't a coward, Sir, I'm sure of that, it's just that he's convinced that his father sees him as a failure, and he's terrified he will fail when he's flying, and kill not only himself, but also his Observer. I don't think he really has trouble seeing in the dark, it's something far deeper than that, and I was wondering if you could talk to him and help him in some way?'

'You could be right, Mary,' the Commander said thoughtfully, 'but what made you so sure that he had a problem in the first place?'

'Intuition I suppose, I just felt that he was asking for help without actually saying so out loud, and I wondered whether failing the Night Vision Test was his way of asking for the help he needed. He seems to be convinced that he is a failure; he told me that was what his father had told him ever since he was a little boy.'

Commander Timpston stared at me with interest and then asked, 'Do you really believe that you can read people's thoughts sometimes, particularly when they're distressed?'

'Yes Sir, I believe I can,' I answered honestly, looking him straight in the eye.

'Let me have the pilot's name,' he said, 'and I'll see what I can do to help him. It's an area that interests me too. I have a very interesting book on ESP at home, which I'll bring in for you, as I think you'll find it interesting.'

'Thank you very much, Sir,' I replied, 'What does ESP stand for?'

'Extra Sensory Perception and I think you may have this gift, Mary, so read the book and then we can discuss it all another time.'

When Lydia returned from leave, she looked rested and in good spirits, and told me that she was delighted to see that I'd managed so well on my own. As a reward I could take a forty-eight and have a long weekend at home, so that evening I wrote to Elsie to suggest that we meet up for lunch in Portsmouth on the Saturday before I went home to see my family.

'I'll treat you to fish and chips and we can have a good gossip before I catch the train to Woking,' I wrote, enclosing a stamped addressed envelope to save her the cost. I couldn't wait to see Elsie again to tell her all about my first few weeks at HMS Daedalus.

The next day I was typing out a report when the Commander came into the office.

'Here's the book I mentioned to you,' he said kindly.

'Thank you Sir, I'll save it to read when I next go home on leave.'

'I know when that is Mary,' he said, looking at me intensely and putting one of his fingers to his forehead as though he was concentrating hard and trying to read my thoughts.

'E-S-P?' I asked him in all seriousness.

'No, 4-8-P,' he chuckled, 'I have just approved your weekend pass!'

It was good to see Elsie again, and while we ate our fish and chips we were chattering non-stop about what we had both been up to since we last saw each other.

'What are the pilots like Mary? Are they givin' you any trouble?' Elsie enquired.

'What sort of trouble do you mean, Elsie?'

'Like pinching yer bum when the lights are out!'

'Elsie! You are naughty, trust you to think of that,' I giggled. 'The answer is no, they are all perfect gentlemen.'

'Oh, are they?' Elsie said raising one eyebrow, 'So have you've been asked out then?'

'Well, yes, actually, I have,' I told her.

'Oh you h'ave, h'ave you, h'actually!' Elsie said trying to copy the way I spoke, which made us both laugh.

I then told her that I had turned down all the invitations to go out, as I had so much to learn for my new job, and after I had done my studying, I was just too tired to go anywhere.

I asked Elsie if she had met anyone and she replied, 'Fat chance with me 'air smelling of boiled cabbage and fried onions! By the time we've finished our shift all we want to do is collapse and go back to our 'ut!'

We continued nattering for over an hour before it was time for me to leave.

'Could you get me permission to 'ave a look at where yer working next time I gets a forty-eight?' Elsie asked, as I kissed her goodbye. 'Then I could get one of your nice h'officers to take me down the pub, 'specially as yer too bloomin' busy to go out with 'em!'

'I am sure they would be delighted to meet such a lovely young lady as you,' I joked back. 'And I am sure there must be one of them that has no sense of smell and won't mind the fried onions!'

Elsie roared with laughter and said, 'Cheeky cow! You'd better get yer skates on Mary or you'll miss yer train.' I looked at my watch and realised she was right.

'See you later alligator!' Elsie shouted as I hurried towards the station.

As the train pulled into Woking, I felt overjoyed to be home again and told my parents everything that I'd been up to, since I had last seen them.

That evening, I rang Archie McIndoe to tell him my news and how grateful I was that he'd suggested I join the Wrens. Uncle Archie and I talked for ages and he pulled my leg mercilessly about sitting in a pitch-dark room with six burly men.

The next day I went next door to see Mrs Derwent to get the latest news of her boys. She told me that Robert was now in the desert somewhere, which I could tell was worrying her, and that Edward had got married and that they were expecting their first baby. It suddenly struck me how sad Edward must feel that his dear friend Henry would never see his first child, as I am sure he would have been the godfather.

When I rang Jane, who was staying at her Uncle Oliver's house in Cornwall, while she was working as his private secretary, we had our usual long gossip. I was delighted to hear what a lively social life she was having. Her Uncle regularly invited young Army officers to the house when they were off duty and she was also meeting-up with several of her long-lost cousins. She then mentioned that there was one special cousin, who she rather liked, called James.

For the rest of my leave, I tried to finish reading the book that Daddy-T had lent me. My mother had also found time to read it, and told me that she thought that I must have ESP, as I often said what she was about to say just before she had a chance to say it. She had spoken to Uncle Archie about my strange ability once, and he had told her that he hoped I would be able to use it to help others one day.

Before I left home to go back to HMS Daedalus, I did as Lydia had suggested and swapped over my lighter summer clothes for warmer autumn wear. I was glad that I had decided to stay an extra night with my parents and catch the five-thirty milk train on the Monday morning, as it gave me a chance to listen to ITMA with my parents. They loved the programme as it was so funny and such a contrast from the seriousness of the war.

We then listened to the news and were heartened to hear that the British Eighth Army commanded by General Montgomery or Monty, as everyone now called him, had halted Irwin Rommel's offensive at Alam el Halfa.

When I woke up at 5 a.m. to catch the early-morning milk train from Woking to Portsmouth, I had no idea that this day would nearly turn out to be my last.

Catching the milk train early on a Monday morning was a tip that I had got from some of my Wren friends. It meant that I could spend an extra night at home rather than having to leave after tea on the Sunday. Still yawning, I quickly picked up my overnight case, slung my gasmask case over my shoulder and leapt onto the platform. The elderly guard grinned, as he helped me lift my bicycle out of the guard's van, its basket over-flowing with things I hadn't been able to fit into my case. I had always tried to travel light since joining the WRNS, but so far had never succeeded, as there always seemed to be extras to take back with me: a mackintosh, a bed rug, a new novel, more civilian clothes, which I would squash into my basket or tie onto the grid at the back of my bicycle along with my overnight case.

As soon as the train arrived in Portsmouth, I hurried towards the 'Green Ferry' waiting to cross the bay to Gosport, and then decided to pay a visit to the Ladies before the half-hour ride to HMS Daedalus, the Royal Naval air station where I was working as a Night Vision Tester. I did think it rather odd, when I came out of the WC, that no one seemed to be about: there were no cars with drivers waiting to collect the officers, or even sailors waiting patiently to be picked up by lorries but just assumed that everyone must have already left for the Naval base while I was in the loo.

As I cycled along the deserted road towards Lee-on-Solent I thought how beautiful and quiet it was, apart from the sound of birds. When I got about halfway I looked at the church clock and was relieved to see that I still had plenty of time to get there.

Just as I reached the avenue that led to HMS Daedalus, a small aircraft flew directly over my head. It was flying very low and the downdraft was so violent that it made the leaves fall from the trees. I glanced up as the aircraft turned away above one of the houses and disappeared from view; then suddenly there is was again. It was almost as if the road had become the runway and it was now heading straight towards me.

Wobbling all over the road and shaking with fear, I yelled angrily at the pilot, 'I'll report you to your Commanding Officer!'

I then saw two aircraft following each other across the sea. I could see that one of them was a British plane, but the other one was unfamiliar to me. Both aircraft were flying very fast and low, as if they were chasing one another. Low flying was forbidden in a built-up area and I thought you silly boys, you will get into real trouble.

Both aircraft then swung towards the hill near my billet on the seafront and disappeared from view. I sighed with relief and was just regaining my composure, when I heard a loud engine roar getting closer and closer and when I looked up I couldn't believe what I was seeing. On the wings of the plane flying in my direction were black crosses. It was a German Messerschmitt. I braked sharply.

I then heard the sound of gunfire followed by a different sound, the roar of another plane. It was one of ours.

My goodness, a dogfight is going on right above my head, I now realised, as more gunfire sent me into a cold sweat. Suddenly a hail of bullets hit the road not very far from where I was, and that's when instinct took over. I dropped my bicycle in the middle of the road and quickly ran for cover. I saw a high garden wall and decided that the sooner I got behind it the better. It was a life-saving decision. I only just made it over the wall, as more bullets hit the road right at the spot where I had been standing only seconds before.

I pressed my body as close as possible to the base of the garden wall, hoping that any stray bullets would hit the wall on the roadside and not on my side of the wall. I lay there shaking for at least five minutes before I dared to move again. Just as I was about to stand up the sound of more gunfire getting closer and closer stopped me in my tracks. I was ridged with fear.

'Please God… I am too young to die!' I screamed at the sky, hoping God was listening. Up until now I had only been scared for the people I knew and cared about being killed, but now the thought that I might die too suddenly occurred to me.

The reality came as quite a shock. My parents would have been devastated if I had died. I was still only eighteen, the war having started when I was just fifteen, when passing my school exams had been my priority. Remembering the summer of '39 that I'd spent without a care in the world, I now thought how utterly and unbelievably different my life was now to how it was back then.

I stayed curled up at the base of the wall until I felt safe enough to stand up again. I was a bit wobbly, so put my hand on the wall to steady myself. It was a good four and a-half feet tall: how the hell had I managed to jump over that?

When I went to pick up my bicycle, I noticed that the front wheel was now twisted at a funny angle, which would make it impossible for me to ride, so I'd have to push it the rest of the way. I then looked at my watch and realised with horror that I'd be very late for work.

Just as I got back to the base, I heard the All Clear siren. So that's why I hadn't seen anybody in Gosport, I now realised. Everyone must have taken cover in the air raid shelters. Somehow I had missed the siren going off while I was in the loo.

I propped my damaged bike against the Sick Bay wall, grabbed my belongings and gas mask and made my way towards the Sick Bay side-door, which all ranks other than the officers used. Suddenly the door burst open and three Sick Bay attendants (SBAs) ran out. They were presumably coming up for a breath of air from the cellar, which was used as an air raid shelter. One of the SBAs looked at me aghast, as I staggered towards them. The reason became clear as I looked down and saw that my legs were covered in cuts, still dripping with blood, and my skirt was covered with dirt.

'There was a dogfight and I had to run for cover,' I was able to say, before my legs gave way beneath me and I fainted.

When I regained consciousness, I was in the sickbay, and Commander Timpston's angry face glared down at me.

'Where the hell have you been?'

'I'm sorry I'm late Sir, I left myself plenty of time to get here, but I got caught up in a dogfight. I had no idea there was an air raid on, as I didn't hear the warning signal.'

Commander Timpston barked, 'For God's sake girl, what's all this nonsense about a dogfight? There haven't been any dogfights that I know about this morning. And where were you this morning? When the siren went off we couldn't find you anywhere, you had me worried sick. Look at the state you're in. Did you fall off your bicycle?'

'No Sir, I didn't fall off,' I replied indignantly, 'I was being shot at, so I had to jump off, and then take shelter behind a wall, as quickly as possible.'

'I don't believe you. You obviously didn't come back to the base last night, and just decided to waltz in at your leisure this morning. You have taken advantage of my trust in you, which I am not happy about. Come to my office at one-thirty,' he ordered 'and then I want a full explanation as to why you are almost two hours late. Meanwhile, you'd better get those legs attended to.'

After he left, one of the SBAs gave me a tetanus jab, which gave me time to think about why Daddy-T had been so angry with me. I realised that he wouldn't have heard the planes fly overhead if he had been in the air raid shelter, so maybe that's why my story had sounded far-fetched to him and he had thought I was lying.

While the SBA tended to my cuts and grazes, I asked him if he knew anybody at the air base who might be able to mend my bicycle, 'The front wheel's all askew; it must have happened when I leapt off the bike, and I can't ride it again until it's mended.'

'I have a pal in the transport section,' he replied, 'if anyone can fix it, he will. I'll let you know later, leave it to me.'

After I'd told Lydia what had happened and that I felt sick, she offered to do my work for me, but I didn't wanted to make a fuss, so told her I could manage.

Later that morning, the SBA came to our office and told me that I should go to the transport division at lunchtime to see Chief Marsden, as he was willing to mend my bicycle. So I did exactly that. The chief asked light heartedly whether I'd been doing some target practice firing bullets at it. I looked at the mudguard and realised it must have been hit by one of the bullets from the plane. 'I'll hammer the sharp edge flat,' he offered, 'but if I were you. I would replace it later.'

At one-thirty sharp, I knocked at Commander's Timpston's office door. He called me in, but didn't invite me to sit down, as he usually did so I guessed I was still in trouble.

'I must say Mary, I am disappointed that you abused my trust and lied to me about why you were late this morning.' He then brusquely ordered me to sit down pointing to a chair. 'So I now want you to tell me exactly what happened, why you weren't sleeping here last night as you should have been, and why you were so late, because I'm obliged to make out a report when anyone I'm responsible for gets hurt in any way, so it's important that you tell me the truth. Is that understood?'

As I fought back tears, I told him what had happened to me, 'In order to have an extra night at home with my family last night, I took the milk train very early this morning. I have done this before and always had plenty of time to get here before nine. But this time there must have been an air raid on when I arrived in Gosport, but I never heard any siren so I was totally unaware that there was any danger. I did think it was a bit odd that there was nobody about; but I didn't think anything more of it other than that it was a bit unusual. When I got to the halfway mark, where the church is, I looked at the clock and it said half-past eight, so I knew I still had plenty of time so didn't have to ride too fast.'

'Then why the hell were you so late, girl?' he snapped.

'Suddenly I heard two planes overheard having a dogfight and bullets were raining down all over the place, so I leapt off my bike and somehow managed to jump over a garden wall. I landed on the other side and that's how I cut my legs.'

'And your hands, how did you hurt them?' he asked.

'I must have injured them at the same time, Sir, but I don't remember. I was just so frightened.'

'All right Mary. Go back to work and I'll talk to you later.'

I tried to keep myself busy all afternoon, and not think about what had happened that morning but it was hard not to. I knew that I was lucky to still be alive.

At the end of the day, Commander Timpston asked me to come back to his office, and to my relief he apologised for being so brusque with me that morning.

'Since I spoke to you, I have discovered that a German plane was shot down in the sea between Lee-on-Solent and Portsmouth this morning. The pilot was rescued by lifeboat and is now, I assume, a POW. Apparently, several other people in Portsmouth witnessed the dogfight in which you were unfortunate enough to be involved in. I am sorry for not believing you but it seemed farfetched at the time. In future if you are planning to stay an extra night with your parents, please let either Lydia or myself know, that way we won't wonder where the hell you are!'

I was relieved that my story had been verified, but was a little hurt that the Commander had not believed me right away.

That night, Lydia suggested that I went to bed early and gave me a couple of aspirins to help me sleep, but the terrifying experience of having bullets fired so close to me kept me awake and I relived the moment again and again, before finally drifting off to sleep.

When I arrived at the eye unit, the following morning, the senior male nurse at the sick bay exclaimed, 'My God Mary! I went to see the place where you said that you were caught up in the dogfight on my way home last night and there was debris all over the road. It was a right old mess I can tell you. That wall is riddled with bullet holes, so you were one damn lucky girl, not to get hit.'

Having done my best to try and forget the incident, it all came rushing back and I thought I might faint again, but Lydia was standing nearby and seeing that I was a bit wobbly, made me sit down until I had recovered. She then offered to do my tests for me until I felt better, but I assured her that doing the tests would take my mind off it all, which they did thank goodness.

The following week, I asked Commander Timpston whether I could invite my friend Elsie over to the air base next time she had leave, so that she could see where I worked. He asked me who she was so I told him what a good friend she had been to me. He said that he had no objection, so that night, I wrote to Elsie to let her know that I was looking forward to seeing her and that I would meet her off the ferry. She wrote back giving me the date and estimated time of arrival.

The day before Elsie was due to arrive, Commander Timpston called me into his office, and I was worried that he might have changed his mind, but instead he said, 'First Officer Smitherson has just spoken to me on the phone, and I'm afraid she has asked me to convey some very sad news to you. Your friend, Elsie, was killed during an air raid two nights ago, while she was visiting her family in London.'

I sat in total shock for a moment and then shut my eyes and whispered quietly, 'I thought I was bad luck to boys, not girls as well. It looks like I am bad luck to everyone I get fond of.'

'What do you mean by that Mary?' the Commander asked.

So I told him about Andrew, Henry and Charles all being killed, and how hard it had hit me.

'This war is not your fault, it's the Nazis', so you must never think that you are in any way responsible for the death of your friends. We have all lost friends in this damn war, Mary, so all we can do is put on a brave face, and try to win it.'

Although Daddy-T's kind words were a big help, I felt very sad and cried myself to sleep that night. When I went back to work the next day, I decided that all I could do was 'carry on as usual', so although I was grieving for yet another friend, I managed to get all the tests done without a problem.

The following week I received a long brown envelope in the post, which contained my new chequebook and a two-page bank statement. I glanced through it quickly, noticing with surprise that the last six items were marked in red ink and wondered why that was, so wrote back to the bank to ask them if they had run out of black ink, or whether there was some other reason.

Two days later, I received a letter from the Head Bank Clerk telling me that, no they had not run out of black ink; the reason they had used red ink was because my current account was overdrawn. He suggested that to stop it happening again, he could automatically transfer money from my deposit account into my current account, as soon as I went below ten pounds. He had enclosed a form for me to sign and send back, which would authorise them to do this, so I filled it in and posted it later that same day.

The next time I went home on leave, my father told me that my letter had caused so much amusement at the bank, that they'd telephoned him to share the 'red ink' joke with him. I was very embarrassed.

My father sat me down and made me add up all the expenses that I had recorded in my chequebook stubs and then gave me another lesson in bookkeeping. He suggested that I limit my spending each month from now on to avoid going overdrawn again.

When I got back to HMS Daedalus on the Monday morning, one of the Wren Writers came rushing into our office and yelled to Lydia and me, 'Good news girls. All Other Rank Wrens are now to be issued with new navy blue sailor-style hats, so at last those hideous schoolgirl pudding-basin hats are no longer!' We all cheered.

That evening, Lydia and I took the hatbands from our old hats and happily sewed them onto our new ones; we then admired ourselves in the mirror. I couldn't wait to show my mother, as she would think this new hat was rather stylish, especially when tipped slightly to one side.

The next day, Daddy-T called me to his office, 'I hope you don't mind, Mary, but I urgently need you to go to HMS Heron at Yeovilton in Somerset. Anne Briscoe who is in charge there, is overworked and really is in need of another Wren to help her out; she is well overdue some leave, so once you are settled, you will be expected to take over her duties. Do you think you will be able to manage that?'

'If you think I can, Sir, then I'm sure I can,' I replied. 'I don't mind where I go, but I've no idea where Yeovilton is.'

'I'll show you on the map later,' Daddy-T said and then told me that he'd arranged for me to take a week's leave, so that I could take my belongings home to Woking and re-pack whatever I thought I might need for the winter, as he thought it was unlikely that I'd have any additional leave for at least the next four months.

'You've done well here, Mary, and I'm proud of you,' he said.

'Thank for all the time you've spent teaching me about psychology and for lending me some of your books. I'll miss you Sir,' I said. 'You're my first 'Boss' if you know what I mean?'

'And I won't be the last, Mary,' Commander Timpston now said seriously. 'I'm afraid the war will go on for several years yet, but remember, when you get posted somewhere else after Yeovilton, it'll be me that's sending you, and I'll be in touch personally before you go. I never send any of my Wrens anywhere unless they're quite happy about it.'

'Thank you again Sir, for being so kind to me,' I said sincerely, 'after the war I hope you and your wife will come and meet my parents, I know they'd like to meet you one day.'

'I'll look forward to that!' Daddy-T said with a big grin.

When I told Lydia that I would be leaving soon she said, 'Lucky you! I will have to stay here and train another girl who will most probably be even more stupid than you!'

'Thank you so much my dear, dear friend!' I laughed.

As the train pulled into Woking station, I was glad to see my father waiting on the platform for me rather than by his car. I had two cases, an overnight case and my bicycle to get out of the guard's van, and I definitely needed his help. We piled my luggage into his car, and as he drove off, I rode my bicycle all the way home in hot pursuit.

When I arrived home, my mother told me that she was a bit upset because she had only just realised that when I went to Yeovilton the following week, it would mean that I would be away for Christmas for the first time in my life.

'You'll be homesick,' she fussed, 'and won't know anyone.'

My father pointed out how lucky we had all been that I had been allowed to come backwards and forwards at weekends, as often as I had over the last few months.

The next day, after my mother had helped me work out what I needed to take with me, my father organised for my luggage to be sent to Yeovil, via Carter Paterson, in advance along with my bicycle. This, he told me, would mean that I wouldn't have to lug more than one suitcase and an overnight bag on the train journey.

The day before I was due to leave, I went and said goodbye to all my friends, and then I called in at Aunt Nora's to get news of the Derwent boys, and to let her know where they could all contact me.

On the morning of my departure, Mrs Green, our new cook, armed me with a large packet of sandwiches, two apples and bar of chocolate to sustain me on the journey. I also received a present from Agnes who'd saved up two weeks' rations working at the 'Munitions' to buy me some sweets to suck on the train.

Although I wasn't quite sure what I was letting myself in for, I felt quite excited as I waved goodbye to my family.

I had to change trains at Southampton, and I was glad to see an old porter with a barrow who I got to help me take my case to the correct platform for the connecting train to Salisbury, where I would then have to change trains again, to go on to Yeovil. I was glad that my father had sent most of my luggage in advance, so that I didn't have to lug my bicycle from platform to platform.

When the train finally arrived at Yeovil, I got off the train and saw a Chief Petty Officer looking around and scratching his head; he was obviously waiting for someone, so I hoped it was me.

'Excuse me have you come to take me to HMS Heron?' I asked hopefully. The Chief turned and asked, 'Leading Wren Arden?'

'That's me,' I said cheerfully, putting out my hand. 'Good afternoon.'

The Chief looked quite taken aback, wiped his hand on the back of his trousers, and then shook my hand.

'I am sorry, but I was expecting someone much older,' he said, and then looking at my luggage asked me, 'is this all you have?'

'I'm afraid not,' I said apologetically, 'my bicycle should be waiting for me in Left Luggage, as well as another case.'

'Oh dear, I am sorry, but I will have to organise a lorry to pick them up for you later, as there is not enough room in the car,' the Chief said, explaining that he also had to pick up two Officers, and as their train had been delayed we would have to wait for them. He suggested that I went to check to see if my luggage had arrived, while we waited.

I found the stationmaster who asked to see my Carter Paterson receipt, confirmed that my things had arrived, and assured me that he would personally check that it was all loaded onto the lorry when it arrived.

When I went back to the car, the Chief asked me if I felt like a cup of tea, 'It'll fill in the time and it's nice and warm in the café,' he explained. After a short drive, he drew up opposite a row of tiny shops, one of which was called Polly's Tearoom.

'Go on in while I park up, and tell Dot that TNT is following up behind,' he said with a wink.

'TNT?' I asked.

'Well, it's short for Tony, and I work in Transport,' he explained patiently. 'So it's a joke, see, Tony N' Transport!'

I walked into the café, and asked, 'Excuse me, is there someone here called Dot?'

'Who's asking?' a middle aged woman replied looking a bit surprised.

'TNT told me to say that he was following up behind,' I replied.

Dot looked me up and down for a moment and then a broad grin spread across her face and she roared with laughter.

'Tea for two,' I asked, and then I noticed some delicious Bath buns in the glass cabinet, 'and could I have two of those, as well please.'

'So that's TFT for TNT is it love?' Dot asked which made us both laugh.

TNT then came into the café and sat down on the chair next to me. As we sipped our tea and ate our buns, TNT very firmly put some money on the table and said jokingly, 'If we're to make a habit of this Wren Arden, we'd better go Dutch!'

When it was time to collect the Officers, TNT told me to stay inside the cafe to keep warm while he collected them, and then he would pick me up. About fifteen minutes later I spotted his car outside, so I quickly thanked Dot for the delicious tea, telling her that I would come back soon.

I ran across the road to the car where TNT was waiting with two young Sub-Lieutenants sitting in the back seat. I hopped in the front seat next to TNT, and then turned around to the back seat and said 'Good afternoon'. The Officers smiled back at me, but I kept quiet as TNT drove us back to the air station, as I wasn't sure whether it was against the rules to talk to him while he was driving with two Officers in the back, and I didn't want to get him into trouble.

Arriving at the gates of HMS Heron, a guard came up to the car and I showed him my pass. He then checked the Officers' passes and we drove on to the Wren Billeting Officers' hut, where TNT dropped me off. As he lifted my luggage out of the boot I thanked him for looking after me so well, and then asked how I would contact him to find out when he had the time to collect my bicycle and cases.

'I'll leave a note at the NAAFI with one of the tea ladies.' TNT assured me, hurrying back over to the car. 'Good luck Mary,' he called as he drove off.

I knocked on the door of the small building and when I went in the Petty Officer said, 'I was expecting you an hour ago.' I apologised for keeping her waiting and explained that the driver had to wait for two other passengers arriving on a later train.

The Petty Officer told me that I was to be billeted in quarters at an old Inn in a nearby village, which was five miles from HMS Heron. Transport would be provided to and fro to work each day.

I told her that I'd brought my bicycle with me, and that Transport would be picking it up the following day along with my luggage. I then asked, 'Am I allowed to use my bicycle instead of the official transport on a fine day?'

'It's up to you,' the Petty Officer said 'as long as you're not late for work, but personally, I wouldn't recommend it at night, especially at this time of year, as the lanes are narrow and dark and with only the light from your bicycle lamp, it wouldn't really be safe. But, certainly, in the summer it would be all right.'

The Petty Officer then went on to explain that the rules and regulations for the billet were pinned on a board there, and that it was essential I familiarise myself with all the rules. 'I expect you're familiar with the system for late passes, permissions, and signing the book and so on?'

I told her that I'd never required a late pass, but that if I intended being late I would ask one of the other girls what to do.

'This will be your first Christmas away from home, I expect, but you will find it's a happy time here at HMS Heron,' the Petty Officer said kindly. 'We try and make it as homely as possible. Heron is a small air station, so you'll soon make friends.'

The Petty Officer now handed me a piece of paper with my new address on it and told me to take my suitcase up to the NAAFI, where I could leave it until the official transport arrived to take me to my billet. She then said that the other Night Vision Tester, Anne Briscoe, was not in the same billet as me because she'd specifically asked to stay on the air station. Apparently, she was nervous about being in the countryside. How strange, I thought. Personally, I loved the smell of horses and cows and newly mowed hay; and as I was in Somerset, I thought there would most probably be a lovely smell of cider apples too. I couldn't wait for the weekend to get out on my bicycle and explore.

I went to the NAAFI and left my case with a kind lady called Bella who told me she would keep an eye on it while I had a meal in the Wren's mess.

The mess was a home from home, as they all looked the same. I was delighted to find that there were baked potatoes in their jackets for tea and that slabs of butter had been placed on each table along with a bowl brimming with grated cheese. I assumed that all the produce was sourced from the local farms.

As usual, it was noisy with everyone talking at once, but I was pleased to hear happy chatter and see that everyone seemed to be cheerful and laughing. I looked around and saw that all the girls seemed to have healthy complexions; red cheeks, sparkling eyes and wore little or no makeup, which was different to the Wrens I'd got used to seeing at Vernon and Daedalus with their pale faces and bright red lipstick.

Finding an empty seat at a table I sat down and began to eat hungrily, while one of the other girls, still busy chatting to another girl, pushed the butter and cheese towards me. Then the Wren suddenly stood up and yelled, 'Hands up for tea.'

I put up my hand up with everyone else and watched as she walked over to a big table, put six cups and saucers on a tray, poured milk into each cup, and then tipped in the tea from the spout of an industrial-size teapot. The girl then carried the tray back to our table.

As I was handed my tea, I very nearly said, 'Thanks awfully,' but managed to stop myself in the nick of time. One of the girls, realising that I was new here, began to ask me all about myself: where had I been stationed before, what category I belonged to, and where I was going to be living. I took out the piece of paper I'd been given and read out the address.

'Oh, you lucky thing,' one of the girls said, 'You're billeted at the Inn in Queen Camel. Us lot are at Charlton Hawthorn.'

We all chatted for a bit and then I excused myself so that I could walk slowly back to the NAAFI to pick up my case and wait for the official transport. As I walked, I noticed the Administrative Office, where the billeting Petty Officer had told me to report first thing in the morning, I asked a Wren where the Paymaster's Office was, as I needed to leave my pay-book there, and the girl pointed to a path on the left.

I arrived at the NAAFI with plenty of time to spare before my transport arrived, so I went inside and bought myself a cup of coffee. When I went to collect my case, I thanked Bella for keeping an eye on it for me, and then a man's voice called out, 'Anyone for Queen Camel?'

As usual the transport was a lorry, but there was a wooden crate acting as a step, which made it easier for us all to clamber into the back. I listened to the other girls chattering as we drove down the dark country lanes and realised that my billet was out in the sticks. Arriving at the billet, I followed everyone around to the back door, and as we entered, I was grateful to discover that the Inn was properly heated.

There was a Petty Officer sitting by the check-in book watching the girls put a tick against their names. When I was the only one left she looked at me and asked, 'Leading Wren Arden?'

'Yes Petty Officer, that's me,' I replied warily.

The woman looked at me with a puzzled expression and asked if I was the Special Category Night Vision Tester she was expecting. I replied that I was.

'Ah,' the Petty Officer said, 'you're in training I assume?' I thought it was easier just to say yes than to explain that I was now as qualified as Anne Briscoe.

'You're in Room 8,' the Petty Officer said. 'You'll find it overlooking the courtyard at the front of the building, but watch out as you climb the stairs,' she warned, 'the ceilings are very low because that's how coaching inns were built.' Then she handed me two pieces of paper: on one was the times of the transport neatly typed out, and on the other, the rules and regulations of the billet. 'The bath rota is pinned on the bathroom door,' she instructed. 'Ask one of the other Wrens about the ablutions block; sometimes you'll bathe upstairs, and at other times, you'll use the showers behind the bar. I'm off duty now,' she said already heading for the door 'so if there's anything else you need you'll have to ask one of the other Wrens.' She then disappeared through a door at the back of the hall and shut it firmly behind her.

Room 8 I discovered was down a little corridor and on the right. I put my overnight case down and knocked, but there was silence. I opened the door a bit and looked inside. Seeing that it was empty, I went in and noticed that only one bed had been made up and that there was only one set of towels folded on an old-fashioned towel-horse near the washbasin. Is it possible that I've got a room to myself, I thought with glee, what luxury!

I needed the lavatory, so wandered along a corridor where I thought the bathroom would be. I came to a sharp bend on the landing and was confronted by three girls standing in a small laundry room. Some of the girls were helping each other put curlers in their hair while they waited for the kettle to boil to fill their hot-water bottles.

'Excuse me,' I said politely, 'is the lavatory near here? I was told there was a bathroom on this landing, or do I need to use the one downstairs?'

'I'd use the lav' in the ablutions block downstairs,' one of the girls suggested. 'The bathroom up here will be in use for at least the next hour.' She then gave me directions.

'May I use the kettle to fill my hot water bottle a bit later?' I asked somewhat timidly.

'This kettle belongs to Margaret,' a girl with pink rollers in her hair replied. 'I'm sure she won't mind if you use it, but kettles don't last very long here, so we take it in turns to chip in and buy a new one every so often. But meanwhile, you're very welcome to use it.'

'Are you the new girl in number eight?' another girl in a green dressing gown asked.

'Yes I am,' I said, and introduced myself to them all.

I was too tired to unpack everything, so I just emptied out most of my belongings on to one of the beds and hung up my skirt and jacket. I then summoned the energy to empty my gas-mask case of its gas mask and refill it with the usual lipstick and so on, and also pack my day bag with emergency spares; a shirt, stockings, and so on, which from then on I intended to leave permanently at the Sick Bay. With my hot-water bottle now filled to the brim, and my alarm clock set for seven sharp, I was soon sound asleep.

I awoke the following morning bright and early and quickly got washed and dressed. I was ready far too early, but it was just as well because as the Inn slowly came alive, bedlam ensued with half-dressed girls charging up and down the stairs in their panic to get ready for the transport. Sure enough, it arrived on the dot of eight and drove off at five-past.

After breakfast, I familiarised myself with the air station, so that I'd know where all the various offices were, but saw no sign of the Sick Bay and had to ask someone where it was. I was directed to the far end of the airfield towards the Control Tower, which was a good five minutes walk away from all the other buildings.

It was so different to what I'd known at HMS Vernon and Daedalus, but when I pushed lightly on the Sick Bay's swing doors, they opened very easily and I thought that they must be used for stretcher access if an accident occurred on the airfield. Venturing further inside, I realised that the Sick Bay here was in fact a mini-hospital. I approached an SBA and asked, 'Excuse me, does a Wren called Anne Briscoe work in this building?'

The SBA, took his head out of the cupboard, turned around, and grinned at me. 'Who's asking?'

'Leading Wren Arden,' I said brightly. 'I'm the new Night Vision Tester.'

CHAPTER 8

1942

I walked towards the Night Vision Tester office, and knocked on the door. A very quiet voice said, 'Come in.'

'Hello Anne,' I said with a smile, 'I'm Mary Arden. Commander Timpston sent me to help you with the testing.'

Anne Briscoe's face dropped. She was obviously hoping for someone a bit older and more experienced.

'Lydia trained me personally,' I explained, feeling the need to justify myself. 'I've had five months experience, and often been left in charge of the Testing Unit when Lydia was away on leave. I do know what I'm doing and I am here to help you.'

Anne was obviously embarrassed that I'd read her thoughts so clearly, and mumbled something about me looking so young. Then she gave me a rather weak smile and we shook hands. She showed me around the Tester's office, which looked very bare, equipped with only one typewriter, one chair, no proper cupboards for anything, no table lamps and, looking up at the ceiling, I noticed a naked light bulb without a shade.

'Where do you keep your things?' I asked.

'What things?' Anne asked.

'Well, you know all the things you need when you're shut out of your billet all day?' I asked.

'Oh, I see,' Anne said flatly, 'I don't need to bring anything over as I'm allowed into my hut after lunch.' She pointed out of the window to a Nissen hut next to several others hidden among some trees. 'That one is mine.'

'But where do you keep all the stationery? Where's the electric kettle and coffee-making things?' I asked.

Anne looked at me as though I'd just landed from the moon, 'Oh, I don't make coffee here. You can go to the NAAFI when you have a coffee break, but I don't bother, it's too far to go.' She then bent down and pointed to a box under a long wide shelf beneath the window, where she said she kept the stationery, and the files in the box next to it.

'We'll need another typewriter and another chair, so when I put in a chit for those, shall I tell them we also need a filing cabinet and maybe one or two other things as well?' I asked.

'Well I suppose you could do that, ' Anne replied with a worried look on her face, 'but we could just take it in turns to use my typewriter,' she suggested, looking almost frightened, as she then explained, 'Surgeon Commander Lewis is worked off his feet and is very stern. I don't like to ask him for anything.'

'You won't have to, Anne, Daddy-T told me when I left Daedalus that if I found anything that wasn't quite right, that I should call him and he would speak to the Senior Doctor himself.'

'Oh, no, I don't want to make a fuss,' Anne remonstrated.

'It's not making a fuss when you are doing your best and don't have the proper equipment to do it with,' I reassured her 'and, by the way, working under a glaring light bulb like that with no shade is terribly bad for your eyes, and Daddy-T would be horrified if he knew about it.'

Anne smiled now with relief, 'I'd forgotten what a kind, lovely man he is. I have thought of buying a lampshade, because I do find the glare rather trying in the evenings, but it would have meant going to Yeovil to find one, and to be honest, even if I found my way there, I might not find my way back.'

'Leave it to me,' I told her.

I soon discovered that although Anne was obviously lacking in self-esteem, when it came to her job she was very self-assured, and possibly, even more efficient than Lydia.

I asked Anne if she minded if I sat in on one of her tests to see if she did it any differently to Lydia, and if she did, then maybe she would prefer me to do it her way. She said it was up to me.

We went into the Testing room where it felt damp and cold; a small heater of some sort would make all the difference, I thought. Soon six reluctant-looking young pilots turned up, and I positioned myself quietly in a corner and listened.

I was glad that Anne did the test in exactly the same way as Lydia had taught me, very efficiently, but what struck me that morning was that there was not a single laugh during the whole hour we were in the room. As the pilots hurriedly filed out of the room at the end of the test, they looked bored, except for one of them, who waited behind and asked me cheekily, 'Why were you sitting quietly in the corner Little Miss Muffet?'

'I'm here to help the Senior Night Vision Tester, Simple Simon,' I replied, laughing, and then added, 'Aren't you a bit old for nursery rhymes?'

'You can never be too old for a nursery rhyme!' he said, laughing.

'Oh, so are you more of a Peter Pan than a Simple Simon then?'

'That's for you to find out,' the pilot replied, giving me a wink as he left the testing room.

As I turned around to help Anne tidy the braille boards she remarked, 'I wish I was able to be as at ease with the pilots, as you obviously are.'

'It's not so hard, Anne,' I told her, 'I just treat them as though they are my big brothers.'

'I don't have any brothers,' Anne said, in a rather forlorn voice.

'You can share mine!' I joked, and I was rewarded with a huge smile and a small giggle. Well that's a start, I thought, Anne is obviously going to need me around to cheer her up as well as organise her light fittings.

During the afternoon I made a list of all the things I thought we were missing in the office and then made a second list of things that I thought might lift morale, such as a lampshade, an electric kettle, a heater in the Testing room, and a mat on the floor of our office. I then went through Anne's filing system, which consisted of a large cardboard box full of files. It was so heavy that I couldn't lift it off the floor, so I decided there and then to request an extra table and a proper filing cabinet.

After work Anne took me to see her billet. It was quite cosy for a Nissen hut, with pretty curtains at the windows, a small jar of flowers on a table and, I noticed, that there were only four beds instead of the usual six.

As I lay in my bed that night, with a lovely hot water bottle at my feet, I was thankful that I was billeted at the Inn, as it was much better having my own room.

The next morning I decided that I'd better go and introduce myself to Commander Lewis, so went in search of CPO Turner to see whether it was necessary to make an appointment to see the Commander; apparently it was, and the Chief said that he'd arrange it for me. He then called over his two young SBAs, 'Mary, may I introduce my two colleagues. This is Laurel and Hardy.'

'How do you do, Laurel? Hello Hardy, I'm Mary Arden,' I said, shaking their hands. The two SBAs then left and the CPO, realising that I hadn't understood that 'Laurel and Hardy' were just their nicknames, roared with laughter and explained that in the Navy, all tall thin men were given the nickname Laurel, and all short fat men were called Hardy, after the famous silent-movie comedy duo.

'Don't they mind?' I asked, a bit concerned that they might take offence.

'I think they're so used to their nicknames that they've forgotten their real ones,' the CPO joked, 'and I bet they wouldn't answer to their real names if we called out to them now.'

When I got to our office, Anne told me that, as there were now two of us, we would be able to do four tests a day rather than just two. We agreed to do alternate tests, like I had done with Lydia.

The CPO then popped his head around the door and said, 'Surgeon Commander Lewis will see you at 10.30 this morning, Mary.'

'Thanks Chief, by the way we need another typewriter and an extra chair in here. Do you know how we go about getting these things?'

'I'll see to getting these things for you once you have authorisation from the Commander,' the CPO promised.

'There are a few other things we could do with as well.' I said cheekily.

'Well, good luck with that!' he said laughing, as he left the room.

On my way to Commander Lewis's office, I noticed that the door to the Wren Writers' office was ajar, so I decided to go in, introduce myself, and then explain why I was there. I noticed that these girls had everything a proper office should have, including a filing cabinet, a built-in cupboard for stationery, table lamps and plenty of chairs and typewriters.

'Excuse me for asking, but where do you make your coffee and tea?' I asked one of the girls. She opened one of the cupboard doors, and inside there was a tray with mugs, a tin of coffee, a packet of tea leaves, a bowl of sugar, a bottle of milk, and best of all an electric kettle.

Aha, I thought, deciding then and there that I'd definitely add a built-in cupboard to our list of priorities.

'Where's the power point?' I asked, 'Do you plug the kettle in next to the typewriters?'

'And have some nosey Wren PO ticking us off; not on your Nelly!' the girl replied, and pointed to a power socket hidden underneath the shelf in the cupboard. That's exactly what I will ask to have done in our room too, I thought.

One of the other girls then whispered, 'You won't say a word about our electric kettle and secret brewing things, will you?'

'Of course not,' I said, thankful that I wasn't the only one to have problems with bossy Wren POs.

At 10.30 on the dot I knocked on Commander Lewis' door and waited.

A deep voice said, 'Come in.'

The Commander was reading some papers on his desk and gestured for me to sit in one of the chairs without looking up. I could tell immediately that he was overworked and fussed, so decided that I'd better keep my second list with the electric kettle and a lampshade for another time.

'This Testing thing?' he said, still looking down at his papers, 'Is it really worth doing?'

'Yes Sir, I believe it is, ' I said honestly, 'We have recently carried out a special test with some of the pilots where they have had to refrain from drinking for forty-eight hours, and we discovered that their night vision was then twice as good as usual. We now make a special point of reminding pilots and their observers not to drink when night-flying. It would of course be better if they didn't drink at all, but it's asking a bit much isn't it?'

Commander Lewis finally decided to give me his full attention: 'Tell me more.'

I then told him in much more detail about what we had been doing, and how Commander Timpston insisted that the pilots abstain from drinking alcohol for twenty-four hours before flying, day or night. Commander Lewis then told me about the recent spate of careless accidents at HMS Heron, which he thought might have been caused by the pilots drinking too much alcohol, although he admitted that he had no evidence to support this theory. I suggested that he might consider trying the no drinking before flying rule here at HMS Heron, and he nodded agreement.

Now that I had the Commander onside, I thought I'd better take advantage of the moment.

'I understand that at the moment you make all the bookings personally for the Night Visions Tests directly with the Commander Flying,' I said, 'but might I suggest Sir, that if we had some sort of internal telephone extension in the NVT office, we could relieve you of all that work? At Daedalus, the Testers made their own arrangements.'

The Commander looked surprised. 'I only have to organise up to twelve young men a day to come for tests – and an occasional re-testing whatever that is – on a Saturday morning.'

'Yes Sir,' I replied, 'but now there are two of us testing that will mean twenty four or even more tests for you to organise every day.'

'Oh God!' the Commander sighed, 'I hadn't thought of that.'

'If you have no objection, Sir, perhaps you could have a word with the Commander Flying, and once we've got a telephone organised in our office you won't need to concern yourself about our unit at all.'

'I'll think about it,' the Commander said and then went back to reading the papers on his desk. Our meeting was obviously over, but as I still wanted to mention my lists to him, I thought, it's now or never, so spoke up.

'Now that there are two of us, Sir, and there's only equipment for one, we need a few more things for the office; another typewriter, another chair, a proper filing cabinet and somewhere to put all the extra stationery. May I write you a list and leave it with you, perhaps tomorrow?'

'Yes, yes' he said impatiently wanting to get on with his work, 'once I have approved your list, I will authorise CPO Turner to make the necessary arrangements.'

I left Commander Lewis's office and walked as quickly as I could back to tell Anne the good news. She was thrilled and made me recount my whole conversation with the Commander; we agreed that all we had to do now was make one list rather than two, and to my delight, Anne immediately put a fresh sheet of paper in her typewriter and began to make up our new list.

'There is no hurry, Anne,' I said, 'it doesn't have to be in until tomorrow.'

'Let's hand it in this evening, just in case he changes his mind!' Anne said laughing. It was the first time I had seen her look really happy since I had arrived.

The following morning after my first test was finished CPO Turner put his head around the corner of our office door and asked me if I could come to his office for a few minutes, as he had something he needed to discuss with me.

'You've got a nerve, Mary,' CPO Turner chuckled, as he pulled up a chair for me to sit on. To my delight Commander Lewis had said 'no problem' to everything on the list except the built-in cupboard, which he queried. I explained to the CPO that we needed to have somewhere to store stationery and somewhere secure in which to put our personal belongings. 'And somewhere to hide an electric kettle and our tea-making things,' I added cheekily with a grin.

Chief threw his head back and laughed, 'You've been in the Writers' office haven't you?'

'Yes I have,' I replied, 'we don't mind buying our own kettle, but we would need a socket hidden underneath the shelf like they have, if that's possible.'

'Yes Madam!' he joked, 'Anything else I can do for you?'

'Well we do need somewhere to hang our coats and mackintoshes if it's been raining and perhaps a hook inside the cupboard door would be useful too, to hang our gas mask cases on.'

'I think you mean somewhere to hang your handbags!' he grinned.

'How do you know that?' I gasped.

'Nothing gets past me, Mary, and you would do well to remember that,' he said with such a straight face that I wasn't completely sure whether he was pulling my leg or deadly serious, so decided not to push my luck any further.

'I am amazed that the Commander authorised everything.'

'So am I; I suspect that he is so busy that he hasn't really gone through it thoroughly, he's left that to me, so you are jolly lucky that I am in a good mood today,' Chief said wagging a finger at me, but smiling again.

I thanked the Chief and was just about to leave when I remembered the most important thing of all that I had omitted from the list.

'I couldn't help noticing that we haven't got what we called at Daedalus a 'Panic Button' on the NV Testing Room door.'

'What's that?' Chief asked.

'Imagine a girl on her own locked in a pitch-dark room with several young men. Obviously, things could get out of hand, and if it did, then she could press a panic button, which sets off an alarm in the corridor to alert someone outside the room to come to her rescue,' I explained and suggested that a spare key should be kept in his office for this purpose.

After work that day, on the way to the NAAFI, I heard someone singing in one of the hangars, so went to investigate. At the back of the hangar there was a small stage with a piano on it and standing next to it were two women in civilian clothes who were sorting out some sheet music. There was also a small group of people sitting at a table reading scripts. One of the people sitting at the table then noticed me and asked if I needed any help. I asked him if he would mind me sitting quietly and watching the rehearsal, which he said was no problem and pointed to a chair. A woman began playing tunes from some of the latest London shows that I recognised at once. I looked at the people at the table and realised they were mostly Officers, and a few civilians, so hoped they wouldn't mind a mere Leading Wren barging in on them but they seemed to be totally oblivious to my presence. On the stage, the younger of the two women began to sing, but it was obvious that something was wrong with her voice and it sounded as if she had laryngitis. She suddenly stopped singing and apologised saying that she wasn't feeling well enough to go on.

'Do you know anybody else who could go through these songs instead of you?' a Third Officer Wren asked the young woman, whose voice had just let her down. The woman shook her head, and said she had asked everybody that she knew in the village, but no one was willing to spare the time.

'I know the words,' I blurted out.

Everybody turned around and stared at me in surprise. One of the men then asked if I'd been to any of the West End shows recently. I replied that I had seen a few of the shows the previous year and that's why I knew the words of the songs.

'Would you be willing to help us out?' the woman at the piano pleaded. I told them that I would love to, and started to walk towards the stage. One of the men then suggested that we should run through a song before making any decisions, as to who would replace the girl with the cold; who I noticed, had made a discreet exit.

'The revue is going to be held in one of the hangars, and as we don't have any microphones you will need to sing as loudly as you possibly can,' he informed me, as I made my way nervously up to the stage.

'Are you a soprano or a contralto?' the pianist asked.

'I'm a soprano, but I can sing fairly low too if required,' I said quietly.

The pianist played a few lines of the music and asked me if it was in the right key. I began to sing quietly, surprised that I could remember so many of the words.

'Sing a little louder dear,' the pianist instructed, 'in fact, sing as loudly as you can. Can you hear the words back there?' she asked loudly, aimed at the group round the table.

I felt a bit shy at first, but once I'd got into the song I forgot about everybody, and began to enjoy myself. When I finished the song there was silence for a moment and I started to wonder if they didn't like my voice so I asked, 'Was that all right?'

'We heard every word,' one of the Officers said, standing up and coming towards the stage, 'what's your name?'

'Mary, Sir, I mean Wren Arden, Sir.'

'Don't worry; first names are fine in here! Can you sing Christmas carols, Mary?' he asked.

'Oh yes, Sir, we learned them at school.'

'Can you sing one for us?'

I then turned to the pianist and asked her if she knew 'Silent Night', which thankfully she did, and as she played, I sang the song in German, as we had been taught to do at school, much to the amazement of all those watching me.

When I had finished, the Officer said, 'Thank you Mary, but do you know the words in English?'

'Yes I do, but I thought that it might be an idea to sing it in German for your revue to remind everyone that not all Germans are Nazis.'

'Are you a German sympathiser then?' one of the women at the table asked sarcastically.

'No Ma'am, certainly not, but as it's Christmas aren't we supposed to forgive our enemies?'

There was a deathly hush for a moment, and then one of the other Wren Officers stood up and said, 'You are quite right. It's a super idea.' The male Officers then all looked at each other grinning and nodded their agreement.

The Wren Officer then asked me if I could act, and when I said that I loved acting, she told me that they were about to start rehearsals for some sketches the following week, and so she wanted me to attend the rehearsals. But when she told me the times I would be required, I suddenly realised that I wouldn't be able to come, as my transport back to Queen Camel left at eight sharp, and the rehearsals would go on well past that time.

'Oh, that's no problem,' one of the Officers replied, 'you can request a late pass; I'll make sure of that!'

'And Freddy can take you home after the rehearsals are over, as he lives quite near Queen Camel.'

'Which one of you is Freddy?' I asked.

'Ah, Freddy,' said an Officer: 'or I should say, Sir Frederick Marshall; he is our esteemed director of the show, and a lovely old gentleman to boot.'

The pianist joined in, laughing, 'I think Freddy has only agreed to do the show so that he can get some extra petrol coupons!'

The following week, we rehearsed every night, and I discovered that Freddy was actually a very good director, with plenty of experience so we were in good hands. On the Friday evening, a local woman came along to measure us for our costumes. For my part as an angel in the Nativity play, she said she would make my costume out of a pretty white nightgown, which had belonged to her elderly aunt. Another woman said she would make my wings from transparent organza, bits of Christmas tinsel, and strong fuse wire and then sew them on to the back of my gown.

When I tried the outfit on during the first fitting a week later, the wings started to flap about on their own instead of staying rigid on my back, so it was decided that they should be taped firmly around my chest to keep them steady. However, this created another problem, as it now made my breasts stick out even more than they did already. This was very embarrassing, and it didn't help that the three kings forgot their lines, as they had been looking at my bust instead of the shining star above their heads. Freddy wasn't impressed at all and let everyone know in no uncertain terms.

Fortunately, the costume lady was able to rectify the situation, using a small, loose-fitting white-net over-garment, which had been made from an old net curtain. It hung loosely down the front of my gown disguising the tape and my bosoms, while at the back my wings were now threaded through slots. Problem solved.

There were other little hitches like these, but as the rehearsals progressed, the revue started to become quite professional and the whole cast was now taking it much more seriously.

Over the weeks, the dusty hangar was transformed by a dedicated group of volunteers who spent days dusting, scrubbing and cleaning, so that by the time we were doing our final dress rehearsal, it resembled a Christmas grotto, complete with fir-tree branches provided by the Forestry Commission, camouflage netting balanced over frames around the walls, and paper chains hanging from the ceiling in the auditorium. Everyone felt that the hard work was worth it because the hangar was the centre for all the entertainments over Christmas; which now included a film show on Boxing Day afternoon, and a dance that evening, and the New Year's Cinderella Ball.

During those busy weeks of rehearsal, I seldom got to bed before eleven but somehow still managed to do all my NVT work without falling asleep in the dark Testing Room. Freddy gave me a lift back to the Coach Inn in his car most evenings, and when he couldn't do it, one of TNT's night drivers came to my rescue.

Anne was very understanding and had volunteered to do the re-tests on Saturdays, so that I could go to Yeovil to do my shopping.

I was now getting to know my way around Yeovil a bit better, and would ask transport to drop me off and pick me up at Polly's tea rooms. My Christmas shopping took ages, as I was trying to find things that didn't require coupons. I was delighted when I found a second-hand shop that sold china ornaments and books along with hundreds of other things that were suitable to buy as Christmas presents. I decided to wrap the presents in brown laundry paper and then paint Christmas scenes on them to make them look a bit more festive.

On Christmas Eve morning, I woke up feeling as nervous as a kitten about the evening's performance. I made myself eat something for breakfast, but by lunchtime, I was too tense to even drink a cup of tea without feeling sick. The whole cast had spent the morning checking that we all knew where we were supposed to be on the stage that night, so that the lighting crew could get their spotlights in the right place at the right time. One of the lighting engineers reminded me to stand as close to the manger as possible so that they could then guide the star directly to the point above my head and make a light look as though it was shining down on baby Jesus, which was actually a baby doll.

The costume area had been organised with military precision, as there was so little room for anyone to get changed between acts, and to avoid any muddle, each member of the cast was allotted their own little corner where their outfits were displayed on hangers.

The curtain went up on time, and the opening act, The Can-Can, went down so well that we got three encores, which meant that the whole revue would now run half an hour late, but no-one seemed to mind. We then performed a few sketches and most of us remembered our lines perfectly, and those that didn't managed to cover it up so cleverly that the audience didn't notice, and the prompter was not required to call out once, thank goodness. The audience joined in the choruses for all the songs we did next, during which a large board was lowered from the ceiling illuminated by a spotlight, so that they could read the words. Everyone then sang a few Christmas carols together, while a scenery change took place behind the drawn curtains. Finally it was time for the big finale, the Nativity play.

Earlier that day a patriotic farmer had donated a bale of straw to cover the floor of the stage to make it look more like a stable, but unfortunately, nobody had realised that Joseph suffered from hay fever, and he was now doubled up sneezing.

'Can't anyone stop the man sneezing, this won't do at all,' our director Freddy complained, 'the curtain is due to go up in less than a minute.'

'What we need now is a miracle!' one of the Shepherds joked, but soon stopped laughing when Freddy gave him one of his now infamous glares.

The Wren Officer who was playing the part of the Virgin Mary solved the problem by grabbing the nappy the Baby Jesus was wearing and handing it to Joseph, who promptly blew his nose into it, but then realising what he had just done, looked up to Heaven, and said a quick 'Sorry Lord' before placing it back in the manger, just as the curtain went up.

The play started well and thankfully Joseph didn't sneeze once. But then I noticed that one of the Shepherds false beards was starting to peel off. Obviously it needed more glue, but it was too late to do anything about it now, so he would just have to hold it on. The Three Kings then began to walk towards Mary and Joseph to place their presents at the foot of the manger. The First King was a rather tall Lieutenant Commander; the Second King a Sub-Lieutenant, whom I'd recently tested in the NVT unit, and the Third King was a sailor who had been chosen for his weather-beaten skin, which was made even darker with make-up. They all wore magnificent dressing gowns which had been found in the dressing up box, and then embellished with gold braid, red ribbon and sparkling sequins. Their cardboard crowns made them look really quite regal.

It was now my turn, so I softly began to sing 'Silent Night, Holy Night' in German, as had been agreed and then started to walk slowly out of the darkness at the back of the stage, towards the centre. The electricians, or Sparks as they were called, who were working above me in the rafters, slowly moved the star in time with my slow steps across the stage; unfortunately the star suddenly began to wobble, and the light that reflected off it started to jump all around the hangar, which was a little distracting but thankfully, they soon got it back under control.

As the song came to an end, I raised one of my arms with my palm facing the Shepherds and the Kings to bless them, and then the spotlight was turned off exactly on cue. I suddenly felt so overcome with the holiness of the moment, that instead of disappearing backstage into the darkness, as I'd done correctly every time in rehearsals, I walked to the front of the stage, raised both hands and blessed everyone in the audience. Everyone appeared to be so stunned by my gesture, that they all lowered their heads as one for the blessing, at which point I suddenly snapped out of my Angel mode and exited stage left, as quickly as possible.

I thought that Freddy would be furious with me for improvising, but when I saw his face, I could see tears running down his cheeks, and fortunately he was also smiling.

The audience applauded for a while and then someone shouted 'Happy Christmas!' which was followed by a loud cheer and the sound of people getting up to leave. Meanwhile, backstage we were all relieved that the revue had been such a success and everyone shook hands and slapped each other on the back. Someone put a glass of cider in my hand, informing me that it was a local brew called 'Scrumpy', so to drink it slowly, but I was so thirsty that I drank it all in a couple of gulps and then had a second glass. It tasted a little strange, not at all like any of the bottled cider I had had before. Ten minutes later, having finished my third glass, I began to wonder why I now had four feet instead of two.

When it was time to go, I kissed almost everyone in the room goodnight, forgetting that most of them were Officers. When one of them asked me who was taking me back to my billet, as all the other Wrens had gone, I said, 'Freddy of course.'

'Sir Frederick is being entertained by the Captain with some local dignitaries and their families in the Wardroom,' I was told, 'so he won't be taking you anywhere.'

'I suppose I could go on my bicycle,' I said miserably, 'but it's very dark down those lanes to Queen Camel.'

'We'll take you Angel,' a slightly worse-for-wear Lieutenant Commander, who had played one of the Kings said cheerfully, 'Won't we Johnny?' he asked turning to his colleague, who was one of the Shepherds.

'Yes we will, we'll just follow the brightest star all the way!'

A Third Officer Wren sitting next to me, offered to come with me so that there would be two girls with the two boys in the car, 'I'll keep the men in order,' she promised.

As we weaved our way dangerously through the narrow lanes, we sang carols and when we eventually got to my billet, I got out and thanked the driver.

'I'll see you to the door,' the young Sub-Lieutenant offered, leaping out of the car and nearly falling over his feet, as he did so. He then insisted on helping me to open the door but I told him that I could manage 'Purf... fectly well... on my own... Thank you ve... very much!'

I promptly dropped my keys on the ground, but soon retrieved them, and all I had to do now was to find the keyhole. But just as I was about to put the key in the lock, the door opened, and an angry looking Wren Petty Officer glared at me.

'You're late Leading Wren I'll have to report you in the morning,' she snapped.

'If you report Leading Wren Angel on Christmas Day I will speak to the Captain!' the outraged young Sub-Lieutenant shouted back at her. He then saluted me and did a Hornpipe back to the car. The Wren Petty Officer was speechless.

'I'm sorry I'm late but I had to wait for transport back,' I said quietly. 'If you wish to speak to the Third Officer, she's still in the car.'

'Well don't be late again or I shall refuse to give you a late pass next time,' the bossy Petty Officer said grudgingly.

I went upstairs to my room and just as I was about to get undressed, the door opened and a group of smiling faces appeared. One of the girls then said, 'You were fantastic, Mary; the Captain was so moved after you blessed us all that he had to blow his nose to hide the fact that he had tears in his eyes. Happy Christmas Mary!'

On Christmas Day, we had plenty of time to unwrap our presents and chatter amongst ourselves before a lorry arrived to take us to a special service being held at the air station. We sang Christmas carols and said a few prayers, and after the service, we all trooped out onto the parade ground, where everyone, Officers and Other Ranks, shook hands and wished one another a happy day.

A voice behind me said, 'Leading Wren, Angel. Stand to attention!' It was the cheeky Sub-Lieutenant from the night before. I saluted him and he smiled at me, saying, 'If you have any trouble with that rather unpleasant Petty Officer that I had the misfortune to meet last night please let me know and I will have a word with the Captain. We can't have an Angel being told what to do by the Devil now, can we?'

He went off to join his friends, as some of the young pilots I'd met through work came up to me to shake my hand. Then the Captain and the vicar who had just given the service walked towards me.

'Happy Christmas Sir,' I said, saluting the Captain. He congratulated me on my performance the previous evening.

'I'm afraid I got a bit carried away,' I said smiling awkwardly at the vicar, 'but it seemed to be the right thing to do at the time.'

'It was the right thing to do,' the vicar said, 'Bless you my child.'

I walked over to the Wren's mess, where a special Christmas lunch had been organised and the cooks had done us proud; the food was almost pre-war standard, as it had all been bought locally. In order to speed up the proceedings, the turkey had been carved in the kitchen and all the trimmings put on the plate. Tradition was kept alive, with the naval and Wren Officers serving the first course to the Other Ranks. They would have their lunch an hour or so later in their own mess.

I was delighted to see that there was bread sauce and three sorts of vegetables and delicious roast potatoes. How the cooks had managed to produce a meal for so many people, I will never know. They must have been up half the night.

When the meal was finished, three cheers were called for the cooks and the stewards who all came out of the kitchen and into the mess to take a bow.

After lunch special transport for those in billets outside the air station was laid on and, when we got back to the Inn, I took myself up to my room to open my presents. My mother had sent me some new white knickers, and a few other things that she thought might be useful to me, which was thoughtful of her.

At three o'clock we all gathered together in the recreation room to hear the King's speech on the wireless. Thankfully he didn't stutter too much on this occasion and I wondered whether he had been getting some help, as he sounded so much more confident than usual. I had always felt a bit sorry for him; it must have been such an ordeal to talk clearly publicly with such a bad speech impediment. The King spoke about the 'family circle' and that immediately made me picture my family all sitting around the fire listening to the speech at home, and suddenly I felt very homesick, so as soon as I could, I rang my parents reverse charges and spoke to them for over an hour.

On the way back to the airfield that evening, the other girls were talking about the following evening's dance, and about who they hoped would ask them for the Last Waltz. I didn't really feel like going but thought that I should.

The film show that night started with a Laurel and Hardy short film, which made us all laugh. I looked around at the interval to see if I could see our 'Laurel and Hardy', before I realised that the SBAs would most probably be on duty.

The main film was a Whodunit and when it was over, we all sang the National Anthem, before filing out to return to our billets. When we arrived back at the Inn someone had already lit the sitting room fire. There weren't enough seats for all of us, so some of the girls who had arrived the previous year and therefore knew the routine, brought down their bed rugs and pillows and settled down comfortably on the floor. We shared the chocolates and sweets that many of us had been sent and tried to decide on a game to play: someone suggested Charades, which prompted loud groans, so in the end we all decided we were far too tired to play anything, and just sat and chatted among ourselves until bedtime.

Boxing Day was a day off for everyone, except for those working in essential and emergency services. Breakfast was a specially laid-on help-yourself affair at the Inn and we had lunch at the base, which consisted of yesterday's leftovers, which was fine, as we had eaten so much the day before and all we really wanted to do was tidy our rooms, wash our hair, and put out on our smartest uniforms ready for the dance that evening.

The dance was held in the same hangar that the revue had taken place, but had now been transformed with festive decorations, which looked quite jolly. I looked around for somewhere to sit, but to my dismay there were no chairs and only long, hard benches against each wall. And although the band was amateur, it made up for its shortcomings by playing very loudly and keeping in time. When each new dance started there was a mad rush as sailors virtually ran across the room to make sure that they got the girl of their choice before their friends did. But everyone always managed to find a partner, as there were so many of us. It was impossible to sit out a dance, because as soon as I tried to sit down, three sailors would appear almost immediately and demand that I dance with them, so I'd find myself shuffling or galloping around the room again, depending on the music.

Anne Briscoe had spent most of the evening hiding behind the Christmas tree and had hardly danced all evening, so I went over to talk to her to make sure she was all right. She told me that it wasn't because she didn't enjoy dancing but because she was desperately shy, and only felt comfortable dancing with someone she knew already. Just then, a crowd of young Officers pushed through the entrance and made a beeline for the bar. I noticed Anne's face suddenly light up, when she recognised one of the Officers, a Junior Sick Bay doctor called David Mount, and after a few minutes, he came over to ask her to dance, which she accepted without hesitation.

A few dances later, a Paul Jones was called. The first time the music stopped, I found myself standing opposite Laurel, who surprised me by dancing rather well, but when it came to Hardy's turn, my poor toes were so squashed that I prayed for the music to stop as quickly as possible.

For the rest of the evening I danced with one Officer after another, most of whom I'd tested in the NVT unit, and was thankful when the Last Waltz was called, as I'd had so many late nights since arriving at Heron, that I was longing to get back to my warm bed.

As the music began I suddenly had an image of myself dancing with Charles to the same tune, which made me feel very sad, and I had to hold back the tears. A young RN Lieutenant must have noticed the sad look on my face because he came up to me and whispered, 'Are you missing your boyfriend?'

I nodded, thinking that he must be a very nice young man to have so intuitively picked up how I felt. 'He's dead,' I told him quietly, fighting desperately to stop the tears that were now cascading down my cheek. 'I'm sorry I didn't mean to cry.'

'Don't ever say sorry for crying over somebody you loved,' he said kindly, 'I still miss my brother who was killed on Boxing Day last year and there isn't a day that goes by that I don't feel like crying.'

I was utterly shocked and suddenly felt very ashamed of my own selfish feelings. Looking at this young Lieutenant and then around me at the hangar, it was abundantly clear that many people at this dance were putting on brave faces; doing their utmost to appear happy even when they were not. Squeezing the young man's hand, I said, 'Thank you,' and after telling me his name was Anthony Ross, he led me onto the dance floor to join in for the rest of the Last Waltz.

When the dance was over there was a lot of activity as people milled around talking, collecting jackets, coats, bags and gasmask cases. Anthony asked whether I was intending go to the New Year dance.

'Yes, are you?' I replied.

'Yes I am Mary, so I'll look out for you there,' he said smiling.

As I climbed into bed that night, I realised to my surprise that I was already looking forward to New Year's Eve and seeing Anthony again. I didn't have any romantic feelings for him and sensed that he didn't feel that way about me either, but he was obviously a very kind and sensitive man and I hoped that we might become friends.

Four days later it was my nineteenth birthday, so the girls at my billet took me out for a drink, but we didn't make a big night of it, as the following night was the New Year's Eve dance and we wanted to save our energy. As we stepped into the hangar on New Year's Eve, I was delighted to see that it had now been redecorated with brightly coloured paper-chains and lanterns. There was a much better band this time, including two talented young naval Officers, one on drums and the other on the saxophone. When the saxophonist waved at me, I realised that it was my new friend Anthony. I waved back, but before I had a chance to go and talk to him, I was whisked onto the dance floor and didn't stop dancing until it was time for refreshments.

As I was helping myself to the food, Anthony came up to me with a drink and insisted that I keep the last dance for him, as the saxophone wouldn't be needed for the Last Waltz.

'New Year's Eve is going to be a bit rough for both of us this year, and so I thought that we could give each other a comforting hug at midnight,' he suggested.

'That would be lovely, Anthony, a hug is always welcome,' I replied. I was so glad that he had asked me for a hug rather than a kiss, as it confirmed that he felt the same way about me as I did about him, and he just wanted to be friends.

When midnight finally arrived and everyone else welcomed in the New Year, Anthony and I hugged each other tight. This time, it was his tears I felt on my cheek.

CHAPTER 9

1943

Anne and I returned to work the day after New Year's Day and were kept busy with two new squadrons that had just flown in. There were several French and Dutch pilots that required NVT tests but none of them spoke good enough English to understand our rather complicated lecture. Fortunately my schoolgirl French was adequate enough for the French pilots to understand me, but all I could do for the Dutch pilots was to try speaking in German while miming the content of the test at the same time, before turning out the lights, which caused much laughter. But somehow it worked, and after several attempts they all passed.

Work carried on as usual for the next couple of months but at the end of February Anne caught a bad cold, so I had to do all the tests for the next few days. She wasn't the only one who was ill. On the radio one evening, we heard that Winston Churchill had had pneumonia, but was now sitting up in bed and smoking a cigar, a sure sign that he was back on the road to recovery!

In the spring, a substantial number of Fairey Barracuda three seat torpedo bombers arrived at the base, to replace the much loved Swordfish and Albacores, or 'Applecores', as some of the pilots affectionately called them.

'The Barracuda is the first of its type used by the Fleet Air Arm to be fabricated entirely from metal,' one of the pilots told me after taking his NV test.

'Oh gosh! How on earth does it stay up?' I asked him, meaning it as a joke.

'That's a good question,' he replied seriously. I found out later that this replacement plane wasn't proving to be very popular with some of the pilots.

When the weather finally started to get warmer, I decided it was time to start using my bicycle more often. The hedgerows near my billet had started to come alive, and the banks were covered with primroses, so it was a joy to spend my weekends exploring the local area on my bike.

One day I saw a lane running through a farm that I thought might be a shortcut to the airfield, so I decided to ask permission from the farmer. When I knocked on the farmhouse door, a middle-aged man opened it and looked me up and down. He was wearing a cloth cap, a well-worn waistcoat, and a pair of britches. He had a huge belly and very red cheeks covered in grey whiskers. There was a twinkle in his eye as he asked me what I wanted.

I explained that I was a Wren billeted nearby, and that I was looking for a shortcut to get to the naval airbase, so wondered if he would mind me riding my bike though his farm. He looked at me for a moment without saying a word and then beckoned me to follow him though his yard and into a large orchard. We walked in silence until we got to some trees covered in blossom. The farmer then began talking to me in such a broad Somerset accent, that I had no idea what he was saying until I heard the word, 'Zider', and then guessed that he must be telling me all the names of the different apples in his orchard. I nodded and did my best to look interested, which must have done the trick, because when we returned to the farmhouse to collect my bicycle, he then pointed to the gate that led to the lane I had spotted earlier and said, 'Make'e sure that you cloze yon gate behind thyself.'

I promised him that I would, and thanking him, put out my hand to shake his. He looked at his hand to make sure it was clean and then decided that he needed to rub it on his britches before taking my hand in his. As I left he touched the brim of his hat and gave me a huge smile, which showed off his few remaining teeth to good effect.

The following weekend I decided to look for some riding stables near my billet, so cycled around the local lanes and villages for the next two hours, but there didn't seem to be any stables anywhere.

However, on my way back to my billet, I noticed a woman teaching some young children to ride in one of the fields, so after propping my bike against the hedge, I walked over to her to ask if she knew of any local stables that might let me help at weekends in exchange for some free rides.

'Well actually, my sister could do with some help, as she has a livery stable and is looking after several hunters for Services personnel on her own,' the woman said in a very upper class accent. 'She also runs a small riding stable for the pony club, so it might just solve both your problems.' She then pointed to a farmhouse about a quarter of a mile across the fields, and explained how I could get there and that her sister's name was Mrs Swallow.

When I got to the farmhouse, I saw a lady mucking out the stables, so presuming it must be Mrs Swallow, went and introduced myself and then told her why I was there.

'Well, I certainly do need some help with the hunters,' Mrs Swallow said to my delight. 'In fact, I've applied for a land girl to come and work for me, but at the moment there aren't any available.' She then suggested that I come again the following day, so that she could see me ride. 'Do forgive me, I don't want to appear rude,' she said, 'but I do need to be satisfied that you can ride well enough to exercise my horses.'

As I made my way back to the Inn that afternoon, I made a point of looking carefully for landmarks and made a mental note of a gate with a broken bar, a tree with a missing branch, and a church steeple in the distance, so that I wouldn't get lost trying to find my way back to the stables the following day.

When I arrived at Mrs Swallow's the next morning, she was still having her breakfast, so I joined her for a cup of tea until she had finished eating. She then took me out to see the horses, explaining which ones were livery horses, which ones she hired out to ride and the sort of things she'd like me to help her with like cleaning the tack, mucking out the stables and putting fresh hay in the feed boxes. She then let me select a pony and I chose a bay called Maize, which suited someone of my stature. After I had saddled up and mounted, I began to walk Maize towards the field and then broke into a canter. It felt wonderful to be riding again after so long and Maize was a dream to handle.

'I can tell that you are an experienced rider Mary,' Mrs Swallow said patting Maize affectionately, 'Why don't we go for a ride together next Sunday? Then you can familiarize yourself with the bridle paths and the fields that the farmers allow us to use.' She then asked me to help her with the grooming for the next hour or so, which I was more than happy to do.

Just before it was time for me to go, Mrs Swallow told me the terms for my free rides: 'Two hours riding exercising the horses, one hour mucking out and another cleaning tack, and in exchange, I will make you a sandwich for lunch and if you stay late for any reason, an egg for tea!' We shook hands on the deal and I then went back to my billet, happy but exhausted.

For the next two months I rode nearly every Saturday afternoon and most Sundays. It didn't take long before Mrs Swallow began to trust me with some of the lovely hunters she was looking after, and my relationship with her developed into a happy and relaxed one built on our mutual love of horses. I thoroughly enjoyed going there and, as the locals got used to seeing me ride to the stables on my bicycle or pass by on Maize or on one of the other horses, they would wave to me from their gardens as I went by.

One Saturday after my ride, I decided to take a slightly different route back to the Inn and as I passed a house on the edge of a small village, I saw a woman tidying her garden, so I stopped for a chat. The woman introduced herself as Margaret Fuller and said that she hadn't seen me around before, so I explained that I was a Wren stationed at HMS Heron.

'Oh, really! My husband is at Heron every day,' Margaret said with a big smile. 'What do you do?' I explained my work to her and she seemed fascinated. She then told me a bit about her family and we were getting on so well that it was well past five o'clock by the time we'd finished chatting.

'You must come and have tea with us tomorrow,' Margaret said cheerfully. 'I'll bake a cake.'

I was just getting on my bicycle when I turned round and called out 'By the way, what does your husband do at the air station? It's possible that I've met him.'

'For his sins' Margaret replied, smiling, 'he's the Air Station Captain.'

Without thinking, I said, 'Oh that lovely man; I met him on Christmas morning with the chaplain after the service.'

Margaret laughed and said, 'Yes, my husband is a lovely man, and he'd be delighted to hear that someone besides me thinks so too. Most of the time he has to be very strict with both his Senior and Junior Officers because they're inclined to lark about too much when off duty.'

'I think they 'lark about' as you say to cover up being homesick or missing their wives, and I know that many of them are worried that they won't make it to the end of the war,' I said quietly.

'You're a wise girl for one so young,' Margaret said with a gentle smile.

The following day it was pouring with rain, so I rang Margaret and asked if I could come the following weekend instead. When I turned up at the Fullers the following Sunday I was met by their youngest child, Anthea, who was playing with her guinea pig in the garden.

'Are you an angel?' she asked, staring at me with interest.

'I used to be, but now I'm a stable girl!' I replied laughing.

Margaret then joined us and explained that they had told their daughter about me being an angel in the play, but when she had first seen me she had thought I was a real one. We both laughed and when we went indoors, Anthea asked me if I would play Monopoly with her, because she didn't want to play with her two brothers anymore, as they cheated. I told her that my older brother was just as bad and sulked if he didn't win.

'Aren't boys a bore?' Anthea said, which made her mother and I laugh again.

Margaret's husband then came into the kitchen, 'Oh Justin, this is Mary Arden, the girl I told you about.'

'How do you do Sir?'

'When you're under my roof, there's no need to call me Sir,' Justin said with a grin, 'so how's our resident angel doing?'

'She's not an angel anymore, she's a stable girl!' Anthea butted in, 'And she's going to play Monopoly with me, aren't you?'

'Yes I am,' I told her.

'Well, if you are willing to entertain our children, you'll be more than welcome, as a regular visitor to this house,' Justin chuckled.

Suddenly there was a commotion at the door, as the Fuller's two sons barged into the room to see what was going on. I was then introduced to David, aged fourteen and James, who was two years younger.

When we were halfway through our game of Monopoly, Margaret called us all through to have a piece of homemade sponge cake and a cup of tea. I noticed that David had very nice manners, and I asked him where he went to school. He told me, and then asked me the same question. When I mentioned the name of my school Margaret told me that she knew one of the girls that I'd been friends with there, who had been a prefect when I was in my first year. Small world, I thought.

Before I left, I asked Justin to not tell anyone at the airfield that I had visited his home. 'I don't mind the Wren Officers knowing because they're friendly, but I do seem to have trouble with the Petty Officers,' I explained. 'They don't seem to like the way I speak and they do their best to pull me down all the time.'

'Yes they can be right cows at times!' Justin said smiling and all three of his children giggled and made mooing sounds. I laughed too and promised them that I would teach them how to play Animal Snap next time I came to visit.

As the weeks went by, every time I saw Captain Fuller at the airfield he was always friendly but very professional and didn't let on that I knew his family socially. If we saw each other, we'd salute each other with a straight face, but Justin would often say quietly under his breath 'moo', as we passed one another, which always made me laugh.

Although I was extremely busy working during the week, I still managed to find the time to ride at the weekends, and spent most Sunday afternoons with the Fullers. However, I knew that this lovely routine would have to come to an end eventually.

'I can't expect you to help me forever,' Mrs Swallow said, 'and I can't get a land girl unless I have a proper farm, so there's nothing for it but to advertise the ponies for sale,' she told me sadly. I felt really upset, as I'd grown very fond of the little, fat ponies that I'd been grooming for the past few months, but I did understand her situation.

The following Sunday morning I decided to cycle to church, so that I could say a special prayer for Peter's safety. My father had told me that my brother was now in Burma and that he had been informed by the War Office things were 'rather unpleasant' over there, so we were all worried about him and I prayed for him every night. As many of the younger vicars were serving as chaplains to the armed services, it was not a surprise that a very old and doddery clergyman took our service. Afterwards, I decided to stop off in the next village for lunch. I found a lovely old pub with a garden and noticed a group of young naval Officers were sitting outside sipping mugs of beer, and to my delight, one of the young men was my friend Anthony Ross, the saxophonist.

'Long time no see!' I said.

'That's hardly my fault, you are always too busy riding, or so I've been told!' he teased.

Anthony offered to come into the pub with me to order a glass of cider, and insisted that I try one of the Devon pasties, which he assured me were delicious. We then returned to the garden to join the others, and I thought I recognised two of his friends, as I'd given them a Night Vision Test fairly recently. They asked me where I'd been, and I said that I'd just been exploring and looking for a church I could attend sometimes, instead of always going to the service at the airbase. We had our lunch and chatted for the next hour, and when it was time to leave, Anthony told me that his squadron was going on active service the following week, and that he would miss me while he was away.

'I will miss you too, Anthony, and I would just like to thank you for your friendship. It has meant a great deal to me to have a male friend that is happy just being my friend rather than something more,' I told him earnestly.

'That certainly doesn't mean that I didn't think about wanting more,' he said honestly, 'but I can understand why you are not ready to allow someone special into your life again yet.'

'Thanks, Anthony, you're right. I'm not ready, but when I am, I hope I meet someone who is as kind and thoughtful as you are.'

Just as I was about to get back on my bicycle to head home to Heron, I noticed a poster in the pub window, which advertised for volunteers to help the farmers bring in the harvest. Three telephone numbers were given, so I went back inside and asked the landlord if he knew which farm was the nearest to Queen Camel.

'They all be quite close Miss,' the landlord said, 'but let me warn ye that it's a job for men, not young girls, and it be very 'ard work.'

I then flexed my arm muscles and laughing, said that I was as strong as an ox, so surely I could do something useful? The landlord was so amused that he promised he'd have a word with his friend, Ted Bridges, when he next saw him. He then told me that Ted's wife might like some help making meals for the farm-hands, cleaning out the hen-houses, and other jobs of a similar nature.

That evening I wrote a postcard to William that I knew would make him laugh: 'Volunteered to clean out hen houses on a farm… for free! Wish I had kept my big mouth shut! Love Mary.'

When I went to work the next day I asked Anne whether she'd be willing to do the re-tests on Saturday mornings, so that I could help with the harvest and then asked her if she would be interested in volunteering too. Her reply was emphatic.

'You must be joking! I have no intention of breaking my nails or tearing my clothes on thorns, but I have no objection if you want to!'

She then suggested that I ask the First Officer Wren and Surgeon Commander Lewis's permission before doing anything more about it.

Surgeon Commander Lewis said that he had no objection, so long as I did it in my free time.

'Actually I think it will be good for you to be out in the sunshine a bit more,' he said, 'Working in that dark room for so long is not healthy. In fact, I think you should take some iron tablets as you are looking a bit anemic.'

The First Officer had no objection either, so the following weekend I went back to the pub and the landlord said that he would telephone his farmer friend, Ted Bridges, while I waited. He returned a moment later and told me that Ted was interested to meet me, and then explained how to find the Bridges' Farm, which was much farther away from Queen Camel than I'd hoped.

By the time I arrived, I was a bit sweaty and more than ready for a drink of cold water. When I knocked on the door, a middle aged woman, who I presumed was Mrs Bridges, opened it and said in a broad Somerset accent, 'Yes, Miss, can I help you?'

I smiled and said, 'I hope it will be the other way round!' I explained that I was a Wren at HMS Heron and that I'd seen a poster in a pub asking for volunteers to help bring in the harvest, and that the pub landlord had already spoken to her husband, which is why I was there now. The farmer's wife invited me in and guided me towards her kitchen. 'You aren't very big are you?' she said, taking a tea towel and dusting a chair for me to sit on, 'Farming is man's work.'

'I know that I don't look very strong, Mrs Bridges, and I certainly couldn't drive a plough, but there must be something I can do to help you, like preparing lunch for the farm workers, feeding the hens or mucking out the stables. I'm more than willing to give you a hand about the farmhouse and help you to feed the animals,' I said enthusiastically.

Mrs Bridges then asked me if I was comfortable with horses. I told her that I had ridden all my life and loved horses. She then asked me if I knew how to drive a pony cart, as that could be useful as I would then be able to deliver farm produce around the villages. I told her that I'd only driven one for fun, but that I was sure I could soon learn to do it properly, if her husband had time to give me a lesson.

'I'm very willing to learn anything new. The thing is,' I said emphatically, 'there's a war on, and you need help, and I'm willing to give it, so here I am!'

I noticed that there was a large pile of crockery waiting to be washed up in the sink and a bucket of potatoes nearby ready to be peeled, so I stood up and said, 'As I'm already here, perhaps I could make myself useful and do those dishes for you and then have a go at the potatoes?'

She looked a bit taken aback, but then smiled and said that if I was sure, she would be very grateful, as she had to admit that it was starting to get too much for her to do so much on her own. She then told me that a few local girls had helped her in the past, but they were all working in factories making uniforms and things like that now.

As we worked, Mrs Bridges told me that she provided her farmhands with lunch everyday, which usually consisted of a bowl of vegetable soup with bread and cheese. I asked her how she managed the rations, and she explained that farmers received extra coupons at harvest time and that they made their own cheese when they had surplus milk. They also grew their own vegetables, and that she also made stock for the soup from chicken, mutton and beef bones.

'And if we need the men on a Saturday, I make them a pasty for a treat,' she said smiling, now starting to relax in my company.

'Oh, may I watch you make them?' I asked delightedly. 'I've never learned to make a pasty, neither has our cook.'

'I am rather proud of my pasties, I don't mind telling you. In fact I've won a few prizes in my time,' she told me beaming from ear to ear.

As I peeled the potatoes, Mrs Bridges prepared the vegetables for the soup, and told me about her daughter, who had left home to join the ATS. She said how much she missed having her to chatter with while cooking and doing the household chores.

Suddenly the back door opened and a man's voice called out, 'I'm back, put the kettle on love.' I presumed it must be Ted Bridges. I heard him kick off his boots and wash his hands under a tap in the adjoining scullery, and when he came into the kitchen and saw me, he asked his wife, 'So who's this then?'

'This is Miss Arden, Ted, and she is helping me in the kitchen this morning.'

'Is that right love? In that case, now that my dear wife has her own maid to help her, perhaps she could make me a cup of tea?'

'Oh, now Ted, don't you start with your teasing!' Mrs Bridges exclaimed.

'Actually, I haven't just come to help your wife in the kitchen; I want to help you in the fields and with the animals too,' I said to Mr Bridges, as I put the heavy kettle on to the hob to boil.

'What, you mean like a Land Girl?' Mr Bridges asked. 'I applied for one of those a long time ago, but I was told that there weren't enough to go around at present.'

'I know that, which is why I decided to volunteer my help,' I explained.

Mrs Bridges beckoned me to sit down and then cut three large slices of apple cake to go with our tea.

'What we really need is a young, strong man rather than a little lass like you,' Mr Bridges said kindly, as he drank his tea.

'I'm willing to feed the hens, collect the eggs and jobs like that,' I said eagerly, before Mrs Bridges interrupted.

'Bobby can show her what to do, Ted.' She then turned to me and explained that Bobby was a local boy, who often helped them with things like cleaning out the henhouses and the stables.

'He's a bit simple in the head,' Mrs Bridges continued 'and he looks a bit strange too, but he wouldn't hurt a fly. He doesn't say much either, and when he does try to talk, he dribbles a bit, but if you talk to him slow and quiet like and never shout at him, he soon learns a new task. I hope you won't be afraid of him,' she said looking a bit concerned, so I told her not to worry and that I was very good with young boys, as I had a younger brother who I used to clean out our hen house with, so felt sure Bobby and I would get on just fine.

Mrs Bridges then taught me how she made her special soup, so that in future I would be able to make it the same way myself. I asked her whether it mattered which vegetables were selected and whether she used chicken, beef or mutton bones to make the stock. She tut-tutted and said that she couldn't afford to be so fussy; she made the soup out of vegetables that were in season or that she had spare; as for the stock, she used whatever was available.

'If Mrs B's soup is orange, that means we have too many carrots needing eating, if it's green, then it means the beans and peas are in season, and if it's just white, that means its leeks and potatoes again,' Mr Bridges butted in with a big grin on his face.

'Mrs B' then told me that she always wanted plenty of onions in her soup, and so one of my tasks would be to dig them up from the garden behind the stables, along with some parsley from the herb garden.

A week later I started my new job as a 'Weekend Land Girl' and was put to work straightaway: Mrs B asked me to lay the newly scrubbed kitchen table, putting out the plates, breadboard, spoons, knives and forks ready for lunch. When the farmhands came into the kitchen, one by one, I was surprised that many of them looked quite old. I had assumed that they'd be young, healthy boys between fifteen and twenty, but then realised that all the young, healthy country lads had been called up at the beginning of the war, and that the men now sitting around the table represented the available manpower.

As I served the bread and cheese not one of the men looked up from their plates, or said a word except to ask one another for the salt, butter or the jug of cider. They looked worn out, although they still had half a day's work ahead of them. It really must be hard work, I thought to myself.

After I'd washed up, Mrs B took me to the barn, where I noticed some old carthorse tackle hanging up next to the cart; she said that Mr Bridges would teach me how to drive it when he had the time. She then took me to a field to show me their daughter's pony, Star. My eyes lit up, 'I'd love to take her out for a ride one day, if you'll trust me with her.'

Mrs B smiled and said sadly, 'Star seems to pine for our Hilary almost as much as we do. I warn you, Miss, that pony has become very difficult to handle, and might even need breaking-in again. There are plenty of bridle paths all around us, and most of the farmers have never objected to Hilary riding around the fields, but make sure you shut all the gates firmly behind you, nobody has time to go chasing after loose cattle these days.' She then paused and looked at me quizzically, 'Have you done much riding? Star can be quite frisky and she'll have you off in a jiffy given half a chance.'

I explained that I'd ridden plenty of bad-tempered or naughty ponies in the past, so felt sure that I could handle Star.

When we went back to the kitchen to discuss arrangements for the following weekend, Mrs B said, 'You do understand that we have no spare cash to pay you, Miss Arden, and that this is voluntary work?' I reassured her that it had been made perfectly clear on all the posters that the work was voluntary and that I was happy to help.

'I'll feed you when you are here, of course,' she insisted, 'and I will ask Mr Bridges if he will let you ride Star from time to time.'

'There's just one other thing, Mrs Bridges,' I said, smiling, as I was about to leave. 'I'd be very grateful if you'd call me Mary, I am called by my surname so much in the Wrens, that I fear I will forget my own name soon!'

'Well my name is Susan,' Mrs B announced, 'and the old man's called Ted.'

Early the following Saturday, I found Ted in the barn sorting out the feed. He explained what he wanted me to do, pointed out the different sacks of grain, and then told me what mixture to give all the various animals on the farm.

'If you can feed the animals for me, Mary, that would be a big help as it will allow me to get on with some of the heavier work that's needed around here.'

He then walked me around the farm, giving me a list of small jobs that he felt I could manage, including cleaning the horses' tackle and collecting eggs from the henhouses. He asked me to wipe the eggs clean in the scullery, before putting them in racks in the larder for Susan to sort. They sold dozens of eggs each week, which was a big help with their finances he confided, as they fetched a good price.

'Bobby used to do it, but he's a bit clumsy and crushes them in his hands sometimes,' Ted told me. 'He doesn't seem to know his own strength, so I would rather you do it when you are here.'

As if on cue, a gangly boy appeared by the gate with a herd of cows.

'That's our Bobby, bringing my girls in to be milked,' Ted said, pointing at Bobby and laughing; 'he loves them cows like they be 'is own sisters!'

When I took a closer look at Bobby, I could see that he was singing happily to the cows and patting their rumps. As he came towards us, he looked at me and then quickly averted his eyes shyly for a moment. When he looked at me again, I gave him a big smile and was rewarded with a crooked smile back.

Ted looked at me and nodded, 'I think he's taken to you already, Mary.'

'That's good,' I replied.

'I will teach you how to churn the butter next time you come,' Ted said, 'but for now, can you go and help Susan?'

When I went into the kitchen Susan grinned at me and said, 'So your mother has a cook does she? I thought you must come from a well-to-do family by the way you talks.'

'Yes, Susan, I'm sorry about that,' I giggled apologetically, 'I do hope I don't appear too high and mighty. The truth is that my mother hates cooking, and as she drives an ambulance all day, she needs someone to help her in the kitchen.'

'No need to apologize, I need someone to help me in the kitchen too these days, and that's why you're here!' She pointed to the soup, 'Now stir that please, will you Mary, while I cut some bread up?'

On the Monday morning, I requested permission to see the First Officer Wren and asked her permission to work at the farm one afternoon each week, as well as the Saturdays that had already been agreed. She said yes but on condition that it did not interfere with my work and that I was sensible and did not take on more than I could manage. As two squadrons had recently left for a tour of duty our workload was now less than usual, so Anne was more than happy for me to spend additional time as an unofficial Land Girl.

Over the next few weeks I worked harder than I'd ever worked in my life before, and didn't even find the time to ride Star, but it felt right to be doing all I could to help the War effort.

I also managed to make friends with Bobby, who enjoyed practical jokes just like my brother William did. One day he placed an egg on the kitchen chair hoping that I would squash it when I sat down for lunch, but fortunately, I noticed it just in time. Not to disappoint him, however, I lowered myself gently over it, and then after making loud cluck-clucking noises and moving my arms around like chicken wings, I stood up and produced the egg as if by magic. He shrieked with laughter and clapped his hands with delight. The farm hands all applauded too, and after that, Bobby said he would do anything for 'Miss Mary.'

When I arrived at the Bridges the following Saturday, I was a bit surprised to find a number of the local farmers and their wives all standing in the kitchen.

'We've come to cheer you on,' one of the farmers said to me with a broad grin. When I looked blankly at him, he explained, 'We've come to watch you ride Star.'

Apparently Ted couldn't wait to see how I managed his daughter's frisky pony, and he had invited his neighbours to watch me make a fool of myself. While I changed into my jodhpurs, Ted saddled up Star, and then when I mounted her, he held her head firmly for me while I tightened her girth.

'Will you open the gate for me please, Ted, as there's no point in getting Star excited before I have had a chance to ride her?'

Ted and his friends grinned at one another, obviously thinking that Star would throw me off in a couple of seconds, and they would have a good laugh at my expense, but what they didn't know was that I had been feeding Star with carrots and apples over the past few weeks and gaining her trust; so I felt quite confident that she would do as I asked of her.

I leaned forward to give Star a friendly pat, and gently guided her through the gate; she was as good as gold. Then, suddenly, with no warning at all, she lifted her head, sniffed the air, and decided it was time to have a good old gallop, but fortunately, I was prepared and we took off like a bullet. I held the reins tight to control her and then kicked her on with my heels.

By the time we had reached the top of the steep field, Star was already exhausted and slowed down to a canter of her own free will. I then loosened the reins and allowed her to carry on at her own pace, eventually trotting through a gap in the hedge and into the next field in a very dignified manner. Behind me I heard a loud cheer.

When I went back into the farmhouse to change, Ted and his friends were standing outside the back door waiting for me, clapping.

The atmosphere was very different the next time I came to the farm. As I walked into the kitchen to say hello to Susan, I sensed that something was very wrong. Susan had her arm around another lady, who I had never seen before, and they were both crying. I wondered whether there had been an accident and one of the farm workers had been hurt, but when Susan pointed to a fawn envelope on her kitchen table, I knew what it was at once: a telegram bringing bad news. Susan's friend's son had been killed in action, while serving on Special Ops. He was her only son.

We had all felt so light-hearted the week before, when we were working in the fields; but the reality of what was going on elsewhere was never far away and this sad news brought the war close to home.

I suggested to Susan that she took her friend home and stayed with her for as long as she needed, and that I was quite capable of giving the farm hands their meals by myself today. She took me up on the offer, so I set to and made a soup in the way that Susan had taught me. There were no complaints from the men, and Bobby stayed behind to help me wash up.

A month later, Ted announced that, as it was now time to get the main harvest in, there would be a lot more faces to feed over the coming weeks, so they'd really need my help. All the local farmers were going to come and help at the Bridges farm and in return Ted and his men would return the favour for them later on.

'I could do with help turning stooks, and that. Do you know what stooks are Mary?'

'Well no, not really,' I said honestly.

'Stooks is sheaves of hay, wheat, corn or barley freshly cut and tied into bunches and balanced six at a time into the shape of a pyramid. They then 'ave to be turned each day so that the wet side is turned to the outside, and so on, all down a row, understand?'

I nodded, 'I am a quick learner, just show me once, and I will do my best.'

Ted showed me how to lift the sheaves, and then Bobby and I, along with some of the other farm workers, gathered them together into stooks. I had no problem doing this work, but when it was time to turn them, so that the wet hay inside the sheaves was on the outside in order to dry in the sun, that was a different matter altogether. When it came to the last two remaining sheaves in each stook, there always seemed to be a little field mouse hiding inside them; it would then run over my feet, which would make me squeal, as I was terrified that they would run up my trouser legs. This made Bobby double up and cry with laughter every time. When I explained my fear to Bobby he suggested, 'I do inside; you do outside' so from then on, I would leave the last two sheaves in each stook for him to de-mouse, and move on to the next one.

Apparently when Ted heard his new Land Girl screaming, he wondered what on earth was going on, so had asked Bobby, who then told him about my phobia with mice, which made him roar with laughter. Susan told me that Ted had thought that it was hilarious, and that when he had told the other farmers they had fallen about laughing too, so now I was known as 'Mary Mouse.'

Ted told me the next day that he was concerned that, as the weather was so sultry, the men would need to have several rest breaks, and it was likely that they would run out of cider by midday, so he asked me if I would ride Star to the local pub, and carry back a small barrel of cider.

'A drink of cider will help refresh everyone, but you're not to pay for the barrel, just ask 'im to mark it up on the slate,' Ted instructed. After giving me the landlord's name, and writing down directions of how to get there, I left the Bridges' farm and decided to take a short-cut across the fields where there would be no gates to open or shut.

When I arrived at the pub, the landlord was standing outside to greet me. He told me not to dismount, as he had the barrel ready. Disappearing for a few minutes, the landlord returned with the cider barrel and a lad to hold Star's head, while he secured the barrel between the stirrup leather and the saddle. He fixed a strong rope around the barrel, like a handle, so that I'd be able to hold it steady, but he had tied my leg to the barrel by mistake, which made us both laugh. Thankfully, he soon got it sorted out, and once the barrel was secure, I turned Star around and kicked her on.

Just as I passed the window of the pub, one of the Petty Officers from Heron, who was sitting inside the pub, saw me and if looks could kill she could have put pay to an entire army. It was obvious that this Petty Officer had immediately got the wrong end of the stick, as she rushed out of the pub and yelled, 'Leading Wren Arden, what do you think you are doing?'

She must have assumed that I was collecting the barrel of booze to take to a party with my friends, but before I could reply and explain what I was doing and why, the Petty Officer started shouting about how I had lied about working in the fields and that she would report me immediately.

Meanwhile, frightened by her voice and general demeanor, Star began to turn in circles. I begged the Petty Officer not to talk so loudly or she would frighten the horse, but my words were like a red rag to a bull.

'How dare you talk back to a Petty Officer!' she barked. 'I'm putting your name on Charge for insolence. Report to the First Officer Wren first thing tomorrow morning.'

More concerned about getting Star to calm down, I carefully balanced the wooden cider barrel against my thigh, and told the landlord, who appeared to be dumbstruck at the PO's outburst, that I would sort it out once I got back to the airfield, so not to worry.

I was almost in tears by the time I got back to the Bridges farm and handed the barrel to Ted. As I dismounted Ted asked me what was wrong, so I told him what had happened, and that it was possible that I'd be forbidden from working on the farm again.

'That isn't fair,' Ted said, 'but, don't you fuss yourself my dear, I will write a letter saying that I told you to go and fetch the barrel and why, and if your Officer don't believe me, I'll get Jack at the local to ring up and explain.'

The following day I reported to the First Officer's office and she told me how disappointed she was, and that she hadn't expected me, of all people, to take advantage of the extra leave I'd been allowed, supposedly to volunteer in the fields, just to take the time off to enjoy myself drinking with friends instead.

I then very politely asked her if she'd be so good as to read the letter that Mr Bridges had kindly written for me in my defence.

The First Officer read Ted's letter, but instead of apologizing to me, she began to defend the Petty Officer instead, saying that it must have just been a silly misunderstanding. She then called the PO into her office and asked her to explain the reason why she had put me on this charge.

'Leading Wren Arden was collecting alcohol from the pub on horseback! It was obvious to me that she was on her way to a party, rather than working on the farm, as she had claimed she was doing, so I have put her on report,' the PO said.

The First Officer then asked the Petty Officer if she thought that it could also be possible that Leading Wren Arden might have been at the pub, because she had been sent by the farmer she was working for, to collect refreshments for his hard working men who needed cooling down in this unusually hot weather, and that Leading Wren Arden might have had no intention of attending any party at all.

The look on the Petty Officer's face was a picture. First she looked surprised, as it was obvious that she'd never thought of such a thing, and then she looked really disappointed, as it slowly dawned on her that I hadn't broken any rules and therefore she could not put me on a charge.

'No, that didn't occur to me Ma'am. Is that her excuse? If so, I find it very hard to believe,' the PO said with a smirk.

The First Officer then picked up Ted's letter and handed it to the Petty Officer to read.

'This is a letter from the farmer that Leading Wren Arden is working for. It explains that he had asked her to collect the barrel for him, and to save time, he asked her to ride there on one of his horses.'

The Petty Officer then looked at me with contempt and said that it hadn't looked like that to her; I had been laughing and fooling about with the landlord in an unseemly manner. This was an outright lie, of course, and it was obvious that she had taken a dislike to me and was determined to have me punished. The First Officer then looked at me with a raised eyebrow and enquired if I had anything to say for myself.

'Yes, Ma'am I would like to explain that I was laughing with the landlord because he had mistakenly tied my leg to the barrel instead of to the stirrup leather, but there was nothing unseemly about it at all. The landlord will verify all this if necessary Ma'am.'

'That won't be necessary. Case dismissed,' the First Officer concluded, and while I was still standing in the room, she warned the Petty Officer to make sure of her facts in future before wasting her time.

After the red-faced Petty Officer had left the room, the First Officer asked me to sit down. I was grateful to do so, as my legs were shaking by now.

'I'm sorry to have caused a problem Ma'am,' I said, 'but the Bridges have been very good to me, so when I was asked to collect the cider I agreed to do so without hesitation.'

'I would have done exactly the same thing myself, but you must see how easy it was for the Petty Officer to take the whole episode the wrong way?'

'Yes Ma'am, I suppose so,' I replied, still convinced that the PO had it in for me just because she didn't like anybody who came from a privileged background.

'I advise you not to mention this incident to anyone outside this door, and I will tell the Petty Officer the same thing,' she said before I left her office.

On the way back to the NVT office, I noticed a poster advertising some upcoming musical evenings, starting the following Thursday, and they were open to All Ranks. The concerts would only be someone playing gramophone records but I thought it would be a very good way to relax in the evenings, so mentioned it to Anne to see if she'd like to join me, but she politely declined, saying that she'd much rather read her book in the evenings.

I arrived at eight sharp, as advertised, and found my way to a seat in the middle of the Entertainments hut. Looking around, there didn't seem to be any Other Ranks there except me, but the hut soon began to fill up with Wren and naval Officers. I took off my jacket so that no one would notice the anchor on the sleeve identifying me as a Leading Wren, and then I sat quietly, waiting for the concert to begin.

As the lights went down I felt my chair move slightly, as someone sat down right behind me, and then as the music started, I became completely entranced with the deep, resounding sound of an organ filling the room. I closed my eyes, and succumbed to its beauty.

This first piece of music was a Bach Fugue, which I loved and that was followed by some rather serious Italian opera, and then the last piece was Faure's Requiem. I recognised it instantly, but couldn't remember when or where I had heard it before, but it was so beautiful that it moved me to tears. Trying not to disturb anyone, I fumbled in my jacket pocket for a handkerchief to wipe away the tears that were now tumbling down my cheeks, but I couldn't find one.

Suddenly, a handkerchief appeared over my shoulder, which I gratefully took and wiped away my tears. I then turned sideways to acknowledge my gratitude mouthing a quiet 'thank you' to whoever had come to my rescue, but could not see who it was in the dark. I decided that I would thank whoever it was after the music finished. As the glorious, spiritual music came to an end, there was complete silence for a moment. Perhaps everyone else had been as moved by it, as I had, I thought.

The lights were then turned on and as everyone stood up, I turned around to thank the person that had lent me the handkerchief.

I was met by the biggest smile I had ever seen. The next thing I noticed was that the owner of the smile also had the most amazing coloured hair. It was what my mother would have called Titian, a lovely, rich mahogany red.

'Thank you,' I said to the man who, I could now see was an Officer. He lent forward and looking into my eyes, he asked, 'Are your eyes grey or green?'

'Usually blue, but they are a bit red at the moment as I have been crying,' I said smiling; 'the music was so beautiful that it reduced me to tears; aren't I silly?'

'Not at all,' the young Officer said in a deep, soft voice. 'I must admit it almost moved me to tears too,' he grinned, before adding, 'but it was a good thing it didn't because you had my handkerchief!'

We both laughed and I immediately felt at ease with this kind young man.

'I'm so glad that someone else feels the way I do about music,' I told him.

I saw him glance at the sodden handkerchief I was still clutching in my hand.

'I'll wash it when I get back to my billet and let you have it back nicely washed and ironed, I promise,' I assured him.

As I picked up my jacket, I saw the surprise on his face when he noticed the anchor sewn on the arm, which told him that I was only a Leading Wren and not a Wren Officer.

'May I help you with your jacket?' he offered gallantly.

'Oh, thank you very much,' I said, handing it to him.

'Do you live on the base?' he asked, as he helped me with my jacket.

'No, I'm lucky,' I told him, 'I have been billeted with some other Wrens in an old Inn at Queen Camel, which is much more comfortable than a Nissen hut!'

As we walked down the path the Officer asked me how I got to and from the airfield, so I explained that I was trying to use my bicycle, as much as possible, rather than the naval transport. When we reached the bicycle racks, he helped me lift my bicycle out and I said, 'I must rush now or I'll be late. If I'm not back by ten I'll be in big trouble!'

The Officer stared at me for a moment and then asked quietly, 'Do you like reading poetry?'

'Yes I do as a matter of fact,' I replied.

'That's something else we have in common then,' he said, smiling at me. 'By the way I don't remember you telling me your name.'

'Mary Arden, Sir,' I replied. 'And what's yours if I may ask?'

'I won't tell you if you call me 'Sir',' he replied. 'It's ridiculous, and it makes me feel ancient!'

'But I have to, Sir: rules is rules!' I said, laughing.

'But once we're outside these gates, you are allowed to call Officers by their Christian names, aren't you?'

'Only if one or other of us is in civilian clothes,' I reminded him.

'I could always go back and get my pyjamas!' he suggested, with a broad grin.

I laughed out loud and said mischievously, 'That would cause a bit of gossip.'

'Well, I wouldn't like to start a scandal,' he laughed, 'so I had better introduce myself without further ado: I'm Duncan Ogilvie.'

'That sounds like a Scottish name,' I remarked, 'but you don't sound like all the other Scottish people I've ever heard talk before.'

'And you don't sound like all the other Ordinary Leading Wrens, do you Mary Arden?' Duncan said, grinning.

'No, I suppose not,' I replied.

'Then that's another thing we have in common!' Duncan said smiling that big smile again, 'So I think we must be destined to become friends.'

'Will you be at the concert again next week, Duncan?' I asked. 'If so, I will bring your handkerchief back, as I promised, clean and ironed!'

'That would be perfect,' Duncan said, still smiling at me, as I got on my bicycle. It was only then that I noticed how blue his eyes were and that he was really rather handsome.

The moment I got back to the billet, I went up to my bedroom and put Duncan's sodden, screwed up handkerchief in the washbasin to soak. I then put him out of my mind and went to bed.

As fate would have it, the following Tuesday, Duncan's squadron was booked in for Night Vision Tests. I had no idea, which squadron Duncan was attached to and he had no idea that I was one of the NV Testers, so it was a lovely surprise to suddenly see each other again. After the test Duncan stayed behind and told me that he had been trying to find out where I was working, but none of his friends recognised his description of a small, blond Leading Wren by the name of Arden.

'Of course, what I should have done,' Duncan said with that cheeky smile of his, 'was to ask the Officers in the Wardroom where the prettiest girl at the airfield worked, and then I would have found you sooner!'

'Flattery will get you nowhere, Lieutenant Ogilvie,' I giggled.

'So what do I have to do, then, Leading Wren Arden?' Duncan said raising an eyebrow.

'How about offering your services next Sunday on the farm where I am working as a volunteer?' I suggested.

'Sounds like far too much hard work, I will have to think about it,' Duncan replied before leaving.

At the musical evening on Thursday, I saw Duncan sitting next to some other Officers, but as soon as the music was over he came over and asked me whether I had enjoyed the records. I told him that I had, and fortunately hadn't required his handkerchief this time. I then handed his now clean and pressed handkerchief back to him.

Duncan asked whether he could walk part of the way back to my billet with me, and on the way, he told me a little bit about himself: he had never visited England until he joined the Navy, having spent most of his life in Perthshire and then Edinburgh where he spent two years studying for his BSc in Forestry at the University there. His father had begged him to stay on to finish his third year before joining up, but Duncan and his two best friends had insisted that it was their duty to join up at once.

Duncan then said how much he missed the wonderful Scottish heather, deer-stalking and fishing; but admitted that he was entranced by the little English villages in Somerset that he had seen so far, and was going to buy himself a second-hand bicycle so that he could see a bit more of the countryside.

'Good,' I said, 'and once you have your own bicycle, there will be no excuse not to come and work on the farm; they need all the help they can get you know,' I teased.

'Not so fast Mary! I haven't ridden a bike since the war began; I will be lucky to even get to the farm, let alone work once I am there!'

'Well then, you'd better start saving your strength and turn around now and go back to the airfield, as we are almost back at my billet.'

'Goodness, you're right!' Duncan exclaimed, 'I hadn't realised that we had walked quite so far, and I mustn't be too late getting to bed tonight, as I am flying one of our new Seafires first thing in the morning, so I need to be fully alert.'

'Some of the pilots have told me that they are wonderful to fly,' I said.

'Yes, I think it's the next best thing to being a bird, talking of which I must fly!' Duncan said smiling 'that' smile once more, and then he turned away and started walking back to the airfield.

This time, as I went to bed I couldn't put him out of my mind and it took me quite a while to get to sleep.

When I woke up I was still smiling.

CHAPTER 10

1943

I wasn't expecting to see Duncan again before the next musical evening, so when I saw him standing by the bicycle racks after work one day it gave me such a surprise, that instead of saying, 'How lovely to see you again and thank you for walking me back to my billet,' I blurted out, 'What are you doing here?''

'Come and see what I've found!' Duncan said pointing to an old bicycle with a huge basket at the front, which looked like the kind that errand boy's used to deliver meat and fish before the war. 'So what do you think of my trusty steed? I've managed to get one of the grocer's in Yeovil to hire it to me for a shilling a week, while I am stationed here.'

'A shilling a week! Is that with or without brakes?' I asked, laughing. 'Duncan, you can't be seen riding that old contraption, it's not befitting an Officer.'

'Don't worry, I won't ride it when I am wearing my uniform,' Duncan assured me, 'I just want to enjoy the odd ride now and again exploring the country lanes during these lovely summer evenings. Maybe we could even go out together one evening, if you are not too ashamed to be seen with me?'

I laughed and told him that I would be happy to, as long as he would agree to put in a full day on the Bridges' farm.

'That's why I am here,' Duncan then told me, 'I want you to give me the directions to get to the farm, as I thought I'd come and help next Sunday.'

As I explained to Duncan how to get to the Bridges' farm, I warned him that it was a very hilly ride, so he should make sure his brakes worked properly before setting off.

'Maybe we could ride to a pub on the way back for a quick glass of cider together?' he suggested, with a twinkle in his eye.

'Perhaps,' I replied.

The following Sunday I was grooming a huge carthorse, when Bobby patted my back to get my attention and then pointed at a man wheeling a bicycle towards the Bridges farm.

'Don't worry Bobby, he's a friend, you'll like him, come and say hello,' I said to reassure Bobby who was looking nervously at the stranger heading towards us.

Duncan must have immediately realised that Bobby was a bit simple, and might be afraid of a strange man, so he held out his hand and smiling at Bobby, said, 'Hello my name is Duncan, what's yours?'

'This is Bobby,' I said, answering for him. 'He is my knight in shining armour, and my rescuer from field mice!' Bobby grinned from ear to ear.

'In that case, I am very pleased to meet you Bobby!' Duncan said kindly, shaking Bobby's hand.

As we all walked towards the farmhouse, I told Duncan about my fear of mice running up my trouser legs, and he chortled with laughter. He then bent down and lifted up the bottom of one of my trouser legs and waggled his fingers pretending to be a mouse. Bobby started giggling and copied Duncan's mime with his fingers, before heading back to the stables.

'Oh I'm so glad to see you!' I said, beaming, and then added, 'I need to go and feed the hens now to collect the eggs, do you want to help me?'

'Why not?' Duncan replied.

With two of us doing the work, it took half the usual time to feed the hens, ducks and geese, and then collect the eggs. Duncan then surprised me by saying that he had seriously thought about becoming a farmer, but had decided on learning to be a forestry officer instead.

When I took Duncan indoors to meet the Bridges, Susan told us to sit at the kitchen table, while she made a pot of tea, and within a few minutes, Ted and Duncan were chatting away like old friends. I was amazed at how much Duncan knew about trees, hedging, ditching and the conservation of land, and Ted seemed equally impressed. While we drank our tea, Duncan told Ted that he'd be more than willing to check the spinney at the bottom of the hill to see which trees needed thinning, and at the same time, he'd check both the hedges and the ditches to make sure that they were clear for the winter. Ted was delighted with Duncan's kind offer and suggested that they take a walk around the farm together then and there.

After I had changed into my jodhpurs and come back outside, I saw that the two men were now walking towards the spinney, so I went to the stable to saddle-up Star. I then took her for a short ride through the beautiful countryside, and when we got back, I gave her a quick brush down. When I finally got back to the farmhouse, I was surprised to find Duncan and Ted sitting at the kitchen table studying a large map of the farm and the surrounding area. I gathered from their conversation, that quite a lot of work needed doing on the farm: trees in the spinney needed thinning, the hedges required trimming and the ditches needed clearing for better drainage. Duncan suggested that he could show Bobby how to do these jobs; telling Ted that, with supervision, he was sure that Bobby would be able to manage these jobs.

'I'm quite sure it won't be all that different from what you've done over the years anyway,' Duncan told him, 'but if I can teach Bobby the way I was taught then it will be one less job for you to struggle with.'

Ted nodded his agreement and I could see that he respected Duncan and was grateful for any help he could offer him.

When Duncan and I rode our bicycles back towards my billet that evening, we decided to stop off at a pub for a glass of cider. After I thanked him for coming to the farm to offer his help, he said that he was going to try to book the following Wednesday afternoon off, so that he could get Bobby started, as there was a lot to teach him. He was as good as his word and turned up promptly after lunch the following Wednesday, and immediately began showing Bobby what to do. I could tell that Bobby was really enjoying being taught new skills, and when it was time to leave later that evening, I overheard Duncan tell Ted that Bobby was quite capable of doing everything he was teaching him without any problem.

That evening we rode our bikes together side by side, and Duncan mentioned that he had found another pub, which served good food and that today's special was beef casserole with dumplings.

'There may be more dumplings than meat!' I joked 'but I must admit that I'm starving.'

'Just as well, because I have booked a table,' Duncan said grinning. 'So if you're not doing anything else this evening, Miss Arden, would you do me the honour of dining with me tonight?'

'I would love to, but do you mind if we go Dutch?' I asked, 'I always do, even with my brother and his friends.'

'No problem,' Duncan replied.

Actually, there was one problem. I only had half a crown in my pocket, which I always kept on me for emergencies, so I suddenly realized that I would have to borrow another shilling or two off him. Fortunately, Duncan thought this was very funny and agreed to lend me the money, but only if I let him buy the drinks.

When we arrived at the pub, Duncan ordered us two pints of cider and the landlord said, 'So you got the young lass to come I see: I hope she's hungry, as the Missus has kept aside two generous portions for you both!'

When the landlord cleared our empty plates and asked us whether we'd like some blackberry and apple crumble with cream, I said without hesitation, 'Yes, a double portion please!'

Duncan laughed, and told the landlord that he was far too full to have any pudding, but asked him to bring two spoons anyway. For someone who had just said that he had no room to eat anything else, he still managed to eat more crumble than I did, I noticed.

We had another couple of drinks and then, when it was time to leave, I tried to get up to leave, and my legs nearly gave way. Duncan was obviously having similar trouble.

'I think I must be a little bit drunk, but you won't tell anybody will you?' he whispered in my ear.

'I promish,' I slurred, and then started to giggle.

'This cider is a bit stronger than I'm used to,' Duncan admitted, 'I think we'd better go for a bike ride to sober up before I take you back to your billet, then the effects might wear off.'

'Good idea,' I agreed, 'thish Scrumpy makes your legs all wibbly-wobbly!'

As we weaved along the deserted lanes Duncan sang silly ditties and I laughed until I cried, but when we eventually got near my billet, I begged him to be quiet in case a Wren Petty Officer overheard us, and we got in trouble for being drunk and disorderly. However, instead of doing as I had asked, Duncan made up a rude song about Wren Petty Officers, which made me double up with even more giggles, and I very nearly fell off my bicycle.

'Please stop!' I begged him, 'I've got a stitch in my side and I'll be sick in a minute if I laugh anymore.'

The following evening I wrote to Jane to tell her all about Duncan, how we had met and how he made me laugh so much. I had only intended to write a paragraph but ended up writing four pages. I explained that Duncan and I were 'just good friends' but confessed that I was thoroughly enjoying having the company of a man once again.

Over the next few weeks we worked on the farm together quite often and shared meals at different pubs afterwards; we also went for bike rides and talked about what we had done before we had met.

Duncan told me that he had joined the Navy within weeks of war being declared, 'I hardly knew the difference between port and starboard, but I found myself put in command, as a Junior Sub-Lieutenant, of a converted fishing boat and its crew. As my father drove me to Wick, right at the top of Scotland, he gave me some very useful advice, 'just because of your education you have been fortunate to become an Officer automatically, but that doesn't mean to say that you will have anything like the experience of the sea-faring men on board the boat that you will be in charge of. There will be men that have spent their lives at sea, so ask them for their help and get them to teach you the ropes, literally!"

'Did you take his advice?' I asked.

'Yes I did, and it was just as well, because it was pretty obvious, when I presented myself to the skipper, that he was not particularly pleased to see me, so I decided to be honest with him and confess my lack of experience at sea, and told him that I was surprised as he was to have been put in command. I then added that as far as I was concerned, he was still the boss, when it came to anything to do with his fishing boat, and he was much happier after that.'

Duncan then told me that the skipper had asked him if he had had any experience with firearms, as they had a gun hidden in their fishing nets but none of the sailors knew how to use it, so Duncan had told him, 'I've shot game and deer, but thank God, so far, no men!' The skipper had laughed at that apparently and said, 'That must be why you are here then!'

The next time Duncan and I went cycling together, he asked me what my life was like before the war and I could tell that he was a bit surprised to discover what a privileged life I had led. He asked me if I was expected to marry into the aristocracy one day, so I told him all about Charles, and how I would have become an Earl's wife, had he lived. He was very sympathetic when I told him how Charles had died, and afterwards we continued riding side by side in silence for the next few miles, until I said that I needed to stop to have a pee behind a hedge. Duncan then laughed, and yelled, 'Me too!'

We propped our bikes against a gate, and as I went behind the hedge to relieve myself, Duncan went in the other direction to find a suitable spot to have a pee. When I stood up again, I spotted what I thought must be a lame horse in the field.

'Oh, Duncan, look at that poor horse, he's hurt!' I cried out, in distress.

Duncan appeared immediately, still buttoning up his trouser flies and hurried to my side to see where I was pointing.

'The poor thing seems to have five legs instead of four and one of them is terribly deformed,' I said now feeling very distressed, 'is there anything we can do?'

'There's nothing we can do for the old chap I'm afraid, Mary,' Duncan said laughing uncontrollably, 'I am sure that all will be well with him once he has found a mare!'

I looked at him blankly and he then shook his head in disbelief, as it slowly dawned on him that I was genuinely distressed and was obviously totally unaware of how horses mated. Very quietly Duncan said, 'Mary, that is not a deformed leg in the middle of the horse's tummy you silly ninny, it's the horse's willy!'

'What?' I asked, 'you mean his, his… thing?'

Duncan nodded and after coughing in an attempt to conceal his laughter he then said, 'Hasn't your mother ever given you a lesson about the birds and bees?'

'Well, yes sort of,' I replied, 'but not about horses. Why are their things so much bigger?'

So Duncan took the next few minutes to explain why, and then when he saw the expression on my face at his graphic descriptions, he couldn't hold back any longer and laughed until he wept.

After Duncan had escorted me back to the Inn that evening, he told me that he might not be able to see me again for several days because his squadron was due to go back on operations fairly soon and there was intensive training to be done beforehand.

Despite knowing that Duncan's departure was imminent, I thought that I would at least see him the following Thursday at the musical evening, but there was no sign of him. After the concert, as I was collecting my bicycle from the rack and thinking that in future it would be wiser to take the bus now that it was getting dark earlier, I saw Duncan rushing towards me. His face was as white as a sheet.

'Are you unwell, Duncan?' I asked, quite alarmed. 'Is something wrong?'

'My squadron has been told to be ready to leave first thing in the morning, so I couldn't come to the concert, but I didn't want to go without saying goodbye,' Duncan said looking deeply into my eyes.

'Will you write to me, Mary, so that we can keep in touch? If you send letters to me at my parents' address, I'll ask them to read them to me over the phone when I reach a port. I should hate it if we lost touch; we've become such good friends.'

'Of course, I'll write,' I promised, 'often.'

He handed me a card with his parents' address written on it and I wrote down my parents' address for him too, in case I was stationed somewhere else before I saw him again.

'I might not be able to write as often as you Mary, as it's impossible to do so when you're at sea, but just remember, no news is good news,' Duncan said and then taking my hand in his added, 'Will you miss me, Mary?'

I was surprised at the desperate tone in his voice and thought it might be because he was fearful about what he was about to encounter.

'Of course I'll miss you, you silly man!' I told him sincerely.

'Will you kiss me goodbye then?' Duncan asked quietly.

I put my hands on either side of his head and gently pulled him down to my height, so that I could kiss him on both cheeks. 'Please don't try and play the hero, will you Duncan?'

'Don't worry, I'm not going to take any unnecessary risks; I want to live Mary,' Duncan said quietly. 'Especially now that I have met you.'

'Goodbye my dear, kind friend,' I said, and as Duncan walked away, I could feel my eyes begin to fill with tears. Up to that moment, I had resolved not to get too close to anyone again, as I still felt as though I was bad luck to anyone I cared about. However, the fact was that I 'had' got very close to Duncan over the last few weeks, and I couldn't bear it if I never saw him again.

As I went to collect my bicycle, Duncan's hat suddenly landed in my basket, and then, before I knew what was happening, I found myself in Duncan's arms. He kissed me softly at first, and then with more passion. I didn't resist; it felt so wonderful that I didn't want him to stop, and when eventually he did, he looked deep into my eyes and said, 'To hell with being a dear kind friend, I love you Leading Wren Arden!' He then promptly collected his hat from my basket, and headed back to the airfield without saying another word.

I was so surprised and breathless by what had just occurred that I was unable to move from the spot for a good few minutes, and when I finally pulled myself together and got on my bike, I realized that I was trembling like a leaf. As I slowly rode back to the Inn, I felt utterly confused: I hadn't thought of Duncan as anything more than a friend until now, but I couldn't deny that I had enjoyed kissing him, and it was true that I had a warm glow every time I thought of him. Had I been so busy ensuring that no man got too close to me again that perhaps I had been suppressing my true feelings? I just didn't know, so I put off writing to Duncan for some time, as I didn't know quite what to say to him.

Anne then went on leave for two weeks, which meant that I was now doing four tests a day, instead of my usual two. It was exhausting work but at least it made me sleep like a baby every night, and I didn't stay awake worrying about Duncan all the time.

Two months later, I received a call from Commander Lewis telling me to come to his office, as Surgeon Captain Timpston was on the phone for me.

'Commander Timpston don't you mean, Sir?'

'No, he's been promoted,' he confirmed. When I reached the Commander's office he motioned me to the telephone on his desk and left the room.

I picked up the receiver, 'Good morning Surgeon Captain.'

'You'll have to call me 'Sir' every other word now Mary!' he teased,' and do everything I say.'

'As if I haven't always!' I said, giggling down the telephone, 'Did you ring me up for a friendly chat or are you going to promote me as well?'

'I wish I could,' Daddy-T replied, 'but I'm afraid that I still haven't managed to get your category upgraded to a commission.'

He then went on to tell me that he wanted me to leave HMS Heron and go to another air station based in Scotland.

'The name of the station is HMS Condor. It's a very pleasant naval airbase near a pretty little town called Arbroath. I will arrange private billeting, if it's at all possible, but I'm afraid you may have to buy yourself some winter clothes, as it's pretty cold up there' he warned.

'When would you like me to go, Sir?' I asked.

'When did you last have any home leave?'

'I haven't taken any since I have been here, Sir,' I told him.

'In that case, I suggest you take two weeks leave before taking yourself up to Arbroath.'

'Yes Sir,' I replied, and then added cheekily, 'If you insist Sir, Thank you Sir!'

'Good girl I knew you wouldn't make a fuss!' he said chuckling at my insolence. 'Now don't forget that I'm still here if anything needs seeing to or for that matter, if you need permission to rewire the whole naval air station, should your electric kettle fuse the communications in your region!' he added, laughing out loud.

I didn't know whether to laugh or cry: I wanted to laugh because I thought that there might be a possibility of seeing Duncan if he went home to Scotland on leave, but I also wanted to cry because it meant leaving all my dear friends at Heron. I told Commander Lewis about my new instructions, which he already knew about He said with true feeling but in a matter-of-fact way, 'Well, Mary, we'll all miss you.'

'Thank you, Sir, I'll miss you all too,' I replied.

A few days later, while I was sorting through my things, it dawned on me that I might not see the Fullers again until after the war, so I sat down and wrote Margaret a long letter thanking her for her friendship and hospitality during the summer. I told her where I was going and that I would forward the correct postal address as soon as I was settled.

The day before my departure, I set off to see the Bridges and Bobby. It was awful having to say goodbye, I would miss them all terribly. As Susan and I hugged each other, I promised her that I'd stay in touch. I then returned to the NVT office to say a final farewell to Anne, and as I put the kettle on, she wailed, 'What if I don't get on with the new girl?'

'Well, you'll jolly well have to,' I said firmly, 'I'm sure Daddy-T will have chosen well, and I expect she won't be as scatter-brained as I am.'

We both cried for a while and then Anne regained her composure and said, 'Right then, the kettle must have boiled dry by now. How about a cuppa?'

I knew then that she would be all right.

On the morning of my departure, I was delighted to see TNT's car waiting for me outside the Sick Bay. We arrived at the station in good time and TNT kindly waited with me on the platform until my train was ready to leave.

As I boarded the train TNT asked me if I would be seeing my young man again soon. Gossip obviously travels fast on this air base, I thought.

'I hope so,' I said quietly, 'I really hope so.'

It was bliss being at home again, and for the first few days I did nothing but talk to my parents about everything that I'd done since my last visit and spend part of each day with Kay and her children. My goddaughter Julie was now trying to walk, which was a joy to see. I also managed to visit the Derwents several times. Things had changed little for them over the year, but the boys were still alive and well, which was all that mattered.

My parents had received very few letters from my brother Peter, who was still in Burma but William had managed to get home-leave for the weekend, and told me proudly that he was now shaving, but he was still the same giggly little brother that I loved so much.

One evening, my father said that he had noticed that I had mentioned Duncan rather a lot in my conversations, and wanted to know if he was 'special' to me, so I told him that he was a good friend, but nothing more at present, and that I was unlikely to see him again until after the war anyway. He nodded in understanding and then smiled at my mother, who for once said nothing, but I could see that she was smiling too.

Agnes was far more interested to hear all about my 'new young man'. She had eavesdropped shamelessly while she'd been dusting and had overheard me telling Jane on the phone how Duncan had kissed me goodbye. I had told my cousin that, 'It wasn't a brotherly kiss but a long, slow lingering film-star kind of a kiss that had made my legs go all quivery, and not in the same way the Scrumpy did, I can tell you!' Agnes told me that when she had overheard this, she had nearly dropped a precious piece of Dresden china!

As we listened to the nine o'clock news one night, we heard that Italy had signed an unconditional surrender with the Allies. William and I cheered, but my father's reaction was a bit subdued.

'What's wrong Daddy?' I asked.

'The Italians may have surrendered, my dear, but this war is still far from over,' he warned.

The day before I was due to leave, my parents received a letter from Peter to say that he was fit and well but longing for the war to end, so that he could get on with a normal life. He told them that he had just received a batch of letters, all tied up with string that had been written over several months, which had been waiting for him to return to base, hinting that he'd been out in the jungle during that time. My parents told me that they had become used to reading between the lines of the rare and censored letters that Peter managed to send.

He finished his letter, 'Let William know that I will play tennis with him everyday once I get home, and tell him that I'm sorry I was such a nasty brother to him when he was little.'

I felt tears pricking my eyes imagining that Peter must be terrified of getting killed, and that he was wanting to make his peace just in case. I then thought of all the other families that must be receiving similar letters, and I was grateful that I was working in Britain and that my family weren't being put under the same kind of emotional stress about me.

My mother was a bit worried that I would be lonely in Scotland, as I didn't know anybody in that 'distant land', so she offered to write to my Great Aunt, Lady Margaret, to see whether she knew of anyone who lived near Arbroath, as she had good contacts all over England I was informed, 'And possibly even as far away as Scotland!'

On the day of my departure, my father insisted on coming with me up to London to see me safely across the city to Kings Cross station to catch the overnight train to Edinburgh. As I was boarding, he had a word with the guard, who was obviously used to worried fathers, as I overheard him say, 'Don't worry, Sir, I pass up and down the corridor all night long, so I'll keep an eye on the young lady.'

'I'm not your little girl any more, Daddy!' I said laughing, as I kissed him goodbye, 'I can look after myself now.'

It wasn't until we had left the station that I wondered if those words were the reason I had detected tears in my father's eyes, as I had waved farewell to him through the carriage window.

It was a long journey; we had to stop twice on the way due to air raids and I had to change trains at Edinburgh too, so I didn't arrive until the following afternoon, and then I had to arrange for transport to collect me and take me to the naval air station. When I finally I got to HMS Condor, it was nearly dark. I reported to the billeting office and introduced myself to a weary looking Third Officer, who seeing that I was swaying on my feet with fatigue, told me to sit down immediately before I fell over. She spoke in a soft Scottish burr and asked me when I'd last had something to eat. I thought for a minute and then told her that the last thing I had eaten was a Mars Bar in the middle of the night, which my little brother had given me before I left home.

'He must be a very kind boy,' the Third Officer smiled, 'I wouldn't give any of my chocolate away!'

She looked at a piece of paper on her desk and said, 'You're billeted in an old manse called Letham Grange, about a mile away from the air station, but as there's no official transport until eight-thirty this evening, and it isn't your fault that you're so late, I'll ring through to the Transport Office to see if someone's available to take you to your billet straight away. You can leave your cases there, have a quick wash, and then come back here for a hot meal in the Wren's mess.'

I thanked her and then sat quietly until a van arrived about ten minutes later. The driver helped me put my luggage in the back seat and then I sat in the front next him. When we arrived at the old manse, he said that he would come back for me in an hour and take me back to Condor.

I rang the doorbell and a woman of about fifty greeted me. She told me her name was Mrs Anderson, and that she was the housekeeper. To my relief, the house was warm and I noticed that there were big old-fashioned radiators in the hall and on the landing. Mrs Anderson warned me that the lights were inclined to go out every now and again but that I would find candles and matches dotted about the house on many of the shelves and window sills, just in case. I was then shown to a large bedroom with three beds in it. The housekeeper explained that I'd be sharing with two other girls.

On the way to the bathroom she pointed out a cupboard on the landing where the suitcases were kept and explained that the bathroom was shared with one other bedroom. She then told me that there was a bathroom rota pinned on the door, but that there were no strict rules really, and that the girls changed the timetable to suit their ever-changing shift patterns.

When I asked Mrs Anderson who the Petty Officer in charge was, she replied firmly, 'I'm in charge here, but so long as you keep your room tidy there'll be no trouble.' She then added kindly, 'The other lasses will tell you about the timetable for transport, meals, and so forth.'

I asked where I could do my washing and she explained that there was a laundry room downstairs with 'a wee washing line with a 'poolley' on the ceiling, and the girls use the indoor line if the weather is too wet to hang their clothes outside.'

'Oh, there's just one other thing,' I said, suddenly remembering, 'could you please tell me if there's anywhere I can stow my bicycle when it arrives?'

'Aye, in the 'oot hoose',' she said, 'there's another lass that keeps hers in there too.'

When Mrs Anderson left me to unpack, I opened my suitcase and took out some clothes that needed hanging up, but discovered that the wardrobe was already crammed full of my roommate's clothes and that there didn't seem to be any spare coat hangers left. I made a mental note to buy some coat hangers, a bigger torch and some spare batteries in case the lights should go out, and to find out where the 'oot hoose' was.

Once I had washed and changed into clean clothes, I felt much more refreshed and went downstairs to explore the house. The first room I entered was a large sitting room, which I was pleased to see had a big fireplace laid ready for an evening fire. I smiled as it already felt quite homely to me, and I felt grateful to be billeted here.

Before the driver came to pick me up, I decided to let Mrs Anderson know that I hadn't finished putting away all my belongings, but that I would do it later that evening, when I'd negotiated some hanging space in the wardrobe with my roommates. I then asked her if she'd like me to get her anything from the Wren's NAAFI, while I was at the base. She looked at me as if I'd just landed from the moon, 'Nobody has ever asked me if I'd like anything from the NAAFI before.' She then smiled at me and said, 'Well, I could do with some toothpaste, Miss, as I'm a wee bitty short of it, and it's a fair way to the 'toon' from here just for one tube.'

As I was driven back to Condor, I asked the driver, who was the person that I should talk to about collecting my bicycle and my other suitcase from the station, when they eventually turned up.

'McDougal in Transport: he'll know; wait until the morn' at yon office,' he replied, pointing to a collection of sheds in the distance, as we drove through the gates into the base.

As I signed in at the gatehouse, the Petty Officer in charge looked at my pass, but his accent was so strong that at first I couldn't understand what he was saying, so I had to keep asking, 'Sorry, would you mind saying that again?'

'You're a Sassenach,' he said waggling a finger at me.

I hung my head in shame, 'Yes, I'm very sorry, Sir, I'm afraid I am.'

This made him laugh, 'In that case I will speak ver… ree.. slooooow… lee!'

We both laughed and as he handed my pass back to me, he said, 'Welcome to Scotland Leading Wren Sassenach!'

By the time I had found the Wren's mess, I was feeling very hungry. When I opened the door, the familiar chatter and fug enveloped me immediately, as this mess was almost identical as all the other ones I had eaten in since becoming a Wren. I got my meal and then sat down next to a group of girls sitting at one of the tables nearest to the serving counter. One of them looked up and smiled, 'Hello, I haven't seen you around here before.'

It didn't take long before I was chatting with the entire group at my table. When I told them where I was billeted, one of the girls got up and went to a nearby table to fetch a girl with jet-black hair, who was also billeted at The Grange. She introduced herself as Kitty Campbell, and said with a smile, 'Stick with me!'

I couldn't place her accent, as it didn't sound English or Scottish, so I asked her and was surprised when she told me that her mother was French.

'Oh good I can practice my French with you,' I said.

'Yours is most probably better than mine!' she laughed.

When I'd finished my meal, I went to the NAAFI and bought the tube of toothpaste for Mrs Anderson, before going back to The Grange in the lorry with Kitty. On the way, I asked her if she'd heard of a Petty Officer called

McDougal; explaining that I needed to ask him to pick up my bicycle and cases from the station.

'Everyone knows McDougal,' Kitty said with a grin. 'He'll try to get to know you too all right!' she giggled. 'Old Mac has an eye for all you blondies.'

'Too late,' I laughed, 'I'm saving myself for a Scotsman with gorgeous auburn hair, called Duncan Ogilvie!'

'Are you referring to a rather handsome Lieutenant who smokes a pipe?' Kitty asked with a note of astonishment.

'Well, he is certainly handsome, but I don't remember him ever smoking a pipe,' I said a bit surprised. 'How on earth do you know him?'

'His squadron flew in here about two weeks ago, and all we girls noticed him at once, as none of us had ever seen a man with hair that colour before,' Kitty chuckled, 'and such blue eyes!'

'And don't forget his lovely smile!' I giggled, and then asked hopefully, 'Is his squadron still here?'

'Their next operation has been delayed,' Kitty said, 'so they were all sent on leave, and we haven't seen any of them since.'

I found it amusing that Kitty and her friends had thought that Duncan was so handsome, as I hadn't really thought of him as a 'heartthrob' before, although I certainly had noticed that he had lovely deep-blue eyes, and I did rather like his lovely auburn hair, and of course 'that' smile!

After leaving the toothpaste for Mrs Anderson in the kitchen, so that she would find it in the morning, I went straight to my bedroom and introduced myself to my roommates, Glenda and Marie-Anne. I apologised to them for making the room look so untidy, explaining that I needed a bit of wardrobe space and a few coat hangers.

'Are there any spare anywhere?' I asked them.

'I doubt it,' Marie-Anne said. 'The last girl that slept in your bed must have taken them all with her, but there are plenty of spares at the store.'

I then noticed that my hot water bottle wasn't where I had left it on the chair, but was delighted to find out that it had already been filled, and was now warming my bed. Mrs Anderson must have checked our room, seen my hot water bottle, and decided to air my bed, which was a lovely gesture. One good turn deserves another, I thought, as I snuggled in between the sheets.

I was just nodding off, when I heard strange scratching noises behind my bed, and wondered if perhaps the house was haunted but I was so tired that I soon fell back to sleep.

When I arrived at HMS Condor, the next morning, I reported to First Officer McFarlane, who made it clear from the outset that my arrival had caused her some 'considerable inconvenience.' I soon discovered why. Apparently when the other NV Tester had arrived the previous year, the First Officer had been ordered by Surgeon Captain Timpston to find her a quiet billet in Arbroath, and now she had been ordered to find a similar one for me.

'What is so special about you NVTs that you get preferential treatment?' she snapped.

I had to think quickly and replied, 'Well, Ma'am, as we have to work long hours in a dark, sealed room all day and then have hours of paperwork to do at the end of the day, I think that Surgeon Captain Timpston is concerned about our health, so he prefers us to have somewhere quiet to sleep. He also likes us to walk in the fresh air from our billet to work whenever possible,' I added.

Fortunately, the First Officer seemed satisfied with my explanation, although there wasn't an ounce of truth in it.

I was halfway between the Administration hut and the Sick Bay, when I heard alarm bells blaring all over the air base. I then saw two ambulances and two fire engines speeding towards a distant runway past the control tower. I hurried to the Sick Bay, but the moment I arrived I was told to keep out of the way. Two planes had failed to heed the warning, by the runway control officer, to abort their take offs and had collided.

I made my way to the NVT office where I hoped to find the other Tester, Fiona McIntosh, and could wait with her until everything had calmed down a bit, but as I walked down the corridor towards the office, I heard the sound of running feet and doors slamming, and then saw two young doctors buttoning up their white coats, as they hurried towards the emergency room.

When I opened the door to the NVT office, a tall slim girl with brown hair and lovely green eyes looked up.

'Hello, I am Fiona McIntosh. You must be Mary Arden. Come in and shut the door. I don't want to see what is going on out there, as I can't stand the sight of blood.'

Fiona then showed me around the unit and explained her filing system to me, which was very similar to Anne's, so I knew that I wouldn't have any problems.

'This morning's tests will be postponed because of the accident,' Fiona said. 'I suspect it was due to the silly fools larking around and drinking too much last night.'

'At Heron, Anne and I tried to persuade the pilots not to drink for forty-eight hours before night flying,' I told her.

'And did they follow your advice?'

'As a matter of fact most of them did,' I said proudly, 'and it made quite a difference.'

Our conversation was cut short by the sound of two ambulances roaring past our office. I automatically rushed to the window to see what was going on.

'One of the ambulances is driving towards the gates, Fiona,' I said.

'That means that one of the pilots must be very badly injured, so they will be taking him to Dundee,' Fiona replied, 'but what about the other ambulance, which way is that one heading?'

I leaned out of the window, so that I could get a better view, and told her that I could see the second ambulance drawing up outside the Sick Bay. We then heard running feet, followed by one of the doctor's shouting orders. When I asked an SBA if he needed any help he told me that this pilot had been lucky and only broken an ankle, which meant that they could deal with his injury in the Sick Bay, but the other poor chap had crushed his ribs and had head injuries, so he was now on his way to hospital.

Fiona then took me to see the Testing Room to show me where everything was kept. I was glad to see that it was an almost identical layout to the other two NVT units I had worked in. However, there were two things that I noticed were missing: one was our internal telephone, so that we could arrange tests directly with Commander Flying instead of having to book them through the doctors, and the other was our own electric kettle! I mentioned this to Fiona.

'We don't need one,' Fiona said, 'we have a kettle in the cloakroom ante-room which we share with the Writers, that's where we make our teas and coffees.'

'I could do with one now,' I said cheekily, looking at my watch and was surprised to see that it was already eleven.

While the kettle was boiling, we went to the Writer's office so that Fiona could introduce me to the three Wrens, who worked as private secretaries to the doctors. We then carried our hot mugs back to our office and while we enjoyed our coffee Fiona asked me a bit about myself.

'Why did you choose to be an NVT?' she asked.

'I didn't choose it, it chose me,' I said, and told her all about my dear friend Andrew, who had been caught in searchlights, and how I had felt when I had found out that there was something positive I could do to try and help other pilots see better in the dark and possibly avoid a similar tragedy.

'Goodness, Mary, what a strange thing,' Fiona said. 'It's almost as if you were meant to do it.'

'Yes,' I replied quietly 'that's what I thought, at the time, and, thankfully, so did Daddy-T.'

During the lunch break, I went to the Transport Office and asked to see CPO McDougal. A young mechanic took me through a door and into a shed where the Chief was sitting at his desk. I told him that my bicycle and suitcase needed collecting from the station and asked him if he could help me retrieve them.

'You'll need authorisation first and then I can make arrangements to collect them for you,' he explained, finding the necessary form and showing me where to sign it. 'Do you have a padlock and chain for your bike?' he enquired.

I stared at him and asked, 'Why? Surely no one would steal my bicycle in wartime? I've never had to lock it up before.'

'Argh-aye, you see, there's no' very much transport here about, and the young officers like to visit the public houses, so they are inclined to 'borrow' any bicycles left around to get to Arbroath,' he explained. 'Then they forget which pub they've left the bike at, so then get a wee taxi home to their beds,' he chuckled. 'So it's best you make sure you lock it up, lassie, so they don't pinch it.'

As I was leaving McDougal informed me that he just happened to have both a spare padlock and a chain that I could buy from him if I wanted to, rather than having to go to a shop. When McDougal handed me the padlock and chain, I could see straight away that they were second-hand, although he hadn't mentioned this fact before taking my money. It was obvious they were not new because the key for the padlock still had a lucky charm attached to it, so must have belonged to someone else at some stage. Oh well, I thought, perhaps the charm will bring me luck.

McDougal said that he would make arrangements for my suitcase and my bicycle to be delivered to Letham Grange, as soon as possible, but when I returned to the manse that evening there was no sign of either. Then, I had a hunch, and went to look in the 'oot hoose', and sure enough there they were. McDougal was a wily old man, but at least he had been true to his word.

The next morning I decided to introduce myself to the doctors. Unfortunately Surgeon Commander Scott was away on leave but his next in command, Dr Marchant, was temporarily in charge while he was away, and the moment I introduced myself to him, a large grin appeared on his face.

'Leading Wren Arden eh?' the doctor said, laughing and then told me that 'Red' had been asking all week if anyone had seen me around, so he had promised to let him know when I arrived by hoisting a windsock on the Sick Bay roof, which Red would be able to see from anywhere on the airfield.'

I looked blankly, ''Red', who's Red?' I asked.

'Red, you know, as in red hair? As in Lieutenant Ogilvie!' he said, a little taken aback that I didn't know Duncan's nickname.

'Oh,' I exclaimed, feeling my face suddenly light up with joy. 'You mean Duncan?' I gasped, blushing profusely.

'Maybe you should be the one called 'Red'!' Dr Marchant teased. 'I'll put the windsock up first thing in the morning, as it's too dark now,' the amused doctor assured me before saying goodbye and going back to his office.

I nearly drove Fiona mad the following morning: every time I left the room I would say, 'Don't let him go if he comes in, tell him I won't be a minute.'

'Gosh you've got it badly,' Fiona said, laughing.

I hadn't realised that I had, but it looked as if she was right, I admitted to myself, surprised at the intensity of my feelings.

By the time I got to the NAAFI, I was beginning to feel sick to the stomach. Duncan still hadn't turned up and I was worried that I must have missed him. He obviously hadn't seen the windsock, or so I thought, until I suddenly heard a voice call out, 'Anyone called Mary Arden in here?'

Leaping to my feet I nearly tripped over my gasmask case, and yelled, 'Yes, yes that's me, who wants me?'

The girl who had called out my name then said, 'There's an Officer outside who asked me to find out whether you were inside.'

Clutching my gasmask case to my chest, I went outside and there standing right in front of me, with a huge grin on his face, was Duncan.

Without saying a word he saluted, so I saluted back, automatically, without even thinking, and then he took my hand in both of his and put them to his lips and whispered, 'Meet me outside the main gate at seven-thirty. We're going out to dinner!' He then saluted again and disappeared.

It took me a few moments to snap out of the shock of seeing Duncan again, and then I suddenly realised that I couldn't possibly have dinner with him tonight, at least not in a public place because we were both in uniform, so what on earth could I do? I could feel my eyes start to well up.

When I went back into the NAAFI, I noticed a red jacket hanging up behind the counter on a hook. Thinking that it might belong to the lady who was on duty, I decided to ask her if she would lend it to me for the evening, but had to wait for her to finish serving before explaining my predicament. I told her that if I didn't go out with Duncan that evening, I might not get another chance to see him for months. Fortunately, she took pity on me, and looking at my uniform suggested that if I take off my jacket and tie, it would look like I just had a normal white shirt on under her red jacket.

'Just be sure you smile at everyone brightly, so that they don't notice that you're still in uniform below the waist. Here, try it on,' she said kindly, handing me the jacket.

It was at least one size too big for me, but that was a good thing, as it hung well below my hips. She then suggested that if I turned it inside out, only the lining would show, when I carried it past the guardhouse. I could then change into it on my way to the restaurant.

The lady asked me to wait for a moment and disappeared into the kitchen. When she appeared again she was carrying a navy blue and white silk scarf.

'This belongs to a friend of mine who's helping out with the washing-up tonight, and she says you can borrow it and that if you tie it in a pretty bow, your white shirt will hardly show at all.'

'Thank you so much!' I said, 'I promise to bring everything back tomorrow.'

'You do that and then you can tell us all about your date!' she said laughing.

That evening I showed my pass to the Guard and when I was in the road I saw Duncan waiting by a taxi. He beckoned me to him.

Once I was in the taxi, I relaxed at last and told Duncan about how I had just borrowed a jacket and scarf to disguise my uniform. 'Don't worry about your uniform' he grinned, 'I've borrowed this white pullover and rather gaudy tie so, hopefully, from the waist up I won't be mistaken for an officer… or a gentleman!'

By pure coincidence, we were both wearing red, white and blue clothes.

'We couldn't be more patriotic if we had tried!' I said, and we both laughed. Duncan then put an arm around my shoulders and pulled me close and whispered into my ear how much he had longed to see me again.

When I asked him what he was doing in Arbroath, he explained that his squadron had been sent to HMS Condor between 'ops' and they had been given some leave, so he had gone home to see his parents, who had given him my letter telling him that I had been posted to HMS Condor.

'You didn't give me any specific date in your letter, so I had no idea when you would be arriving here,' Duncan said, 'but I thought you most probably wouldn't get here until my leave was over. I nearly went mad looking out for you and in the end Johnny Marchant offered to fly a windsock on the roof as soon as you reported for duty. But when I eventually saw it, I was too busy to get away, so I just prayed that I would catch you tonight before you left, and God was listening!'

When we arrived at the restaurant. Duncan said quietly, 'See you at the bar,' and then pointed to the ladies' room. Once I was inside, I removed my tie and stiff collar and replaced them with the blue and white scarf, which I tied in a fancy knot. I then draped the red jacket over my shoulders, and taking a deep breath, I joined Duncan at the bar.

'How do you do Miss Arden,' he said, doing a little bow, as if we'd only just met. 'What a lovely surprise that you were able to join me here this evening, I thought you were still in Somerset.'

'And I thought you were still in… ' I hesitated, as I had absolutely no idea where Duncan's squadron had just been on operations, but then noticed that he looked a lot more suntanned compared to the last time I had seen him. 'Actually where have you been? Sunbathing in the Med perhaps?'

He leaned over and whispered in my ear, 'Yes, but it was no picnic and there was certainly no time for any sunbathing.'

'Do you want to talk about it?' I asked.

'I'd rather not, it was very frightening, and I am doing my best not to re-live it all,' Duncan said quietly. 'But I will tell you that I am very proud of my squadron. The boys were all very brave.'

As we sat down to eat our meal and continued chatting, I couldn't help noticing Duncan's deep-blue eyes, and could now see why Kitty and the other girls had given him 'heartthrob' status. The thought must have made me smile, as now Duncan was smiling back at me, with 'that' smile and I suddenly felt my heart beat a little faster than usual.

It was well past nine, when I suddenly remembered that I hadn't had a chance to ask for a late pass, so I told Duncan that we'd have to leave soon so that I would be back at the manse before ten.

'Don't worry,' he said, 'I ordered a taxi for 9.30, so there's plenty of time and you won't be late.'

'Thank goodness!' I sighed.

'But make sure you get a late pass for tomorrow night,' Duncan said grinning, 'as I have booked us in for the local hotel's Saturday dinner dance. That is, if you feel like going, of course?'

'Yes, I'd love to,' I replied but then realised that I had nothing suitable to wear for a dinner dance, so would have to go into Arbroath the next day to do some shopping.

As we saw the taxi draw up outside the restaurant, Duncan asked me to meet him outside the Entertainment's hut the next day at two-thirty to confirm that there was no change of plan, just in case his squadron had to fly off sooner than expected. He held my hand all the way back to my billet, and when we got there he asked the driver to wait while he escorted me to the back door. Before I went inside, Duncan gently kissed me on the lips and whispered, 'I love you.'

It wasn't until I had got to the top of the stairs that I thought to myself, 'and I love you too Duncan Ogilvie!' I then caught a glimpse of myself in the mirror and saw that I was smiling from ear to ear.

The following morning, I made sure that I signed the book for a late pass and collected a key from Mrs Anderson.

As I unlocked my bicycle and set off down the road towards Arbroath, the wind howled around my legs, and I wished I had worn a warm pair of slacks instead of my skirt, as it was bitterly cold.

When I arrived in Arbroath, I saw a poster pinned to a telegraph pole, advertising a Charity Bazaar, which was being held that morning in the Old School Hall.

In small letters at the bottom of the poster I read, 'Books, bric-a-brac, homemade cakes, sweets, second-hand clothes and gifts suitable as Christmas presents on sale.' The mention of second-hand clothes caught my eye immediately. It was just possible that something might be suitable for me to wear that evening.

I propped my bicycle up outside the Old School and went inside. I was thankful to find that it was lovely and warm and soon started to thaw out. As I looked around the hall, I saw a table covered with homemade pincushions, needle-cases, ribbons, knickers-elastic, buttons, and little straw string bags, which I knew Aunt Beth, would simply love.

I asked the stallholder if I was allowed to buy more than one thing, and she replied that I was welcome to buy the lot if I wanted, as the main objective was to make enough money to pay for the special oiled wool they needed to knit comforts for the Merchant Seamen, who had been so brave.

I bought as many items as possible and then asked the woman whether she'd be kind enough to put the things into a bag, while I looked around the other tables.

'It's very kind of you to buy things, dear,' she said, 'we don't get many Wrens coming here.'

'You should put a notice up in our NAAFI,' I suggested. 'I only saw the poster on a lamp post by sheer luck.'

At the next stall, I saw some little felt needle-cases made to look like Father Christmas and reindeers, and also a couple of rag dolls. Although there were still a couple of months to go until Christmas, I decided to buy one of the dolls for my goddaughter, and a couple of felt Father Christmas needle-cases to give to my roommates, just in case I didn't have the opportunity to get anything else before Christmas.

I then looked around for the second-hand clothing stall and when I spotted a clothing rack at the back of the hall, I hurried towards it. A heavily pregnant woman, with a very upper-class English accent, was trying to sell a blouse that looked like a size 34 to a woman who looked much more like a size 40. The pregnant woman winked at me, and I giggled. Then, fortunately, the fat woman finally admitted defeat and realising that the blouse would never fit her, moved on to the next stall.

'Were you looking for something in particular?' the pregnant woman asked, so I explained how I'd been invited to a dinner dance at the Arbroath hotel that evening and that I had nothing suitable to wear.

'I see that you are a Wren, have you been here long?' the woman asked.

'Not even a week.'

'Ah, that explains it then.'

'Explains what?' I asked intrigued.

'Why my husband hasn't mentioned you to me. He's usually the first to spot any new pretty faces that come to the base,' she laughed, and then added with a grin, 'it looks like someone has beaten him to it, anyway, if you have been invited to a dance already!'

'Well actually, I have been invited by a rather lovely Naval Officer that I met when I was stationed in Somerset,' I explained, 'and that's why I am looking for something pretty to wear tonight.'

'Have a look though the rack and see if anything catches your eye,' she offered; 'several of my own frocks are for sale, as I'll never get into them again. This is my fourth baby, and an unintentional one at that,' she sighed.

'Oh!' I said, not knowing quite what to say, as I didn't really understand what she had meant by unintentional.

'You won't believe it, but I was once the same size as you,' she continued, 'and although I am a bit taller than you, I think that one of my dresses might fit you perfectly.'

I watched as she waddled over to serve another customer, and wondered when her baby was due, so when she came back, I asked her.

'Oh, it's not due for weeks yet,' she replied, 'but I seem to be getting tired earlier on in this pregnancy for some reason.'

As I looked through the rack of dresses and skirts, I spotted a turquoise and coffee coloured chiffon dress, which I thought would be perfect.

'Why don't you take yourself to the lav' and try it on?' she suggested. 'By the way, my name is Barbara, what's yours?'

I hastily introduced myself and then asked her if she knew of any shoe shops nearby.

'Yes, there is one, but you'll find a hideous pair of gold shoes at that stall over there. They are dreadfully common, I know, but they were blissfully comfortable when I wore them before my feet began to swell!'

Barbara called over to the lady at the shoe stall, 'Hey, Maggie, will you show this young Wren my Buckingham Palace gold shoes?'

I liked Barbara immediately; she had a good sense of humour and didn't seem to mind a damn what she said.

I collected the gold shoes and took myself to the lavatory to try on my new outfit. As I stripped down to my underwear, I suddenly got the giggles. Here I was half-naked, shivering in a freezing cold church lavatory, trying on someone else's clothes. My mother would have had a fit, but Aunt Beth would have thought it hilarious.

The dress was well below my knees, but as it was an evening 'do', it wouldn't matter. I then tried on the gold shoes, which would fit perfectly if I could find someone to punch another hole in the strap.

When I returned to Barbara's stall to pay for the items, she asked me how they were, 'Lovely,' I told her, 'but the dress is a bit too long.' She suggested that I bought some ribbon to tie around my waist to shorten it a bit, so I went over to the handicrafts stall and found a length of cream velvet ribbon, which was still on its cardboard holder. The stallholder measured my waist and told me that there should be enough ribbon to go around it twice and then showed me how to tie the bow, so that I wouldn't spoil the velvet. I was over the moon with my beautiful 'old-new' dress and gold, 'Buckingham Palace' shoes, and now I had a lovely velvet sash too, all for two pounds and ten shillings!

As I left I said to Barbara, 'If you're ever in need of a babysitter, I'd be more than willing to sit for you.'

'That's very kind of you,' Barbara replied. 'I doubt we will go out much until after this baby is born, but after that I would love to take you up on your offer.'

We said goodbye, and then when I was half-way back to the airfield I realised that I hadn't told Barbara my surname and that I didn't know hers either.

I got to the Entertainments hut at two thirty five and Duncan was already there, waiting.

'Guess what?' I asked, as I came to a halt, before suddenly remembering that I was supposed to salute him. However, saluting with one hand, steadying the bicycle with the other, while also attempting to dismount, was obviously not a very good idea, and as my bike tipped over, all the parcels fell out of the basket.

The absurdity of it all made me laugh. 'I'll end up in the guard house with this unruly behaviour, and then I won't be allowed to go to the dance with you this evening.'

'If you get locked up I will come and kiss you through the bars, and then they will have to put me in the guard house with you, so we can still be together all night!' I noticed that he had a decidedly wicked glint in his eye now.

'Don't be so naughty, Duncan,' I scolded, despite the fact that I rather liked the idea of him kissing me through prison bars. Duncan confirmed that he would pick me up in a taxi that evening from my billet and then we went our own ways.

Once I was back at The Grange, I washed my hair and got ready for the dance and when I was ready, I knocked on the kitchen door to ask Mrs Anderson if I could wait with her in the warmth of her sitting room so that I could hear the front door bell ring. She was happy for me to do so and commented on how pretty I looked.

'Thank you, Mrs Anderson, I do hope my escort thinks so too.'

'He'll be blind if he doesn't,' she said, gesturing for to me to sit down. When I told her how much I had paid for my dress, sash and shoes at the bazaar, she said I was pulling her leg.

Less than an hour later, Duncan and I were on the dance floor doing a Scottish reel.

'Not bad for an English lass!' he teased.

'I learnt Scottish dancing at Finishing School, so that we wouldn't disgrace ourselves at all the various balls we had to attend,' I replied indignantly.

'Oh, did you now, Lady Mary?' he chuckled.

Thankfully the dinner was served early, as I was very hungry. Duncan beckoned to a waitress and asked her to bring us a bottle of wine. 'As I won't be around for Christmas or New Year, let's share a bottle of wine together now and celebrate.'

'That would be lovely, especially as we don't know when we will get the chance to see each other again,' I replied.

After dinner, we started dancing again and Duncan held me close to him.

'I don't know how long I will be away this time, Mary,' Duncan told me, 'but I want you to know that you are very dear to me and that there will never be anyone else.'

As he looked into my eyes, I saw such a genuine look of love that I immediately put my previous fear, of caring for anyone I got close to, to one side and held him as close as I could.

When the dance was over, we took a taxi back to my billet, and as Duncan escorted me to the back door I said, 'Take care, Duncan, I am going to miss you terribly.' He put his arms around me and we kissed each other gently on the lips.

'I love you, Mary, don't ever forget that,' he whispered.

And then he was gone.

CHAPTER 11

1943-44

I didn't know where Duncan's squadron had been sent, although I suspected that it was probably somewhere in the Mediterranean, but I did know that wherever he was he would be in constant danger, so I decided to ride my bicycle to the church in Arbroath to pray for his safety.

I checked with Fiona that we had no re-tests that morning, and then went to collect my bike. To my dismay, I discovered that my front tyre was completely flat so I wheeled it round to the transport sheds to ask one of the mechanics if he'd mend it for me.

'It's a damn nuisance,' I complained, 'as I really want to go to Arbroath this morning.'

The mechanic looked at his watch and told me sympathetically that I'd just missed the bus, but suggested that I could walk there and get the bus back, assuring me that he'd have my tyre mended by the time I returned. That seemed like a good idea, so I set off at a brisk pace.

I had only been walking for about ten minutes or so, when I heard a car horn honking behind me. Thinking that it was probably just one of the junior officers trying to get my attention, I ignored it, but the honking continued. My curiosity eventually got the better of me and when I turned around, I saw a large family car driving slowly towards me. I couldn't see who was inside the car, but as I didn't want to acknowledge the vulgar man who had been honking at me, I tossed my head indignantly and looked the other way.

As the car drove past me the driver honked again, letting out a 'dot-dot-dash' on his horn as loudly as he could, which made me jump sky-high. The car then suddenly stopped and the driver got out. I could see that he was roaring with laughter, so I gave him a filthy look. I was just about to shake my fist at him, when I noticed that he had a thick band of gold braid on his sleeve. Hells bells, I thought, now I'm in for it.

As he came towards me I realised that it was the Commander Flying from HMS Condor.

'I suppose your mother told you not to accept lifts from strangers?' he said smiling.

'Exactly, Sir,' I replied.

'I am sorry if I made you jump, but the thing is that I was trying to attract your attention to see if you would like a lift into Arbroath. It is quite a long walk, you know. I'm not trying to pick you up, young lady, not in that sense I mean. I'm sorry, I should explain myself: I believe you know my wife, Barbara, she sold you a dress at the bazaar about a week ago.'

'Oh, yes,' I said, as the penny finally dropped. I was no longer cross now, and felt a bit of a fool that I had thought he was trying to pick me up. 'I'm terribly sorry, Sir, but I misunderstood and thought you were a junior officer trying to make a pass at me. Now I know who you are, Sir, I'm so glad that you stopped, as I forgot to swap surnames and addresses with your wife, and I'd love to see her again, as we got on so well.'

'Hop in then,' he said, 'and I'll take you home with me now if you have time, as I know my wife would love to see you again too.'

As I got into the passenger seat beside him, he told me his name was Tim Horsfell, and that he had recognised me from his wife's description, so when he spotted me, he had honked his horn purely to get my attention.

As we drove towards Arbroath, he asked me what I did in the Wrens. When I told him that I was a Night Vision Tester, he said, 'In that case you and I must have spoken on the telephone recently; I have to say that those damn tests do disrupt our flying time terribly.'

'Maybe they do Sir, but they are very necessary.'

'So some say,' he said taking his eye off the road for a moment and looking at me, 'though why the hell my pilots do what a pint-sized girl like you tells them to do without question I can't imagine!'

'Because, I tell them that what they learn during the test will save their lives, Sir.'

When we entered his house he took me straight into the kitchen where Barbara was preparing lunch. She let out a squeal of delight when she saw me, 'You have found her at last!'

'Yes,' Tim said, giving me a wink, 'we met on the road, didn't we Mary?'

He then gave me such a naughty smile that I couldn't help but laugh out loud.

Barbara invited me to stay for lunch, and when I met their children I thought they were delightful so offered to babysit for them anytime they needed me. Tim then said that he had to do some food shopping in Arbroath, so he could drop me off at the church and then pick me up again when he was finished and take me back to the base, so that's exactly what I did. We arrived back at Condor just in time to collect my bicycle before the workshop closed.

When Fiona finally went on leave, I got so busy doing her tests, as well as mine, that I didn't have much time to worry about Duncan. And as Christmas was now only a month away, there were also plenty of distractions to keep my over-active mind occupied.

The next time I went to Arbroath I did some Christmas shopping and bought my family a few gifts that were 'Made in Scotland', and while I was there I saw a poster that encouraged us to 'Make Do and Mend' this year, so I decided that all my Christmas cards would be homemade. I then met Barbara at a cafe for a cup of tea and she told me that she would make some shortbread for me to send home to my parents, which I knew my father would love, as he had a very sweet tooth.

To help Barbara with her rations, I begged everybody in the Wrens' mess and the NAAFI to give me any spare sugar they didn't want, and as many of the Wrens had decided to go on a diet before Christmas, I ended up with more than was needed.

'Well, that has solved the problem of what to give all my relations for Christmas for the next two years!' she said when I handed over all the donated sugar.

Christmas Day 1943 was very similar to the previous year, except that there wasn't any turkey or chicken for lunch, as shortages were at their height, but some enterprising soul at the base had come up with 'mock turkeys', which were really lamb and as usual the Officers served meals to Other Ranks before having their own lunch. I wished that Duncan had been there, as it would have been such fun to watch him waiting on all my friends.

I wondered where he was and whether he was having a Christmas lunch too, or whether he was involved in a dogfight at that very moment. The thought made me feel sick, but I was determined not to spoil the day for the others, so pulled myself together and joined in the fun.

Over Christmas and Boxing Day two films were shown, there was also a dance, but no concert. I learned how to dance the 'Dashing White Sergeant', and improved my Scottish dancing skills by dancing countless reels.

Barbara asked me if I would babysit for them on New Year's Eve, as they had been invited to see the New Year in with friends, so I asked for a twenty-four hour pass, which would allow me to spend the night at their house.

On New Year's Eve, I put Carol to bed at around seven o'clock and then gave the older children their supper before playing endless card games with them. By nine o'clock, I was exhausted, and asked the children to get ready for bed, telling them that I would come up and read them a story but they told me, in no uncertain terms, that they were far too old to be read to now, and could read for themselves, which I was thankful for, as I was ready for bed, and the moment my head hit the pillow, I fell asleep.

The next day was 1st January 1944. Over a late breakfast, Tim told me that he thought this would be a better year and that the war might be over by the end of it, but there was no guarantee of course.

That night back at The Grange, I didn't get much sleep at all, as at about one o'clock I was woken up by a scurrying noise, so I switched on my torch and then let out a scream: mice were scampering all over the floor of our bedroom.

'Put on the lights, quickly!' I called out, standing up on my bed and jumping up and down. Grumbling and still half-asleep, my roommates switched on their bedside lights and looked at where I was now pointing.

'Those are my biscuits, you little rascals!' Gloria yelled, as the mice disappeared through a tiny hole in the skirting board.

'Were your biscuits, you mean,' I joked.

Not wanting to wake up anyone else in the house, we got our clothes brushes and tried to sweep up as many of the crumbs as we could and then put the crumbs in the wastepaper basket, which we then left outside our bedroom door, and then filled the hole the mice had made with some newspaper, before going back to bed.

Before heading to work, I asked Mrs Anderson if she could lend us some mousetraps, which we then set up before going to bed with little pieces of cheese that we had saved from lunch. The first trap went off almost before our lights were out, but as none of us knew what to do with the dead mouse or were brave enough to take the victim out of the trap, we decided to throw both mouse and trap out of the window into the garden.

By the morning, all four traps had successfully trapped mice, which had then been duly despatched into the night via the window. Before leaving for work that day, I asked Mrs Anderson if the gardener-handyman, Mr Campbell, would mind emptying the traps and re-setting them for us.

'Mr Campbell is away for the moment,' Mrs Anderson replied. 'He has a cold, so you'll have to set them yourselves.'

None of us wanted to remove the dead mice, so we agreed to pool our resources and buy some new traps, but when they were full too, none of us wanted to empty them either, so by the end of the week there was a disgusting pile of dead mice, still in their traps, outside our bedroom window.

As I left for the airbase one morning, I noticed with relief that Mr Campbell was back. He spotted me immediately and walked towards me wagging his finger and looking very cross, 'I have been sweeping the paths all aroond the hoose,' he said, 'and when I swept under yon window I found some wee dead creatures. Do you know anything about them?'

As 'yon window' happened to be our window, I just hung my head in shame and apologised, explaining that we all had been too cowardly to remove the mice from the traps. I then asked him if he would be willing to dispose of the dead bodies and let us have the empty traps back.

'Aye, but don't do that again, as it's a waste of good wood,' he remonstrated. I stood where I was for a moment and watched as Mr Campbell walked over to a freshly lit bonfire to add some leaves to it from his barrow. I suddenly had visions of the poor wee mice being flung on top of the fire. 'Oh, Mr Campbell,' I called out, 'if it's not too much trouble, could you dig a hole and give the mice a decent burial instead of putting them on the bonfire?'

He shook his head in disbelief. 'I dinna have time for a mice funeral,' he said firmly, and shooed me away. However, the very next morning on my way to collect my bicycle, I noticed a small cross sticking out of the ground near the shed. It was made of kindling wood with 'R.I.P' painted on it!

Tim and Barbara's baby decided to enter the world without any warning whatsoever. One minute Barbara was making the beds, and the next, she was ringing up her husband at the airbase to ask him to come home immediately to take her to the maternity hospital. I had just finished a Night Vision Test when Tim charged into the Sick Bay yelling for me.

'Can you drop everything and come with me? I need someone to stay in the house to look after the children. The baby is on its way!' Tim half asked and half demanded frantically.

Before leaving, I ran to the office and had a quick word with Fiona. She told me to leave straight away and that she would inform the Duty Officer that I had gone on special 'ops' with Commander Flying Horsfell, and needed to take a few days leave.

That night Barbara gave birth to a baby boy, and she stayed in hospital for the next five days. Tim arranged to sleep at the airbase in the Officers' quarters while his wife was in the maternity home, as he thought it was unsuitable for a married man to be alone with a young girl in his house, but he assured me that he would return home first thing every morning to get the children's breakfast and get them off to school, and that he would eat with the children each evening.

When Barbara came home, she proudly showed me their new baby, which was currently called the 'Sprog' because they still hadn't agreed on a name for him. When she noticed how clean the house was, she thanked me for looking after it and the children while she had been away.

'I will never forget this, Mary,' she said gratefully, 'I don't know how we will ever be able to thank you enough.'

Tim must have overheard his wife's comment because later that evening he said, 'How would you like to fly an aeroplane? It would be my way of saying thank you for everything you have done for us.'

'Oh, Tim, I can't imagine anything more wonderful,' I said excitedly.

'If I teach you how to fly you could deliver planes all over the country, which would mean gaining a Commission, without having to wait until you are twenty-one.'

'I am not worried about a Commission, Tim,' I said, 'but I'd simply love to learn to fly.'

'I've been thinking about how we could do it, Mary,' Tim continued, 'Wrens don't fly on naval air stations, but I think that if I dressed you up as one of my ATC cadets no one would ever notice one extra boy. You'll have to cut your hair short,' he said and then looking at my chest added, 'and flatten 'those' somehow, so what do you think about that?'

'I can't wait,' I told him.

'Well, you'll have to, I'm afraid, as the cadets won't be arriving for another month,' Tim said, as he left the room to go and have another look at his new son.

That night I dreamed that I was flying over the manse and waving to all of my friends. Of course, I wouldn't be able to do that at all, because, in reality, my flying lessons would have to remain a secret.

Two days later I was upstairs helping Barbara with the Sprog when I heard Tim call up the stairs, 'There is a Naval Lieutenant here called Ogilvie, he wants to see someone called Mary; do we have a Mary in the house?'

'I will be down in a minute,' I yelled, 'I am changing the Sprog's smelly nappy!'

After handing the baby back to Barbara, I quickly washed my hands and started to go downstairs. When I was about halfway down, I overheard Judy, the Horsfells' oldest daughter, talking to someone in the drawing room.

'Are you one of my Daddy's friends?' she asked. 'Mummy has just come home with our new baby brother whose name is the Sprog.'

'The Sprog?' Duncan's amused voice replied.

'Well, you see,' the little girl tried to explain, 'we were expecting a girl and were going to call her Mary, but it was a boy, and we hadn't thought of a boy's name, so he's called the Sprog.'

I then heard Anthony, the Horsfell's' son, ask in a worried tone, 'Excuse me, Sir. Are you all right? Would you care to sit down?'

As I continued down the stairs into the hallway, I heard Tim call out, 'Mary! Hurry, I think your young chap is about to pass out.'

I rushed into the drawing room and saw Tim helping Duncan to sit down on the sofa and then push his head between his knees. When Duncan looked up again I saw with horror that he was as white as a sheet and his face was drawn and haggard.

Tim whispered to me, 'Don't worry Mary, he'll be right as rain in a minute or two, I have seen this before; it's what we call battle fatigue. I'll get him a drink and that should sort him out soon enough.'

After sipping a large glass of whisky, Duncan apologised to Tim. 'I am sorry for turning up uninvited, Sir, but I was worried about Mary. When I heard she was staying here with you alone in this house, I didn't understand why, so I'm afraid that I got the wrong end of the stick.'

Tim roared with laughter, 'You flatter me young man!' he said. 'But with a wife and four children I haven't the strength to take on someone like Mary too!'

Duncan looked relieved and then he turned to me and said, 'Sorry, Mary, I haven't been thinking straight lately.'

Tim now asked the children to go with him to the kitchen and left us alone.

'What was all that about Duncan?' I asked, feeling a bit upset. 'Did you think that I was behaving badly with a married man? Surely you know I am not that sort of a girl?' I was close to tears now, and when Duncan attempted to put his arm around me, I shrugged him off.

'I am really sorry, Mary, I know you wouldn't do anything like that, but when I was told that you were now living with Commander Flying, I jumped to the wrong conclusion and acted without thinking. Can I tell you the whole story and then you might understand my reaction?'

I sat down on the sofa next to him and taking my hand in his he told me his story. As soon as he had arrived back from ops he'd gone straight to the Sick Bay to find me. He'd hoped that I'd be overjoyed to see him so unexpectedly, but I wasn't there when he arrived, and Fiona must have been busy doing a test because she wasn't there either, so he then went to look for someone else that might know where I was and bumped into his friend, the young doctor Johnny Marchant, who had put the windsock up to alert him to my arrival before.

'Looking for your girlfriend Ogilvie? Bad luck, old man, she's gone off with Horsfell and she's staying with him in his house in Arbroath,' his friend had told him. Duncan then said that if he had not been so exhausted he might have realised that his friend was only teasing him, but being so tired, he had taken his friend's teasing seriously, and felt so angry that he had made his way to the Horsfells without stopping to think it through clearly.

'Try to imagine my surprise,' Duncan continued, 'when the door was opened by a young boy wearing pyjamas and behind him was Commander

Flying holding the hand of a little girl. I realised at once that I had made a terrible mistake. Can you ever forgive me for doubting you Mary?' he said looking down at his feet.

'Oh, Duncan,' I cried out putting out both my hands to him 'of course I forgive you, you silly man.' As Duncan looked up again, I was relieved to see that he was now grinning at me.

'Did you know your blouse is askew? And I can see your bosoms!'

'Duncan!' I exclaimed, 'I was in such a hurry to come down and be with you that I didn't have time to tidy myself, after giving the Sprog his bath.'

He now slowly began to undo the buttons on my shirt, 'what are you doing Duncan?' I shrieked, 'You can't, not here.'

Duncan smiled, and then did my buttons up correctly for me, 'There that's better, everything is shipshape and Bristol fashion again now!'

Tim then came back into the room and asked if Duncan was feeling any better.

'Yes, thank you Sir. I'm sorry for the intrusion,' Duncan said, 'my only excuse is that I feel completely shattered, and I must admit I have been finding it hard to sleep lately.'

Tim recommended that he should report to the Sick Bay to get some help; he knew all about battle fatigue first hand, and assured him that there was no disgrace in asking for help.

'Thank you, Sir,' Duncan said.

'You are always welcome in our house, Ogilvie,' Tim said kindly, 'now let me give you both a lift back to base.'

Over the next three days, Duncan and I spent as much time with each other as we could before he went home to his parents for a week to recuperate.

He telephoned the following evening to let me know that he had arrived safely at his parents, and then passed the phone to his mother, who said that I'd be most welcome to stay with them whenever I felt like it, even if Duncan wasn't there, and that if I found myself alone at Easter I should give them a call and invite myself.

Duncan and I spoke on the phone every other evening, while he was staying with his family, and during our long chats he told me a bit more about his two elder sisters, Janet and Celia. Janet, worked as a dietician in Durham where she lived with her husband, Bertie, and Celia, who was two years younger than her sister, was a teacher whose fiancé had been killed in the Battle of Britain.

Celia had apparently been full of beans before her fiancé had died, but had found life very difficult since then. Having lost Charles I felt that I had some idea of what the poor woman was going through.

I had asked Duncan whether Celia had thought of joining one of the Women's Armed Services, where she might make new friends, and possibly even meet another man. Duncan sighed and said he doubted that she would ever consider doing that, she loved teaching too much, and all she really wanted was to be around children.

I didn't get to see Duncan after his leave was over, as he had to go straight back on 'ops' with his squadron, but his mother wrote to me and asked me to stay with them for Easter, so I then wrote to my parents to tell them. I asked my mother if she would send my old school walking shoes to HMS Condor for my trip to the Ogilvie's, as Ruth, Duncan's mother, had warned me that they liked to go for hearty walks every day.

A huge parcel arrived a week later. My mother had not only sent my shoes but also an afternoon dress, a matching cardigan, and a warm nightdress, and she had inserted a note in one of my shoes, which said that she thought that my Wren's striped pyjamas would be unsuitable to wear as a house guest in case I was seen by the staff going to the bathroom. My mother was obviously under the impression that Duncan must be from a well-to-do family, so I wrote back to her to thank her for the parcel and added a note at the bottom to tell her that the Ogilvies did not have any live-in servants, so nobody would see me in my pyjamas, but there would be no one to help me unpack either!

Ruth Ogilvie had told me to only bring a small suitcase, as I could borrow one of her daughter's jackets or coats if it got chilly. I wracked my brains about what to take as a suitable present to thank them for having me to stay and when I looked around the NAAFI shelves, I spotted a box of Lux Soap Flakes, which were almost impossible to come by, and some bars of sweet-smelling soap that were of a much better quality than those available at the chemist. I also bought two bars of chocolate and a packet of biscuits for Duncan's father, hoping that he might have a sweet tooth like his son.

It was a rather strange assortment of things to give to Duncan's parents, but I thought that they might appreciate these everyday items to supplement their rations.

I caught the early train to Perth on Good Friday morning. Duncan had already told his family what I looked like, and had told me that his father looked a bit like a Scottish bishop, but never actually having seen a Scottish bishop before, I wasn't quite sure what to expect.

When I arrived in Perth, I got off the train and waited on the busy platform until I saw a rather distinguished gentleman start walking towards me.

'Mr Ogilvie?' I asked.

'Yes that's me,' he replied smiling, 'but please call me John.'

'You don't look a bit like a Scottish bishop!' I said.

'Well that's a relief! Was I supposed to?' John said laughing.

'Yes!' I said. 'Your naughty son told me you looked like a Scottish bishop!'

'Ah, I will have to have words with young Duncan next time he's home and not all of them will be the kind that bishop's use!' he said giving me a wink.

John then picked up my suitcase, tucked my arm in his, and guided me to his car. He had the same broad smile as Duncan, and I liked him at once.

As we approached a large Victorian house, John explained that they always used the back entrance, because getting to the front door involved a circuitous route that meant driving past the house and then up the road, round a corner and then back down a lane, and then walking up a long garden path to the front door, so it was much easier to come and go through the back door.

John led me through an old-fashioned scullery into their lovely warm kitchen.

'Hello Mary,' Duncan's mother said, smiling at me.

'Hello Mrs Ogilvie,' I said politely. 'Thank you for inviting me to stay.'

'Please call me Ruth,' she said, before gently kissing me on the cheek.

She introduced me to her daughter, Janet, whose hair was an even redder than Duncan's, and then to her husband, Bertie, who kindly picked up my case and took it upstairs for me. As Ruth and I climbed the rather steep staircase, she apologised for having to put me in such a small bedroom. I told her that it was no problem.

241

She then left me to freshen up, and just as I was about to go back downstairs, Janet popped her head round the door. 'Mary, I just wanted to tell you how glad we all are that Duncan has found someone special like you.'

'Thank you, Janet, that means a lot to me,' I said sincerely.

'Celia will be back at teatime, so you will meet her then, but I thought I should forewarn you, in case Duncan hasn't already told you, that her fiancé was killed during the Battle of Britain,' Janet then confided, 'Poor Celia still hasn't got over it, so if she isn't too welcoming, don't worry, it's not you, it's her!'

'I quite understand, as I have been there myself,' I said quietly.

'Yes, Duncan did mention that you had, so I thought you'd understand. It is quite dreadful the number of young men that are dying, and all the young sweethearts that have been left grieving, it really is so sad.'

'Yes,' I agreed, now starting to feel very sad with thoughts of Andrew, Henry and Charles going through my head.

Seeing my discomfort, Janet quickly said, 'Well, we mustn't think about all that right now, must we? We'd better go down now and join the others, as Mother has made a special lunch in your honour!'

As we began to eat, I remembered that Duncan had told me that his father was a great supporter of the League of Nations, so I asked him to tell me about it, which made Ruth, Janet and Bertie all laugh out loud. When I asked what was so funny Ruth explained, 'That's John's favourite subject. You'll never get him to stop once you get him started!'

When I asked Bertie what his work in the Army involved, he told me that before the war he was a journalist, so when he'd been recruited, he had been asked by the government to write public-information slogans. These wartime slogans were now part and parcel of the war effort, of course, because everywhere in town or city, throughout the country, walls were plastered with posters bearing slogans such as 'Walls have Ears', 'Make Do and Mend' and 'Your Country Needs You!'

'Do you have to call Duncan, Sir?' Janet asked me a little later.

'Only when we are in uniform,' I replied.

'What about when you are out of uniform?' Bertie laughed. 'Do you call him Sir Darling or Darling Sir?'

'Bertie!' Janet admonished him, as she got up to help her mother clear the table, 'Stop teasing poor Mary, you are making her blush!'

After lunch, I helped Ruth with the washing up and looked up when I heard someone come through the back door. It was Celia, Duncan's other sister. She looked exactly like her mother, except that her hair was lighter, and she was a good two inches taller. When she introduced herself, she wasn't impolite but wasn't particularly friendly either, and then she excused herself as quickly as she possibly could before going upstairs. I sensed that something was amiss, but remembering what Janet had told me, I tried not to take her rather strange reaction to me personally.

John then suggested that the 'youngsters' should go out for a walk to make room for the cakes that Janet had brought with her for tea. I laughed and told him that I'd bought my sensible shoes with me, just as Ruth had suggested.

I went upstairs to put on my shoes, and as I was coming out of my bedroom, I bumped into Celia on the landing. I asked her if she would like to come for a walk with us, and to my surprise, she agreed at once.

We 'youngsters' then set off and walked up a steep hill towards the open countryside. We had plenty to chat about as a group, but when Janet and Bertie then went on ahead, I found myself walking side-by-side with Celia, so I decided to take the bull by the horns.

'I'm sorry to hear that your fiancé was killed,' I began. 'I know how you must feel.'

'How could you possibly know how I feel?' Celia spat at me.

'Because someone that I was about to get engaged to died trying to rescue others after an air raid,' I told her quietly, 'and for a while I didn't want to go on living.'

Celia said nothing for several minutes, and then she linked her arm though mine and we walked together in silence for a while, which I suppose was her way of letting me know that we were now friends.

'The thing is Mary,' Celia said almost whispering. 'You are young and pretty and you've met Duncan now, so you will be all right, but how am I ever going to find someone that would be interested in me at my age?'

I didn't know what to say in response, so said nothing and we just continued walking in silence until we caught up with Janet and Bertie.

'Duncan told me that you can cook, and clean and that you can also speak three languages!' Janet said laughing, 'It sounds too good to be true, are you really that perfect?'

'Of course!' I replied giggling, 'but I can't do them all at once.'

'Thank God for that!' Janet laughed. 'That would be just too much.'

I then confessed that I hated housework and that I feared my cooking skills were still a bit limited.

'Can I watch you next time you're baking, so that I can learn a few tips from you?' I asked her. 'I still have a lot to learn in that department.'

On the way back, Celia and I walked together again, but this time she was far more talkative and we soon discovered that we both had a common love for children. I asked her whether she enjoyed being a teacher and which age group she preferred to teach, and it was clear that she loved her job and especially enjoyed teaching the younger ones who, she said, were so eager to learn.

While we had been out for our walk, John had lit a fire in the drawing room and Ruth had put out some delicious cakes and scones for us to have with our afternoon tea. Afterwards, I asked Ruth if she had any photographs of Duncan as a young boy. She seemed pleased that I'd asked, and went to dig out a couple of the photo albums.

As we looked at the photos, Janet told me how she and Celia had treated poor Duncan like a doll, and how they had taken it in turns to give him his bath. She then told a funny anecdote about how they would dress their younger brother in a girl's dress for fun, and that was when they'd discovered that Duncan had quite a temper.

'It was quite a shock,' Janet continued, 'he had been so mild tempered up until then, but I suppose he was just letting us know that he was a wee boy who wanted to play cricket or kick a ball, not be treated like a doll by his bossy sisters!'

Ruth told me that as Duncan got older he became interested in sailing, and insisted on learning to paddle a canoe, and that he also loved going on fishing trips with his cousins, which is where his love of the outdoors really began. I then remembered that I had brought some presents for them, so went upstairs to retrieve them from my room. Ruth clapped her hands with delight when she opened hers, 'It's like Christmas all over again!' I was glad that I had chosen them carefully.

That evening we all sat around the drawing room fire and listened to the nine o'clock news, just as I had done so many times with my own parents.

After it finished I asked John if he was worried about Duncan. 'Yes of course, Mary, and about all of the other young men too,' he said, 'but we will just have to put on brave faces, won't we?'

John took us all to the theatre on the Saturday evening to see the Perth Repertory Company, and then on Easter morning everyone walked to church except Janet, who stayed home to cook lunch. It was a lovely weekend and I really enjoyed meeting Duncan's family. I just wished that he had been there too.

On Monday morning, John drove me to the station to catch my train back to Arbroath, and, as he lifted my case out of the boot, he told me how much they'd enjoyed my visit, and that I could invite myself to stay any time I had leave.

'That would be lovely, if it's not going to make too much extra work for Ruth,' I said.

'Don't worry about my darling wife,' John assured me, chuckling, 'she has always been a busy bee and loves nothing better than to spoil our guests.'

'Well, it's funny that you should say that,' I replied, laughing. 'I had noticed that she hardly ever sits still for a moment and is always buzzing around doing something, so I have given her the nickname 'Bumble'!'

'Perfect! You must call her that the next time you come and stay, she will love it!' John said, roaring with laughter. 'And what about me, Mary, have I got a nickname too?'

'Well, as you're Duncan's Father, I thought Father John might be appropriate,' I said.

'Father John?' he queried, 'I thought I was supposed to look like a Scottish bishop? Not only have you demoted me, but you've changed my religion too!'

I put my arms around him and gave him a big hug, 'As you are Duncan's father, John, I want you to be my Father John too.'

When I arrived back at The Grange, I unpacked my case and took out the framed photograph of Duncan that Ruth had given me, and put it on the locker next to my bed. As I looked at Duncan's portrait, I felt a great wave of love for this special man in a way that I had never experienced before, even with Charles. I couldn't work out why or put any particular logic to this feeling, I just 'knew' that this was the right man for me.

During Sunday lunch the following weekend, Tim Horsfell told me that

I could join his ATC cadets on their first trial flight, which would take place one day that week. 'I've managed to borrow the smallest cadet uniform available and a cap, but to look like a boy I'm afraid you're going to have to cut off all your curls.' He grinned and then added with a cheeky grin, nodding in the direction of my bosoms, 'And I'll see whether I can get hold of a flying jacket for you on the day to cover, err, to cover… the rest of you.' Barbara caught my eye, and we both laughed.

Tim warned me that I'd probably find the initial flight rather boring; explaining that I would be sitting in a specially adapted Anson bomber in seats similar to those fitted in private passenger planes. This, he explained, was in order to give trainee cadets an idea of what it felt like to be in the air, as most of them would have never flown before.

He then explained that I would have to change into my cadet's uniform somewhere where I wouldn't be noticed, such as in the ladies' lavatory, and that I should wear my navy blue Wren's mackintosh over the top to disguise what I was wearing and that I must wear my Wren's hat until I was safely standing inside number three hangar. Only once I was inside should I then swap my hat for the ATC cap, and exchange my mackintosh for my flying jacket.

'And make sure you are wearing no make-up!'

As Violet, one of the Wrens at my billet, had been a hairdresser before the war, I asked her to restyle my hair. 'Please cut my hair short, as I'm fed up with looking like Shirley Temple.' She wasn't happy about cutting off my lovely blond curls, but, fortunately didn't ask any awkward questions and did a good job.

To my relief, my short hair didn't look as peculiar as I had feared, although I now looked a bit like my brother Peter, when he was younger.

On the day of the flight, having done everything, exactly as Tim had instructed me to do, I waited in the queue like all the other fifteen ATC cadets ready to climb the steep steps up to the converted bomber. None of the young cadets took a blind bit of notice of me, and when we were all inside the plane, Tim went from cadet to cadet checking that we were all strapped in safely, carefully avoiding eye contact with me.

We were then given a leaflet to show how the instruments in the cockpit were arranged, and each instrument was marked with an arrow, number, or both, with a typed explanation of what it was used for at the bottom of the leaflet.

As the plane began to taxi along the runway, I noticed that one of the boys on the other side of the gangway had closed his eyes. He must be feeling nervous, I thought. I felt the exact opposite and was very excited. Tim began to explain how the wind affects the aircraft and why they used different runways depending on the direction of the wind. He told us all to sit back, relax and enjoy the flight and not to worry if the engines sounded a bit noisy, like really loud farts, which made the boys laugh. I grinned, thinking how my brother William would have enjoyed Tim's schoolboy humour.

There were a lot of 'oohs' and 'aahs', as the aircraft skimmed the trees after take off; no doubt the pilot was flying as low as possible to give us a thrill. Through the window I could see that we were now in cloud, and I thought how incredible it was that such a heavy piece of machinery could stay up in the air. As the clouds got heavier it became impossible to see anything at all, and I just prayed that the pilot could see a bit more than I could out of my window.

Soon we were out of the clouds, and I could see bright blue sky. Tim then announced that starting from the front of the aircraft, two cadets at a time would sit in the cockpit with the pilot to see how the plane was flown. One of the cadets in front of me was sick when he tried to stand up. Tim was right when he had told me that this exercise would separate the sheep from the goats.

Tim had told me that I had to wait until last, as by then all the other boys would be busy chatting about their experience in the cockpit with each other, so wouldn't notice me. When at last, Tim motioned for me to come forward, I got up and walked to the cockpit, 'Come on, hurry up young man, we haven't got all day!' Tim barked, and I had to look straight down at my feet to avoid eye contact with him, otherwise I wouldn't have been able to stop myself getting the giggles.

When I entered the cockpit, the pilot told me to sit in the co-pilot's seat. It took me straight back to the time I had tried to join the Wrens as a driver but had been unable to reach the control peddles of the lorry with such short legs. It was just the same now, so if I were ever allowed to fly a plane like this, I would need to have a cushion behind my back and another under my bottom.

The pilot pointed out the artificial horizon and explained its importance to me. He then showed me the air-pressure gauge and the fuel-indicator, explaining that when it showed that the fuel was getting low the pilot had two choices. When he asked me if I knew what these choices were, I shook my head.

'Land or crash!' he said smiling. I wondered whether he was trying to frighten me on purpose, but decided that he most probably said the same to all the cadets, to test them. It didn't take long for me to realise that flying a plane was much more complicated than I had thought. As the pilot began the descent, it felt as if we were dropping out of the sky, and my tummy leapt into my throat. I watched wide-eyed as we hurtled at great speed towards the ground.

After we landed, we all made our way back to the hangar and Tim ignored me as I walked past him, not wanting to give the game away, but I caught up with him a few days later at his house, and he asked me then if I'd enjoyed my flying experience, so I told him that I had loved it all except for the landing, which felt like riding a bolting carthorse bareback.

'Do you think it would be possible for me to go up in a smaller plane next time, to see how that feels?' I begged him. Tim said that he'd already decided to take me up in a Walrus, as soon as the opportunity presented itself, which it did a few days later.

Disguised in a flying jacket and helmet, I met Tim on the airfield, and then once I was strapped in, the plane seemed to waddle down the runway like a pregnant duck before finally taking off. The next time Tim took me flying, it was in a Swordfish, nicknamed by the pilots as the 'Stringbag.' It was a thrill to sit in one of the planes that I knew Duncan had flown.

Tim and I then met three times a week over the next month to continue my private flying lessons, until he felt that I was familiar enough with the controls to fly solo. When I eventually had that opportunity, he said that his hand would always be poised ready to take over if necessary. I loved every minute. The only thing he wasn't prepared for me to do was take off and land on my own, just in case I pranged one of the precious planes! Officially, of course, I shouldn't have been allowed to fly at all, and if anything had gone wrong, Tim would have had a lot of explaining to do. Fortunately, it never came to that.

I was just considering having some civilian flying lessons, so that I could fly 'legally,' when I received a telephone call from Daddy-T. He wanted me to go to another airbase called HMS Jackdaw, as soon as possible for six weeks.

The first thing I did on hearing my new orders was to go to the Billeting Officer to ask permission to leave most of my civilian clothes and my bicycle at Letham Grange. I then went to the Transport Department to ask advice about how to get to HMS Jackdaw, which I discovered was in Crail, near Dundee.

I told the Transport Officer that I had no idea how to organise the journey there, so after waiting for a few minutes, another of the Transport Officers came to look at the map and assured me that Crail was easily reached either by train or bus, and told me that when I was ready to leave not to forget to collect the necessary warrants. He also reminded me to go to the Pay Office to make arrangements for my pay to be sent to Jackdaw instead of Condor.

I was concerned about leaving Fiona to cope on her own, but she told me that Daddy-T had thought that as I'd be away for such a short time, there was little point in sending a replacement and after all, she had managed on her own before I'd arrived.

The Billeting Officer came to see me in the Sick Bay the next day to tell me that she'd been in touch with her counterpart at Jackdaw about my accommodation.

'I'm sorry, but you will have to sleep in a Nissen hut at Jackdaw, as that's the only accommodation available, so, you'll just have put up with it.'

HMS Jackdaw was one of the first major Fleet Air Arm training airfields in Britain, and also the main Torpedo training school. When I arrived, I also discovered that it had a dummy runway, which was set up as a flight deck for pilots to practise landing on carriers.

My main duty, the first week I was there, was to give NV tests to a few senior pilots who still hadn't taken it, and some of them rather resented having to do it.

On my second week, I was sent a group of multi-national pilots from European countries such as Poland, Holland and France. It was quite hard to explain about rods and cells to them initially, but between my schoolgirl French and miming and the willingness of a friendly Frenchman to help translate to the others, we muddled through and there were a few laughs along the way.

It soon became apparent that the Chief SBA did not take kindly to foreigners, and he complained endlessly that he couldn't understand what they were saying. On one occasion, after he'd repeated this phrase for the umpteenth time, I said to him sharply, 'You do you realise that these brave men are risking their lives just as much as our chaps, don't you Chief?'

'I suppose so,' he conceded reluctantly, 'but they are still bloody foreigners,' I heard him muttering as he wandered off.

A week later, I received a letter from a lady called Miss Marjorie Henderson, who explained that she had worked with my father at the War Office in London at the beginning of the war, but had since retired and moved home to Dundee.

Apparently, she had recently received a letter from my father, asking her if she'd kindly invite me to her home, as he was worried that I might be a bit lonely. The invitation was to come for tea the following Saturday and she had enclosed a hand-drawn map of how to get to her house.

I asked a young SBA if he knew of any Liberty transport that I could take to get me to and from Dundee at the weekend, which would save me having to pay for a train ticket. He told me that there was Naval Transport available every hour on Saturdays and that the last one back left Dundee at seven o'clock, so if I was going to be late, I would have to get the train and then walk back to the base.

Later that evening I wrote back to Miss Henderson to accept her invitation, and then rang my parents to tell them what I was up to. My father told me that Marjorie was a very clever woman who had taught at the university before the war, so he thought I would find her very interesting. When I spoke to my mother, she was pleased to hear that I was staying in touch with Duncan's family, and happy to know I had done so without her having to remind me to do it.

On Saturday morning, I waited at the designated spot for the liberty lorry to take me into Dundee, and after it had dropped me off near a bus stop, I caught a Number Two bus, which took me within walking distance of Miss Henderson's house, which I soon discovered was a four-story building in a lovely leafy street.

I rang the bell and a moment later, Miss Henderson opened the door, took my hand with a smile and invited me inside. As she led me into the drawing room, I noticed that the walls were lined with beautiful books, many of which were leather bound, and that some of the decorative china displayed neatly in a cabinet came from Dresden.

Miss Henderson told me, in a soft lilting Scottish accent, to call her Marjorie and said that she was delighted to welcome me into her home, saying how lovely it was to have someone young to talk to for a change. She invited me to take off my uniform jacket and then handed, me a bright red cardigan that she suggested I put on if I felt chilly. Marjorie then excused herself to put on the kettle, returning soon after with the tea things and the most delicious-looking homemade cake I had ever seen. When I asked her if she had used up all her food coupons just to feed to me, she laughed and told me that she enjoyed baking, but only did so when she had guests and that she hadn't had any visitors for ages.

We chatted happily together all afternoon, mostly about the books we both enjoyed reading, and when it was time to say goodbye I gave her a hug and felt as if I had known her forever. She suggested that, as we'd got on so well, maybe I'd like to meet her in Dundee the following Saturday, and she could tell me about the history of the docks. When we met up, she told me that she loved coming down to the port, so that she could pretend that the ships in dock were those that her grandmother would have seen, clippers with billowing sails and wooden prows, which brought in spices and other strange produce from far-away places. It was obvious that Marjorie not only knew her local history, but was also a hopeless romantic.

The following Saturday, when I arrived at her house for lunch, I could sense that something was troubling Marjorie, as she wasn't her usual chatty self. I asked her what was wrong, and she told me that she had lost her watch, which was very special to her, as her fiancé, who had been killed in the First World War, had given it to her.

Then something very strange happened. I suddenly had an urge to climb up the little steps, which were leaning against the bookcase, but I couldn't work out why. This odd feeling persisted for the rest of the afternoon and I kept looking from the steps to the books on the top shelf. Marjorie must have noticed me doing this and asked me if there was a particular book that I had seen that I would like to borrow.

'No, it's not a book, Marjorie,' I confessed, feeling rather self-conscious. 'It's more of an impulse feeling that there is something else up there that I am supposed to see, if that makes any sense?'

'Well, let's have a look then, dear,' Marjorie said. 'Personally, I always obey impulses, as there's usually a very good reason for them.'

I watched, as Marjorie set up the steps and then held onto them while she climbed up. When she got to the top she looked left and right, and then suddenly she let out a squeal of delight.

'So that's where I put it!' she exclaimed, as she climbed down the steps holding a small, gold watch in her hand. She handed it to me to have a closer look, and I saw that it was decorated with diamonds and sapphires around the face.

'I can't tell you how glad I am to have found it,' Marjorie said, beaming, 'I've been hunting everywhere for it.' She now took my hand in hers and fixed me with her piercing blue eyes. 'I think you may have the gift, Mary. I thought so, the moment I met you, but couldn't be sure at first, but I am now.'

'What do you mean, the gift?' I asked, not quite sure what she meant.

'You sense things don't you, Mary?' she asked, 'It's just too much of a coincidence that I should suddenly find it like that just after you had felt that there was something up there that we needed to see,' she continued, 'I must have put it there when I was dusting the shelves and then forgotten all about it, but I wouldn't have looked up there if it hadn't been for you.'

I told her that it was very possible that I'd picked up on her worried thoughts, and explained that usually I only sensed this type of thing when I was with somebody who was stressed or upset.

'Unfortunately, it doesn't happen when there's a big horse race, but I wish it did, as then I would be very rich!'

I received a phone call from Daddy-T the next day telling me that he now wanted me to go back to HMS Condor to take over while Fiona had some leave, and after that, he would be posting me to HMS Landrail in Machrihanish on the West coast of Scotland.

'I understand that you've been doing a very good job at Jackdaw, but it's time for your next posting.'

After I'd been back at HMS Condor for a few days it felt as if I'd never been away. I was thankful to be sleeping in a comfortable bed once again, after putting up with the rather hard one in the Nissen hut at Jackdaw. I thoroughly enjoyed catching up on all the gossip with my roommates, however, I was upset that there wouldn't be time to do any more flying lessons, and I also felt sad that I'd have to say goodbye to everyone, especially the Horsfells.

The day that Fiona got back from leave, Daddy-T rang to tell me that it was time to find my way to HMS Landrail. 'Mary, dear,' Daddy-T boomed down the telephone, 'I need you to get on your bicycle, so to speak, and get yourself to the furthest point of the West Coast of Scotland. You'll be helping another Wren with the NV tests, as usual, but one of the doctors has requested a Wren to help him do some experimental tests he's carrying out, so I thought of you. He's doing some research into the altitude pilots can reach without the aid of oxygen. The doctor's name is Graham du Caine. He's a Canadian, and a decent sort. I think you'll like him, as he's very easy to get on with. He'll explain exactly what he wants you to do, but I think it could be interesting for you.'

'Thank you for thinking of me, Sir,' I replied.

'Now remember, Mary, don't talk to any strangers on the way,' he chuckled.

I almost replied, 'Yes Daddy,' but remembered just in time that he was a Senior Officer now as well as my boss, so I'd better show some respect.

'Yes, Sir, goodbye then Sir, I will let you know when I arrive.'

After work the next evening, I went to see the Transport Officer to ask him for a warrant to get to Machrihanish, and when I admitted that I had no idea where it was, he smiled and said that he hadn't a clue either. He then produced a map from under his table, and as he pointed to a small peninsular jutting off mainland Scotland he said, 'Oh goodness me, lassie, it's at the end of the world!'

CHAPTER 12

1944

When I arrived at Glasgow railway station, I asked an elderly porter if he could help me get my bicycle out of the guard's van and take it to the right platform for my next train to Arrochar & Tarbert.

'I'm sorry Miss, but you've missed your connection. The next train will be at least an hour and it will leave from Platform Six,' he said.

'Oh that is a bore,' I exclaimed. 'Is there somewhere I can leave my things while I go and get a cup of tea and a sandwich?' I asked him.

'I would be happy to take your things to left luggage for you miss, if you like, and then I'll bring them to you at Platform Six, a quarter of an hour before your departure.' The old man then carefully checked my luggage labels, before adding, 'make sure that you listen out for announcements in case there are any changes to your departure time or platform, and I'll do the same.'

I went to the station cafe to buy myself a cup of tea and a sandwich and while I was there decided that it might be wise to buy another sandwich for later on, in case I didn't get another chance between here and my destination. When I got back to Platform Six, I found the old porter waiting there for me with my things.

'You have nearly a quarter of an hour before the train leaves Miss,' he reassured me, 'And if I were you I'd choose a carriage with another lady in it if you can.' I was about to ask why when I saw a crowd of noisy soldiers walking towards us.

'Leave it to me, Miss,' the kind porter said. After he had put my bicycle into the guard's van, he beckoned me to follow him down the length of the train, while he looked for a suitable carriage for me. When he found one that he was happy with, he opened the door and said, 'You'll be safe in here, Miss,' I thanked him for his help and gave him a generous tip, which he accepted with a smile. I then climbed on board, and as I took my seat, I said hello to the woman sitting opposite me, who smiled and told me that the two young children in our carriage belonged to her.

As the train began to pull out of the station the woman offered me her newspaper to read, which I accepted gratefully, as I hadn't been able to read a paper for ages. Although we knew that the Allied Forces had landed all along the Normandy coast the previous month, on what we now knew as 'D' day, I didn't know many of the details. It felt very strange and almost surreal to read about what had happened on the beaches in Normandy, a place that I knew so well from all the happy summer holidays I had spent there with my family.

The children began to quarrel and told their mother that they were bored, so as I had brought my cards with me, I asked them if they'd like to play Snap and they both said a loud 'yes'. We played all kinds of card games over the next hour or so, and then suddenly the train jerked to a stop. It didn't move for half an hour and then the train slowly puffed into the next station, where the Guard insisted that we all had to get off. There was hardly enough room on the platform for all the people that had been on the train.

I walked up to the guard to ask him about the next train for Arrochar & Tarbert. 'There isn't another train until tomorrow now,' the guard replied, 'You'll need to find lodgings for the night.'

I looked at my watch and saw that it was already half-past five. 'Would you be able to tell me where I might find somewhere to stay please?' I asked him, 'and is there somewhere I can leave my bicycle overnight?'

The guard asked me to wait a minute, as several lorries had just turned up, and I watched as all the servicemen piled into them, and then drove off. Then a rickety old bus arrived and the civilians got onto that. I was now the only one left. Ten minutes later the guard reappeared and told me that the nearest hotel was a good hour away and that it would be very expensive. However, he knew a local widow called Mrs McTaggart, who might be able to give me a bed for the night, as she often took in guests during the summer. I asked him if he would call her for me, which he did, and half an hour later I was sitting in a lovely warm house having a cup of tea with the kind old lady. I apologized for being a nuisance, explaining the reason why I was stranded, and how grateful I was to her for offering a bed for the night. After I told her where I was heading, she warned me that it was still a good eighteen hours' distance away from where I was now. The idea of another day and night travelling was daunting, but I would just have to cope.

The next morning, I went back to the station to catch the train to Arrochar & Tarbert, and after two more unexpected train changes and a short lorry drive, I finally arrived at my destination. I was pleased to discover that Tarbert was a rather attractive fishing village with multi-coloured houses. There were several fishing boats tied up on the quay, and I stood and watched a fisherman mending his net for a few minutes. I was enchanted at once. It was like a picture postcard.

About ten minutes later, it suddenly dawned on me that I might be waiting on the wrong quay for my ferry, so I went up to the fisherman and said, 'Excuse me, could you tell me where the McBain ferry leaves from please?'

Without saying a word, the fisherman pointed to a notice, near where I'd been standing before. When I looked at the faded notice, I could just make out the name Campbeltown and the time the ferry was due to leave, which was two-thirty. As it was already ten past two, according to my watch, I wondered why the ferry was not there now, unloading its passengers before setting off again. I went back to the fisherman and said, 'I'm sorry for being so stupid, but why is the ferry not here now, if it's supposed to leave at two thirty?'

The fisherman looked up at me as though I was a bit simple and said, 'It does leave at two-thirty, but not today,' and then he went back to his nets.

'Oh, why is that?' I persisted.

'It's because of yesterday,' he said as though I should have known what happened.

'I am sorry, but I still don't understand. What happened yesterday?'

'Big storm,' the fisherman informed me.

'But it seems quite calm now,' I said looking out to sea.

'Aye, that it is, but it's the livestock you understand?'

I didn't understand, of course, but fortunately this time he realised that I hadn't grasped what he meant, and so he continued, 'They have to load all the animals on, but only when the sea is calm, as it's an open deck. It should be leaving Campbeltown about now but it will no' be leaving here until tomorrow.'

'At two-thirty?' I enquired.

'Ach, no, not if there has been a storm. It will leave when it's ready, to make up for yesterday,' the fisherman told me helpfully.

'Of course,' I said, 'that makes complete sense!' Fortunately I don't think the fisherman realised that I was being sarcastic. I now asked him if there was a bed and breakfast or hotel nearby that he could direct me to.

'Are ye a Navy Girl?' he asked looking me up and down.

'I am,' I nodded.

'A wee Army girl was dropped off here in a car this morning, and I believe she put herself in yon hotel, that white building over there,' he said pointing in the direction of the hotel. 'Maybe ye could keep each other company?'

Balancing my overnight case on my bicycle basket, I made my way towards the hotel. When I got a bit closer I saw brightly decorated flower pots balanced on the windowsills, which reminded me of France. When I went in, the reception desk was deserted, so I pressed the bell on the desk and a few moments later an elderly man appeared. I asked him if he had a spare room for the night and explained that I was waiting to catch the ferry to Campbeltown.

'Aye, but I only have a single room left at the back of the hotel and you will have to share the bathroom with the room next to yours,' the old man said thumbing though the book. 'And I expect payment in advance,' he advised.

After I had paid, I was shown up to my room, which had old-fashioned lace curtains on the windows, a linen runner on the dressing table, and a plain bedspread on the bed. It was basic but at least it was clean. I bounced on the bed, and it seemed all right. Beggars can't be choosers, I told myself and was very grateful that my father had given me some extra cash, 'just in case' something like this happened. As I was unpacking, there was a knock at the door.

'Come in,' I called out and was astonished when a strikingly attractive girl with reddish-brown hair stepped into my room.

'Thank 'eavens!' she said with a foreign accent that I couldn't place, 'I was so glad when I 'eard you speaking proper English and not this outlandeesh Scottish dialect.' She must be French, I thought, not just because of her accent but also because she was very elegantly dressed.

'I am Elaine, and you?' she asked, so I introduced myself and told her that I was only staying one night, as there were no ferries until the next day.

'Me too,' Elaine said, as she looked around my room with disdain. 'Mon Dieu Mar-ee, you cannot stay in 'ere, it is, 'ow do you say,' her hands were now stretched out in dismay, 'dreary and suitable only for a servant I think!'

'Exactement!' I said in my best French accent.

'Come and look at my room,' she suggested, 'it is much more elegante.'

I laughed and followed her along a corridor to her room. She then opened the door with a flourish and said, 'Voila!'

I noticed that a uniform was hanging on the wardrobe door, which looked similar to an ATS Officer's, so asked her, 'Are you in the ATS?'

'Mon Dieu, non! I am a sort of French Fann-ee,' she replied with a wicked smile, before adding, 'a very appropriate name, non, for French Female Army personnel?'

I didn't get her joke and stood there looking blankly at her.

'Argh, a little English innocent, I should have guessed,' she said shaking her head and wagging her finger at me.

The penny eventually dropped and it finally dawned on me what she had meant. I was a bit surprised that she had used a 'double entendre', and then realised that the French must have invented the expression, which made me start giggling. I wished my cousin Jane could have been with me, as she would have really loved this vivacious woman with the naughty sense of humour.

Elaine's room was much bigger and nicer than my single room at the back of the hotel, and it was beautifully furnished. I'd have loved to stay the night in a room like hers, but didn't think the Navy would refund me for such luxury accommodation.

'I have a bon idea,' Elaine said, 'why you don't use your room to change your clothes only, and come and sleep in the spare bed in my room tonight and then we can talk all the night together, yes?'

Elaine then suggested that if I changed out of my uniform and put on some civvies, we could both go out for a walk together. I thought that sounded like a very good idea, so I went back to my room and put on my slacks and a shirt, before carefully locking the door to my room. I then went and knocked at Elaine's door and when she called out, I went in. I gasped when I saw her:

she was dressed in long shorts, rather like a divided skirt, called culottes. She was also wearing a very smart white blouse with a red silk scarf tied round her neck. 'Oh, Elaine,' I said enviously, 'You do look so French!'

'And you look just like an English school girl,' she laughed, 'but we see about that later.'

As we left the hotel, Elaine asked which way I would like to walk. 'I haven't a clue,' I replied. 'I've only been here for about an hour, but why don't we get my bicycle and then we can take turns walking and riding, that way we can explore a bit further away from the port,' I suggested.

It was lovely and warm and I couldn't help but smile at what an odd couple we must have appeared: Elaine looking every bit as if she was joining a party at Henley, while I looked as if I was her younger brother, as my hair hadn't grown back yet and was still quite short.

I rode my bicycle for a short distance and then left it propped against a wall for Elaine to collect. I then carried on walking until I heard her ring the bell and whizz past me. She then left my bike a little further up the road for me to collect and catch her up. We did this routine for about twenty minutes and then I started to feel hungry, so suggested that we look for a teashop.

We spotted a board with a picture of teapot painted on it hanging over the doorway of one of the small cottages, and when we got closer I saw a sign in the window, which advertised homemade cakes and scones and the price list was next to it, Everything seemed to cost a shilling and sixpence, much to the amusement of Elaine.

'Always the extra sixpence!' she laughed, 'When I was still in France,' she began, pausing suddenly. I looked up at her, and, noticing that her face looked desperately sad, thought that she must be missing her family, 'When I was last in France, there were no homemade foods of any kind, the Bosh, they take everything.'

We went in and while Elaine went to the ladies, I found us a table and asked the woman who owned the shop if she was still serving tea or whether we were too late.

'I don't stick to times,' she replied sternly, 'if someone's hungry I open up, otherwise I keep the door locked.'

When Elaine came and sat down next to me, the café owner's eyes followed her with such awe that I thought that perhaps she had never seen anyone quite so chic before. I must admit that my new friend did look a bit like a film star with her rather smart attire, which must have appeared out of place in this tiny fishing village. The café owner then regained her composure and announced, 'For tea there are treaclies and sponge.'

'I would rather have a scone,' Elaine suggested politely.

'I told you, there are treaclies and sponge for tea,' the woman repeated deliberately, now realising that Elaine was a 'foreigner'.

'What the 'ell is treaclies?' Elaine whispered.

We found out five minutes later, when the woman placed a large oval china plate on our table that had some brown triangular shaped scones on it. She then returned with another plate that had two huge slices of jam sponge cake on it. There was icing-sugar scattered all over the top.

'Enjoy your tea and treaclies,' she said, and I thought I detected a hint of a smile, as she left.

We both took a scone, cut it in half, and spread it thickly with butter, 'I wish Duncan was here, as he'd love these scones,' I said, without thinking. Elaine immediately wanted to know who Duncan was, so I explained that he was my boyfriend. I then asked Elaine to tell me a bit about her family.

'My father is from Provence but my mother is from Devon, so I am half French and half English,' she explained. 'They are still in France but my brother is working as a translator in London, though I don't get to see him very often.'

'That must be hard for you?' I said.

She now leant forward and whispered, 'Many of my family are working for the Resistance, as they hate the Vichy government.'

After eating the delicious treaclies we were both full, so I suggested that we share one slice of sponge now, and save the other to have the next day on the ferry. She thought that was a good idea, so I wrapped a piece in my handkerchief and then placed it in my gasmask case.

When we got back to the hotel, I told my new friend that I was going to have a rest and change back into my uniform in my own room, but would join her a little later for dinner.

An hour later, I went to Elaine's room and she suggested that I try on her red silk blouse, which she thought would look good with my navy blue skirt, 'You could look almost French if you leave two buttons undone; then nobody will notice how ugly your black shoes and stockings are!' After I had put it on, she put a gold chain around my neck, which she said I could borrow for the evening. She then rearranged my hair, fixing elegant waves with a comb and some setting lotion. She offered me a red lipstick to match the blouse I was wearing, which I applied lightly on my lips, and then she squirted some of her expensive French perfume behind my ears. When I looked in the mirror, I had been transformed.

'I haven't finished with you yet,' she said laughing, as she undid the two top buttons of the blouse, 'You don't want to be mistaken for a school girl do you?'

'No, I suppose not,' I replied, slightly embarrassed, as I wasn't used to revealing the top of my cleavage.

Elaine pinned her hair up on top of her head and changed into a very fetching tight, white pullover that fitted her figure so well that it left very little to the imagination. Satisfied that we both now looked 'très chic', Elaine smiled at me, and announced: 'Right, now we both go downstairs and smile at the gentlemen by the bar.' I didn't want to smile at any gentlemen, but Elaine obviously did.

As we sat down, I noticed a middle-aged man, who had been reading a book, look up and admire Elaine. When he saw that I had caught him looking, he turned back to his book. I wondered if I would ever have the nerve to dress and act the way Elaine did.

Two Naval Officers then entered the bar and immediately made a beeline in our direction. One of them asked Elaine very politely if we had any objection if they joined us at our table. She smiled and gestured for them to sit down, and then to my surprise said, 'May I introduce you to my younger sister, Mar-ee, we have been on 'oliday in the area, but due to the weather and one thing and another, we missed yesterday's ferry, so we find ourselves a bit on our own.'

I had to stifle a giggle at this outright lie, but at the same time, I was intrigued by Elaine's behaviour, so decided to go along with it and see what happened. The men offered to buy us both a drink, and before I had time to refuse or accept, Elaine had accepted for us both, 'Thank you, lemonade for my sister, but perhaps something a little more interesting for me,' she told them.

'I don't think we should be talking to these men, Elaine, we haven't been introduced,' I whispered.

Instead of telling me not to worry, Elaine put a finger to her lips and whispered in my ear, 'Trust me, Mar-ee I do know what I am doing. When you speak, do so with a French accent.'

I was astonished and whispered back, 'Like a game?' She nodded and smiled at me conspiratorially.

After a while, I started to relax and began to enjoy myself. The four of us sat and chatted about all sorts of things and I was intrigued to see how Elaine managed to get the men to talk about themselves so easily. She got them to reveal which ships they had been on, where they were going next, and managed to get them to talk about things that I thought sounded a bit like classified information. All the men learned from Elaine, was our Christian names and that we were on our way to visit an elderly aunt who lived near Campbeltown.

'What's her name?' one of the men asked. 'We might know her.'

'Tante Fanny!' Elaine said, looking straight at me and winking. I had to excuse myself and quickly ran to the ladies before wetting myself in public, and had to hide in one of the cubicles until I had stopped laughing.

By the time I had composed myself and returned to the table the two Naval Officers had gone. Elaine and I then went through to the dining room for our evening meal. As soon as we sat down at our table, and I was sure that we couldn't be overheard, I asked Elaine, 'What was all that about? It was great fun, but why all those lies?'

'Sshh!' she said, as the waitress brought us some soup, 'I will explain later.'

After we had finished our soup, Elaine suddenly began to laugh, 'If only you could have seen your face when I told them that you were my younger sister,' she spluttered.

'I don't like telling lies,' I replied, a little crossly, 'and to tell you the truth, I was getting worried about how we would get rid of them, as you were rather leading them on.' I looked at Elaine and continued, 'You wouldn't have asked them up to our room would you?'

'No my little English virgin,' she replied. 'I would not have done such a dreadful thing,' and then she began to laugh again. 'I will explain everything when we go upstairs, but for now, let us just enjoy our meal.'

As soon as we were back in her room, Elaine explained why it had been necessary for her to be so 'friendly' with the two Officers. 'Part of my work involves asking servicemen questions to find out if the security is good or bad. Sometimes, I have to be a bit flirtatious to loosen their tongues and make them divulge things that they shouldn't tell to a stranger.'

Now I understood what she had been doing and why, I rather admired her, but knew that I wouldn't have the skill or the nerve to do what she had done, and told her so.

'But you played your part as my little sister perfectly!' she giggled.

'Are all the girls in your unit trained to do this sort of thing?' I asked, fascinated by the fact that she must be a spy of some sort, and eager to know more.

'Just a few of them, most do much more dangerous work, but let's not talk about it anymore,' she said, and began to prepare for bed.

I went to the bathroom and changed into my striped Army and Navy stores pyjamas, which were hideous, but warm. Elaine, who was brushing out her hair when I came back into the room, took one look at me and burst into hysterical laughter, 'Oh my goodness me, where on earth did you find those? How unsexy can you get? They look like schoolboy's pyjamas, and if you continue to wear hideous things like this at night you shall remain a virgin forever!'

'You might think of me as prim,' I protested, 'but I see myself as modest, it's the way I was brought up.' Elaine was still laughing, as she went to bathroom.

That night we talked about everything and nothing: English grand old houses, clunky plumbing, Coming-out parties and Debutante balls, my family and her family, and our hopes and fears for the future. When we agreed that it was now time to get some sleep, she said, 'It would be better if we both had breakfast in our civilian clothes tomorrow morning and don't change into our uniforms until after paying the bill. That way we can have breakfast together as friends before having to be Officer and Other Ranks again.'

The following morning Elaine confessed that she loved cooked 'Engleesh' breakfasts and would find it hard to adjust to croissant and coffee again after the war when she returned home to France. After we'd finished breakfast, we both went to pay our separate bills at the reception desk, and I overheard Elaine explain to the housekeeper why both of the beds in her room had been used. 'I found one bed so 'ard that I had to sleep in the other, which was even 'arder, so I went back to the first bed again.' No wonder she's a spy, I thought, she's marvellous at telling lies.

I said goodbye to Elaine and then made my own way to the quay. I was relieved to see that the ferry was already there, so I shouldn't be delayed any further. As I stood waiting to board, I saw Elaine in her smart khaki uniform and when I looked down at my navy blue serge skirt, I thought how drab it was in comparison. I caught Elaine's eye very briefly, and she moved her hand in slow motion in a small wave-like movement. She then turned to join a group of other officers before boarding the ferry with them. Moments later, one of the crew told me to board too. I watched, as he tied my bicycle firmly to a rail near a crate of live chickens, several cases of whisky, and various other sundry boxes.

It was another beautiful clear day, and the sea was calm, which I was thankful for, even though the trip should only take a couple of hours. I remained on deck, entranced, as we approached first one and then another small island to let people on and off. I couldn't believe it when a flock of sheep was herded onboard and then expertly penned right next to my bicycle. I was starting to feel hungry again; it must be the sea air I thought, as I looked longingly at my bicycle basket, where I had left the extra slice of sponge cake, that I had saved from the café. There was no way I could retrieve it now.

I was about to go and see if there was a canteen, where I could get a cup of tea and a bun, when I spotted a Naval Rating munching on a sandwich, so I asked him where he'd bought it and he kindly offered to go and get me something too. I gave him half a crown to get me a cup of tea and a cheese roll. The Rating came back with my refreshments and asked if I was on my way to HMS Landrail like him. I told him I was, so he suggested that I sit with them in the covered area until we arrived at Campbeltown.

My first impression of Campbeltown was that it was a rather picturesque little town. It was at the head of a deep loch and surrounded by hills. Full of anticipation and excitement, as I neared my destination, I wondered if there would be some form of transport waiting to take us to HMS Landrail. We were asked to wait onboard while the sheep were let out of the pen, herded down the ramp, and then loaded into a truck. We then had to wait again while various crates were put neatly on the quayside; and then, finally, the passengers were allowed to disembark. I looked anxiously at my bicycle, and asked the Rating if he'd make sure that the transport lorry didn't leave without me while I collected it.

As I stood on the quayside, I scanned the port for a sight of Elaine, so that I could wave goodbye, as I had not seen her disembark, so thought that I must have missed her, but then I caught sight of her hurrying down the ramp from the ferry and walking briskly towards a waiting car, which looked like army transport. She must have spotted me too, because after handing her suitcase to the driver, a high-ranking Army Officer with red tabs on his uniform who saluted her and put her suitcase in the boot of the car, she walked briskly towards me, handed me an envelope, and whispered in my ear, 'Au revoir petite soeur!' She then hurried back to the waiting car, the driver opened one of the back doors for her, and they drove away. Golly, I thought, Elaine must be very important.

A young sailor broke the spell by tapping me on the shoulder to tell me that he had my bicycle and would put it with my case in the back of the second lorry and that I was to sit in the front with the CPO Alec McPhie.

The road to HMS Landrail was full of potholes, so it was a bumpy ride. On the way the CPO offered to drop my things off at my billet and told me that the Ugadale Hotel, had been an exclusive golfing hotel before the war.

'Gosh! I am lucky, aren't I?' I said, delighted at my good fortune.

When we arrived, a sailor unloaded my bicycle and case out of the back of the lorry and then I followed him, as he took them to the rear of the hotel where there was a garage. 'Your belongings will be quite safe here,' he said with a grin, 'there's only one farm with a few sheep nearby.' I laughed and said I hadn't brought anything precious with me anyway.

I climbed back into the lorry, next to CPO McPhie, and we continued on our way. I gazed out of the window at the deserted countryside. There were steep hills on one side and a flat gorse-covered wilderness on the other. I could hear the sound of the sea through the open window, and thought how utterly different this was to anywhere else I'd ever been before.

When we arrived at HMS Landrail, CPO McPhie informed me that operations at this airfield were mainly focused on training, but that it also served as a base for anti-submarine squadrons, which I thought was interesting. After I was dropped off, I checked in with the Billeting Officer, who was not the least bit fussed by my late arrival, and said that she was quite used to personnel arriving several days later than scheduled.

I went to the Wren's mess to get something to eat, and as I sat down I suddenly remembered that I hadn't read Elaine's letter yet, so when I had finished eating, I began to read it. She said how much she'd enjoyed our crazy bike ride and that she would never forget our tea with treaclies. She then asked me to try and find someone at the air station that she could leave a message for me with, from time to time, so that she could arrange to have lunch with me one day, but added mysteriously, 'Every time you meet up with me, always wear civilian clothes and don't tell anyone where you are going.'

I went to the NAAFI to order a coffee and then waited until the transport lorry arrived to take me back to the hotel. A Wren Petty Officer called Betty Brown showed me to my room, and told me that I would be sharing it with another girl called Hazel Clarke, who drove a petrol bowzer that refueled all the planes on the airfield. I imagined that Hazel must be an Amazon to do such heavy work, as I'd only ever seen men doing that job before.

After Petty Officer Brown had gone, I looked around the room: we had bunk beds, and Hazel had obviously already claimed the bottom one. I changed into my striped pyjamas and climbed up the ladder to the top bunk. I thought the bunk would be uncomfortable, but to my relief it wasn't too bad at all, although I was so tired by then that I would have slept on a bed of nails.

I woke up the following morning to the sound of someone climbing out of the bunk bed below me. Suddenly, I was staring into the face of a girl who looked incredibly similar to me, small and slim with blond curly hair and not the Amazon that I had imagined Hazel to be.

'Hello you must be Mary, I'm Hazel,' she said with a smile and offered her hand to me. I leant over the edge of the bunk and shook it, but before I could say anything to her, she vanished with her sponge bag to go the bathroom.

When we were both washed and dressed, we then had time to have a good look at each other and realised that we could be mistaken for twins.

'My goodness, Mary, how alike we are!' Hazel remarked. 'The only difference between us is that I'm flat chested and you're…' she laughed and pointing at my bosoms, said, 'Well, you're not!'

Before leaving our billet to go for breakfast, Hazel told me that we wouldn't have to sleep in the bunk beds for too much longer because we were going to be given a twin-bedded room when one became available.

On the way to the HMS Landrail, which involved another ride in the back of the transport lorry, I mentioned to her that I had found it hard to locate the Sick Bay the previous evening, so she told me that it wasn't far from the control tower at the edge of the dunes.

'It's quite a long walk from the Wren's mess to the Sick Bay,' Hazel warned me, so I told her that as I had brought my bicycle with me it wouldn't be a problem once I knew my way around.

Although Hazel and I looked quite alike, we soon discovered that we were very different people. She was always talking about boys and wanting to go out for drinks with them whenever she could, whereas I was a church mouse in comparison, and having now met Duncan I had no desire to meet any other men. She told me that her father was a schoolteacher at a boy's school and that he was stricter with her than he had been with his pupils, so I guessed that now she was away from home, she just wanted to enjoy her freedom. Despite our differences, I really liked Hazel, and thought we would become good friends.

After breakfast, I found my way to the Sick Bay, just as Hazel had described but as I was a bit early for work, I decided to take a quick look at the sea. Noticing a path that led over the sand dunes, I walked in the direction of the sound of waves pounding against the shore. The shoreline went on for miles and I couldn't see any houses anywhere. It was a desolate place and yet utterly beautiful at the same time. I stood transfixed as I watched the sand blowing in small circles around the dunes, as though it was dancing just for me, and when I took a closer look at some of the strange looking grasses, I saw tiny clover-like flowers. I must have walked right past a mass of wild flowers on the way to this magical spot, but I could have sworn they weren't there a moment ago. Then, reluctantly, I made my way back to the Sick Bay.

When I made myself known to the Chief SBA, Andy Anderson, he told me that I would be working on my own for a while because the other NV Tester, Rose Bentall, had been called away suddenly on compassionate leave, as her father's ship had been sunk by a torpedo, with all hands lost. I felt awful for the poor girl and told the Chief that I would do my best until she got back. I then rather shamelessly used his compassionate mood to ask him if it would be all right if I could give the Sick Bay phone number to someone just in case they needed to contact me in a hurry. He said he didn't mind, obviously presuming that I meant that I would give the number to my family in case of an emergency, but in truth I intended to give it to Elaine.

I then went to the NVT office where there were two typewriters, two lamps, and a filing cabinet, and to my delight after opening a cupboard door I found an old electric kettle, a stained mug and some tealeaves in a screw jar. There was no coffee, however, and so I made a note to myself to buy a new mug and some Nescafé in the NAAFI later that day.

Underneath the electric kettle, I found an envelope addressed to me, and I chuckled at Rose's choice of a hiding place. She obviously knew that sooner or later the new NV Tester would go in search of a kettle and find the envelope. Inside there was a scribbled note to say that she had cancelled all the tests that had been booked in, and that I was to ask Doctor Du Caine to re-book them whenever I was ready to take over. At the end of the note she'd written a P.S. which read, 'Sorry to leave you on your own but my mother needs me, I am sure you understand.'

When I took a look at the testing room, I discovered that there was no panic button installed, so decided that I would make that one of my priorities. Just as I was leaving the room, a man with a kindly face was walking in and we nearly bumped into each other, which made us both smile. When I saw the stripes on his sleeve I knew that he was my new boss, Doctor Du Caine.

'Good Morning, you must be Leading Wren Arden,' he said, 'I'm Graham Du Caine. I've come to see if you need any help as you are on your own,' he said kindly, extending his right hand, 'I am so sad for Rose, but this is what happens in war I'm afraid.'

'I am sure that I can manage until she gets back, Sir,' I replied. 'But what I do need to know is if it's you or one of the other doctors that make up the NV testing schedule?'

'I've been doing it,' he told me, 'but if you feel you can organise it yourself, I would be very grateful, as I'm so extraordinarily busy with my research work at present. I will tell you more about that once you've settled in.'

I then told him that I would need his authority to have an extension telephone installed, so that I could ring Commander Flying direct to organise the tests, and I also mentioned the absence of the panic button inside the testing room and asked him if he would give me permission to have one fitted.

'What do you need a panic button for, for heaven's sake?' he asked with a smile.

'You would be surprised how many people suffer from claustrophobia. After an hour in a room with no windows it can become quite oppressive I can assure you,' I explained. 'And then, of course, there is the safety issue,' I added.

'Safety? What do you need to be kept safe from when you're locked in a room with six strapping young men?' There was a moment's silence before he added, 'Oh, I see! I hadn't thought that through... I will see to it immediately.'

I asked him if he had ever taken a Night Vision test to experience what it was like and he admitted that he hadn't, but would be interested to take one and would try to persuade Commander Flying to take one too. He then explained that apart from doing my usual work he would also need me to write notes for him while he did his decompression tests.

'I know this extra work will be difficult, especially with Rose away at the moment,' he said, 'but if you can organise your tests in the morning and give me a couple of hours every afternoon, I think we should muddle though it together without causing you too much stress.'

I spent the rest of the morning going though Rose's files to see whether she did her NV tests in the same way that I had been taught, and was thankful to see that she did and had only been doing two tests a day, which meant that if I did both of them in the morning, I would be able to keep the afternoons free for Doctor Du Caine.

At eleven, I felt like having a coffee, so went in search of one.

'I was just about to make a mug for the Chief, so you are in luck,' a young SBA said, 'so if you're not too busy, why not take a seat and join us?'

'Thank you, I will,' I said. 'By the way, I am Leading Wren Arden and I will be working in the NV testing unit.'

'I'm Sandy,' the young SBA said, as he handed me a mug of steaming coffee, 'we keep the milk in the fridge for dangerous drugs, so help yourself anytime!'

'Thank you Sandy, and please call me Mary,' I told him accepting the mug gratefully.

The Chief, Andy Anderson, then joined us and as we sipped our coffee I asked him if he could tell me anything about the decompression research that Doctor Du Caine was doing. He explained that the doctor was doing some simulation tests to find out how high the pilots could fly and still remain in control of their planes with and without oxygen at different altitudes. So far, he had discovered that some of the pilots could fly responsibly without oxygen at quite high altitudes, while others reacted as though they were drunk at quite low altitudes. The doctor wanted to find out why this was. Now that I knew a little about what the tests were all about, I was intrigued, and was looking forward to helping the doctor with his research.

Later that same day, Doctor Du Caine asked me if I would like to see where he did his experiments. I followed him out of the Sick Bay and we started to walk towards one of the other Nissen huts, but instead of going into the building, we continued on for a short distance until he suddenly stopped, and pointing at a large caravan said, 'There. That's my research unit.'

I thought that he was joking to start with, but when he opened the caravan door and we went inside, I realised that he was dead serious.

The doctor explained that the pilots sat in a sealed section at the front, which was a mock-up of a cockpit, while he sat at the back next to a series of controls. I noticed that there were large oxygen cylinders fixed to the wall, and beside them was another console of dials, which the doctor told me were like the dual controls in a training plane.

'All I want you to do Leading Wren… Arden – damn it, what's your first name?'

'Mary, Sir,' I replied.

'All I want you to do when I am conducting a test, Mary, is to follow my instructions to the letter and observe what I'm doing carefully. I want you to write down everything I call out, and using your common sense, if you notice anything strange or different to normal conduct, I want you to jot it down on the facing page.' He handed me a notebook that had a spiral binding down the middle, and when opened up, it exposed two pages at the same time.

'Does it matter which side I write down your observations and which side I write my own?' I asked him not wanting to get it wrong.

'No, it doesn't matter a damn so long as you stick to the same format. I need to go over the notes myself once the tests are over, as I can't possibly remember what I've called out during a test, but it's important to keep your observations separate to mine. What I suggest is that everything on the left is what I tell you to write, and everything on the right is your comments.' He paused and then added, 'As this is the first time I've had an assistant we will just have to work out the most efficient way of working together with the least fuss. How does that sound?'

'Perfect,' I replied, and then I thought that I'd better confess that I might not be able to spell some of medical terms and complicated names correctly at first.

'That's to be expected,' Doctor Du Caine reassured me. 'Until you find your feet, you and I can go through your notes at the end of each test, and I suggest that at the back of the book you make a list of any medical terms with which you're unfamiliar, and then attempt to learn the spellings by heart. Didn't they teach you to spell at school?' he asked, teasing me.

'Yes and I'm word perfect in French, Italian and German, but my English spelling is terrible,' I replied rather cheekily.

'I am sure we will get on famously, Mary, but when we are doing the tests we must be very serious as the pilots' lives are in my hands when I am controlling the oxygen valves.'

As these tests could help save pilots lives in the future, I was determined to do my utmost to be of help. On the way back to the Sick Bay I asked the doctor whether the pilots would be grounded if they failed his test, and I wanted to know if my comments could in any way be responsible for that decision.

Doctor Du Caine smiled and replied, 'Don't worry about that, Mary, whether they pass or fail is all down to me and I always give the chaps a second test before making any big decisions like that.'

'That's a relief,' I sighed.

'I don't expect you to do everything right at first, Mary, but once you get the hang of it, you will be of great assistance to me; doing these experiments on my own I had to write my notes while adjusting the oxygen flow, which as you can imagine, isn't an ideal way of conducting a test like this at all.'

After high tea that evening I went to the NAAFI and found a quiet corner where I wrote some letters to my parents and to Duncan and his family, to let them all know that I had arrived safely and that I had some interesting new work, as well as my normal duties.

I was so busy concentrating on my writing that I didn't hear the call, 'Ugadale girls your transport is here,' but fortunately a Wren who had been on the same lorry as me that morning recognised me, and kindly called out for me to hurry up. I quickly gathered my things, ran out to the lorry, and clambered into the back just in time.

On our arrival, Petty Officer Brown was waiting in the hall to let me know that two suitcases had arrived for me earlier in the day, and had been left in the garage next to my bicycle.

Hazel agreed to help me carry one of my cases up to our bedroom, and as we went back upstairs, I couldn't help noticing that her clothes smelt strongly of diesel fuel. As I began to unpack, Hazel got out of her work clothes and put on her dressing gown, and said, 'I'm allowed to have a bath every night because I have to do such dirty work, but you can hop in first if you like, Mary, so long as you're quick.'

Bliss! From that night on I had a bath almost every night instead of just taking my turn on the rota.

A week later, the internal telephone was connected to the NVT unit. I was now able to contact Commander Flying to arrange the tests for the mornings only, which then allowed me to assist Doctor Du Caine in the afternoons. I asked the Commander to send only six pilots at a time and politely requested that he get them to refrain from drinking any alcohol for twelve hours before the test, as the booze affected the results.

When I had my first experience in the simulator with the doctor, I made notes of everything the pilot did during the test just as I had been asked to do. It wasn't until I had done several tests that I saw for myself how each pilot reacted differently to the lack of oxygen: some became very tense, some lost their temper, but many of them seemed to just relax, and a few of them even started singing or telling rude jokes, but when their language became too blue, Doctor Du Caine suggested that I remove my headphones so that I couldn't hear what they were saying. He needn't have worried, however, as I didn't understand most of the jokes anyway.

It soon became apparent that once the pilots were at the same altitude in the simulator, as they would be in real life in the air, which was at about 10,000 feet, many of them became disorientated, sleepy or completely irresponsible and unable to understand which controls they were supposed to use. Doctor Du Caine told me that this was exactly why the tests were carried out very, very carefully. The ascent had to be gradual, only a few hundred feet at a time, because fast ascents could prove very dangerous, as the altitude got higher and higher. This point was proved to me when I witnessed one of the pilots pass out; the doctor had to give him extra oxygen very quickly. Afterwards, when the pilot had recovered, the doctor explained to him that if he had been in a real plane he would have crashed, and therefore, he would have to ensure that he switched on his oxygen at a lower altitude than some of the other pilots in future. He then told the now rather shaken young man that he would have to take another test the following week to gauge the correct height at which he should start using his oxygen.

Doctor Du Caine asked me later what the indecipherable scribbles on the right hand page were, and when I told him that I had written 'Floppy, drowsy and woozy' he roared with laughter.

'They sound more like the names of three of the seven dwarves!' he said, still laughing. 'I think we might have to think up a list of descriptive words more suitable for use in my official reports.'

I was a bit surprised when one of the older pilots managed to reach an altitude of well over 10,000 feet, without switching on his oxygen. I thought that he intended to keep going until he passed out, but then he seemed to change his mind, and finally switched on his oxygen. The doctor seemed to be impressed, but I sensed that something was very wrong with this man, and wrote down on my page 'death wish'.

The pilot nodded his head, which the doctor took as sign that he was all right and began to lower the altitude in the simulator. Then suddenly, without warning, the pilot put his head in his hands and began to sob uncontrollably. I looked at Doctor Du Caine, but he seemed unconcerned, so I presumed that he had seen this reaction before and put it down to the lack of oxygen. However, my instinct told me that this pilot's despair was very real; it had nothing to do with the test, but was due to something far more personal.

When the doctor went through my notes and saw what I had written he asked me why I had thought that the pilot had a death wish. I told him that I had sensed that this man was terribly unhappy and that he had purposely gone without oxygen for as long as he could, because he had lost the will to live, and meant to kill himself the next time he flew at altitude, but he had then changed his mind at the last minute.

Doctor du Caine looked at me with a frown and said, 'That's a bit fanciful, Mary, unless you know something about the pilot that I don't.'

'No, I have never seen or heard of him before,' I told him honestly. 'I just had this funny feeling that's all.'

'Do you often get these funny feelings?' he enquired.

'Actually, yes, I do,' I said seriously, 'but I haven't experienced any for some time, as I usually only get them when I am near to someone who is really distressed.'

A week later, after this incident Doctor Du Caine came to the NVT office to tell me that I had been right and that the pilot had tried to commit suicide shortly after the test, as his wife had recently left him for someone else.

CHAPTER 13

1944

'I am glad to hear he's all right,' I told Doctor Du Caine earnestly, when he let me know that the stressed pilot's attempt to kill himself had failed, and that he was now in the care of the pastoral team.

'In future, if you sense someone is in trouble and you get one of your 'funny feelings' again, please let me know straight away, then I can decide whether to act on your impulses or not,' the doctor said. I could tell that he was rather sceptical about my intuition, and I couldn't really blame him, as my gut feelings were exactly that and not based on any scientific proof.

Over the next few days, I made friends with the SBAs and the Wren writers and started to feel more settled, which was a relief, as being posted from one naval air field to another was disorienting at times, and sometimes I'd wake up wondering where I was.

One morning Commander Flying Douglas Frazier walked into my office unexpectedly and said, 'Sorry for barging in on you like this, but I wanted to see for myself who this bossy Arden woman was who told me on the phone never to send more than six people at a time for a test and to tell my chaps to abstain from any alcohol beforehand!'

'Good morning Sir, I am Leading Wren bossy Arden,' I replied a bit cheekily, but as I could see the twinkle in his eyes, I thought it worth the risk to be insubordinate.

'Ah, really, I was rather expecting someone a bit older and more like a schoolmarm,' he said looking me up and down with approval.

'I am sorry to disappoint you then, Sir,' I giggled.

He roared with laughter at my reply, 'Not at all, I am delighted,' he said.

'Would you be interested in taking the NV test for yourself Sir?' I asked, now trying to be a bit more professional.

'I would like to take a look at the set-up first,' he said. 'Lead the way, then Leading Wren,' he ordered.

Commander Flying was over six feet tall and almost as wide; his very broad shoulders gave him a typical English bulldog look. I escorted him to the NV testing room and then took him inside where I pointed out the six chairs with clips attached to the backs, and explained the procedure in detail. When I'd finished showing him the equipment, Commander Flying sat down and tried out the braille board. I asked him to shut his eyes to simulate being in the dark, and then asked him to see if he could manage to find the metal bars. We then went back to the office where I showed him the forms that we were required to fill in, in triplicate, and explained why.

He then asked me what proof my department had that the pilots could see better at night if they had no alcohol in their system.

'We have discovered that for some reason alcohol affects the rod cells at the sides of the eyes of anyone who's had a drink or two before taking the test, even if it's the night before,' I told him, and suggested that the next time he drove his car at night after he had been drinking to test his night vision and compare it to another night when he hadn't had a drink.

'I might just do that,' he grinned, and then added, 'I believe you're very friendly with my counterpart at HMS Heron, Tim Horsfell.'

'Yes, I am,' I told him, 'and his wife Barbara and the children too.'

'Well, I had a letter from Horsfell the other day asking if I knew of a nearby civilian airfield where you could take some flying lessons. I understand that Horsfell has already begun putting you through your paces, and in his opinion with a bit more flying practice, it would only be a matter of taking an official pilot's exam. Unfortunately, I had to let him know that there are no private airfields nearby, as this area is far too dangerous for beginners.'

Commander Flying then thanked me for showing him around, and assured me that when he had more time he would sit in on a test, and promised me that he wouldn't touch a drop the night before.

Over the next two weeks, I spent all my spare time exploring the coast road around HMS Landrail on my bicycle. The scenery was spectacular and every time I went for a ride I spotted a huge array of birds, but had no idea what species they were. When I mentioned what I had seen to CPO McPhie, he kindly lent me his bird book, so that I could identify them. The next time I went for a ride, I saw a merlin, a falcon and a buzzard, along with hundreds of seabirds.

Every time I went out on one of my bicycle trips, I noticed that there was another bike in the garage, but didn't know who it belonged to. The mystery was solved the following weekend, when I saw a Wren pumping up the tyres.

'Have you seen any seals on your rides yet?' she asked.

'No I haven't but I would love to,' I replied.

'Well I know a place where we might be lucky to see some but it's a good five miles away along the coast road to the North. I am thinking of going tomorrow, but I get a bit nervous going that far on my own, so would you like to tag along and keep me company?' she suggested.

'I'd like that very much,' I replied and then introduced myself. She told me that her name was Veronica Peters, and that she had just arrived back from leave with her family in Sussex.

The day we went on our seal hunt, Veronica told me that she was a Private Secretary to a Senior Officer, but she didn't mention what her work entailed, so I presumed that it must be confidential and didn't ask her any questions about it. We soon discovered that we'd both been to boarding school, and that our schools had played tennis, netball and lacrosse matches against each other, but because she was nine months older than me, and therefore in the year above me, we had never met before. It was lovely to meet someone who had been brought up in a similar way to me. That day we were lucky enough to see not only seals, but also some otters.

When Rose Bentall, the other NV tester, eventually returned to Landrail, I could see that she was still upset by the death of her father, so I gave her a big hug, and I told her how very sorry I was. She asked me what I'd been doing while she had been away, so I told her that I'd managed to get a new phone extension connected, so that we could make calls directly to Commander Flying, and that I had also asked to have a panic button installed, which she thought was a good idea. I then told her about the additional work I was doing for Doctor Du Caine.

'I don't believe it!' Rose said and then started to laugh, 'I don't suppose you have managed to persuade Surgeon Commander Tapps to take a test too have you?'

'No,' I replied, 'I have only met him briefly, when I had first arrived, so I didn't like to ask him. What's he like?'

'He is such a kind man and I have never seen anyone work so hard,' Rose told me, 'I think that he would be genuinely interested in what we do if he has any time to spare.'

'Why don't you ask him then?' I suggested. 'After all, you are the Senior NVT.'

'Oh, I couldn't possibly, as I don't know him very well,' Rose said, 'but if you have been cheeky enough to get Doctor Du Caine and Commander Flying to agree to come for a test, then perhaps you are the right person to ask Tapps too.'

The following morning, an SBA came rushing into our office to say that there was a call for me on the Sick Bay phone. I thought it must be Elaine, as she was the only person that I'd given the number to, but I was wrong.

'Is that Leading Wren Arden?' a man's voice enquired, when I picked up the phone.

'Yes,' I replied, wondering whom it could be.

'I will be in Commander Tapps office in one hour. Be there without fail,' the man said, and then added, 'it's about your friend, Elaine.' Before I had a chance to ask if he had a message for me from her, the man hung up.

An hour later I went to Commander Tapps office, as instructed and knocked on the door. When I was told to enter, I went in.

Standing beside the Commander was a high-ranking Army Officer, and I could tell that he was in the Intelligence Corps, as I recognised his uniform. He also looked familiar but I couldn't place him straight away.

'This is Colonel Sinclair and he has asked me to remain in the room to witness this meeting, so just sit down on the chair over there, and answer any questions that he puts to you,' Commander Tapps ordered, so I sat down feeling a bit worried and wondered what could be wrong.

'I am most sorry if my presence has alarmed you in any way. Would you mind if I call you Mary in the privacy of this room?' the Army Officer said.

'No, not at all Sir,' I replied.

'Now, Mary, I need to ask you some questions about Elaine,' he said ominously.

'She is all right isn't she, Sir, she's not hurt or anything?' I asked, suddenly fearing the worst.

'Where did you meet Elaine? And how long have you known her?' he said, without answering my question.

'I met her at the hotel in Tarbert, Sir. But we only spent about twenty-four hours or so together.' I then looked up and suddenly remembered where I had seen the man before, 'You're the Officer that met her on the quay at Campbeltown. Are you Elaine's boyfriend, Sir?'

The Officer was lost for words, and I could see that Commander Tapps was trying to suppress a smile.

'If you don't mind, young lady, I will ask the questions here,' the Officer reprimanded me gently.

For the next hour and a half, he asked me one question after another about how and where Elaine and I had met, what we had talked about, where we had been after that, and everything we had done since we met, so I told him everything I could.

'Did Elaine tell you what her duties were?' he asked me rather sharply.

'No Sir, she didn't, but I must admit that the thought crossed my mind that, as she was French, she might be in the Resistance, but she didn't talk about her job, and I didn't ask her any questions about it,' I replied. 'Please tell me that she is all right.'

'Before I can tell you anything, Mary, I want you to sign the Official Secrets Act,' the Officer said taking a form out of his briefcase.

'I did that when I joined up, Sir,' I told him.

'Nonetheless, I want you to sign this one too please' he said gently. 'You know what signing the Official Secrets Act means don't you, Mary? Anything that has passed between us this morning is not to be repeated to anyone, not unless you are given official permission to talk about it.'

I took the form, signed it, and then the Officer explained why he needed to know everything that Elaine and I had done and discussed when we had met in Tarbert.

'Elaine was dropped over France a few days after you last saw her,' he began. 'We kept in contact with her regularly, and then we lost touch with her.'

'Do you think that she… that she has been captured?' I whispered. 'Or do you think she's dead?' I added, with rising panic and a familiar croak in my throat.

'I hope to God not,' he sighed, 'but the truth is, I just don't know. We are doing our utmost to track her movements since her radio went silent. The reason I have had this meeting with you, Mary, is to see whether you and Elaine met or talked to anyone who might have known about the work she was doing; anyone could be responsible for her disappearance, so I want you to now tell me again about the other people you met in the hotel. I am quite sure they are all innocent, but we will need to double check.'

I went back over everything once again, including how Elaine had thought that two young naval Officers' security had been rather lax.

'Elaine looked so pretty in her civilian clothes, Sir, and the Officers obviously had no idea that she was trying to find out as much as she could about them. I do hope they won't get into any trouble, as they were both very pleasant and polite, and didn't try to,' I felt myself go pink in the face, 'Well you know, Sir.'

'Well, I know what?' he asked.

'Try any funny business!' I whispered.

Commander Tapps suddenly had a coughing fit and had to get up and pour himself a glass of water.

When the meeting was over, the Officer apologised for putting me through such an ordeal and before I left he said, 'I want you to know that we are doing our very best to find Elaine and bring her home safely. When we do, I will make sure that you know personally, but meanwhile, not a word, understood?'

'Yes Sir,' I replied and then headed back to the NVT office, as fast as I could. For the rest of that day and most of the night I kept thinking about Elaine and just prayed that she hadn't disappeared without trace.

The following Saturday was a beautiful day, so Veronica and I decided to go for a walk over the hills behind the Ugadale Hotel. She was a bit worried about getting lost, so I assured her that I'd mark the route with little arrows made from stones or twigs, and tie lengths of cotton onto some of the branches, so that we would know whether to turn left or right on our way back.

'Anyway, there's a farmhouse about a mile from the Ugadale, which we can use as a landmark,' I tried to reassure her. 'There's no way we can possibly get lost.'

I told Veronica that I'd learned to do orienteering when I was a Girl Guide and that I'd managed to get my Orientation badge. She laughed at this revelation and admitted that she was more of an indoors type of girl who preferred dressmaking and embroidery, so she would be relying on me to find our way back.

'I don't know why I should trust my life in your hands,' Veronica teased. 'I could be peacefully sitting in the hotel conservatory reading my book instead of puffing and blowing up this narrow path and getting dust all over my lovely clean shoes.'

I giggled and suggested that we sit for a while and have a drink of water and a couple of biscuits each to give us the strength for the remainder of the walk. I then told her that I wanted to take her to a special place that I had found on a previous walk, as it had the most wonderful views in every direction.

When we finally got there, we stood side by side in silence for a while and took in the beauty of the scene. When Veronica finally spoke she said how glad she was that I had dragged her all the way there.

'I had no idea that Machrihanish was so breathtaking. You can't tell, when you are standing on the airfield, because it's so flat, and the dunes seem to go on for miles and miles blending into the sea, but once you're up here, it's like a whole new world.'

Veronica and I sat and chatted in the sunshine for nearly half an hour, before realising that the temperature had dropped significantly. I then noticed that a mist was starting to form, so suggested that it was time to make our way back to the hotel.

As we made our slow descent, the mist was getting thicker by the minute and soon we were unable to see more than a few yards in front of us.

'I think we should walk a bit faster,' I said trying not to sound in the least bit frightened.

'Yes, the fog is getting a bit dense isn't it?' Veronica said nervously.

'All we need to do is to look out for the various signs I made on the way up, so that we don't stray from the path, and then we will be able to find our way down again,' I said, trying to sound confident.

The mist was starting to get really thick now, so I told Veronica to hold onto my cardigan, and that I would lead the way.

'Hells Bells!' Veronica exclaimed, 'I wish I hadn't come now.'

It was hard finding my landmarks with this eerie dense fog now all around us. I even had to get on my hands and knees to check for my signs every so often, because I knew that if we strayed from the path too much we could fall down the hillside, which was extremely steep and covered in prickly gorse. Eventually, I spotted a bit of old rag that I'd tied to a bush earlier that day, so knew exactly where we were and realised that all we had to do now was to stick to the path and keep our eyes skinned for my other landmarks.

We carried on walking silently through the fog concentrating on our every step. A few yards further on I spotted an arrow that I'd made with some sticks, and then found a Cairn that I had built with a pile of stones. I breathed a quiet sigh of relief, now we were almost home, even if not dry, and all we had to do was turn right ahead to get to the farmhouse, which would lead us back to the road to the Ugadale.

A minute later we were lost again, as the fog had become so thick that I couldn't see my foot in front of me, so I said, 'Let go of my cardigan Veronica, and stay put until I have come back to get you.'

'Don't leave me Mary,' Veronica begged.

'Don't worry, Veronica,' I said calmly although I wasn't feeling very calm at all, 'I just need to find the rowan tree, where I tied a piece of string and then I will know which way to go from here and come back and get you. It should be very near here so I won't be far away from you, but as I can hardly see my hand in front of my face, let's keep talking to each other, so I can easily find you again.'

To keep Veronica's spirits up I pretended to be a sheep as I got back on to my hands and knees to feel my way along the path, 'Baa, Baa,' I bleated.

'That's not funny' Veronica said crossly.

My hands were now getting quite sore from feeling around the prickly bushes, and my knees were getting raw from inching along the stony path, so when I bumped my head against a really hard object my first reaction was one of anger.

'Ouch!' I yelled. It then dawned on me that this hard object just might be the Rowan tree that I had been looking for, so I stood up and felt up the trunk and along a branch, and finally found my piece of string.

'Thank you, God,' I whispered. 'I've found the Rowan tree,' I then called out, as casually as I could, 'I'll come back and get you now.'

Just as I grabbed Veronica's hand she yelled, 'Look over there, I can see some lights on in a big house.'

'It's the Ugadale!' I shouted with relief, 'see, I told you I would get us back safely.'

'Hmm, well the next time I come up here with you I'll make sure I get a weather forecast first,' Veronica said grumpily.

When we got back to the hotel, we were met by the anxious face of Petty Officer Brown, 'Where on earth have you two girls been?' she asked. 'I have been worried sick, Mary; your roommate told me that you had gone for a walk up the hill, and then when the mist turned to fog, I was concerned that you might not find your way back.'

Much to my surprise Veronica said cheerfully, 'Oh, we've just been for a lovely country walk. I'm awfully sorry if we've caused you concern.'

Once we had both had a hot bath and a hot drink, I decided to apologise to Veronica for putting her through such an ordeal, as I knew that she'd been really frightened.

'That's quite all right' Veronica said. 'Just as well you got your Orientation badge when you were a Girl Guide, or we might still be up there now!'

The following day on the notice board in the hall of the hotel there was a new notice, which read: 'All Wrens to sign in and out. Please use the book on the hall table if going for anything more than a stroll up the road and write down your intended destination. P.S Yes, that means you too Leading Wren Arden!'

One night, I had such a vivid dream, that when I woke up I decided to draw a sketch of everything that I could remember. It wasn't easy to draw because I had dreamt about rather strange looking objects like radio aerials that were attached to long poles, some of which resembled the crosses that I had seen as a child on the shields of French Knights in armour in my brother William's history books. These crosses were all set in the ground on a hill overlooking the seashore in a number of rows, and I knew it was the seashore, because in my dream I could hear the waves breaking. To indicate that high-pitched sounds were emanating from these crosses I drew little squiggles above them, which looked more like bedsprings, as I had no idea what sound waves looked like.

The following night, I had another strange dream, so I did a sketch of that one too. This time, I drew a man sitting in a cockpit wearing a flying jacket that had a number of tubes coming out of it, and a helmet similar to one that I had seen in a children's comic depicting what Martians might look like if they came to earth. I wondered if I had had this dream because I had overheard Doctor Du Caine talking to some of the pilots about the need to overcome something called G-force, which I hadn't fully understood yet.

When it was time to leave for the day, I tidied my desk as usual, but as I didn't want anyone to see my childish drawings, I hid them in the office drawer and then forgot all about them.

The next morning, I went back to the office to write up some reports, but when I opened the drawer to get the forms I needed, my 'dream' sketches were no longer there. I looked around the office but couldn't find them anywhere, so I thought I would ask Rose if she had put them away somewhere else when she came back to the office.

I was halfway through doing the reports, when one of the Wren writers came into the office and told me that I had to go and see Doctor Du Caine immediately. By the tone of her voice, I could tell that this was an order rather than a request.

I quickly made my way to his office, and, feeling rather apprehensive, knocked on his door before going in. Instead of his usual cheery greeting he just pointed to a chair and glared at me. I couldn't imagine what I could possibly have done to make him so angry, so I asked him in a very quiet voice, 'Have I done something wrong, Sir? If I have, I am sorry, but I have no idea what it is.'

The doctor picked up one of the drawings I had been looking for and said, 'Is this your drawing?'

'Yes, Sir, but I didn't do it during working hours I promise,' I told him, thinking that I must be in trouble for drawing during office hours.

'Why draw these particular things? Why not a vase of flowers, a bowl of fruit, or something else, if you have so much time to spare?' Doctor Du Caine asked sarcastically.

I couldn't work out why he was being so nasty to me. It didn't make sense, so I decided the best thing to do was to tell him the truth and explain that I'd recently had two very strange and vivid dreams that I couldn't get out of my head, so I had decided to draw them with the intention of analysing them later.

'That's a likely story. Now just tell me how the hell you found the originals, which are locked up in the drawer in my desk? Did you take the key, open the drawer, and then copy them?' he asked me furiously.

'I'm sorry, Sir, but I have no idea what you are talking about,' I said honestly.

Doctor Du Caine didn't say anything for a minute, and then asked me slowly and deliberately, 'Have you ever been in my office when I have not been here?'

'Are you accusing me of sneaking in here, unlocking and opening a drawer, and stealing one of your drawings to copy?' I asked, tears now welling up. 'If you are, Sir, I must say that I think that is grossly unfair. Surely you know me better than that, and anyway, why would I? Are your drawings so much better than mine?' Tears were now running down my cheeks and my hands were trembling.

'Stop crying, for God's sake,' Doctor Du Caine said firmly, and then in a slightly gentler tone added, 'Come on Mary, you're making me feel like a real heel, but let me explain to you why I'm so angry.'

He then explained how he had found my drawings when he went looking for one of the pilot's reports in my desk. Apparently, my childish squiggles looked almost exactly the same as some Top Secret research that he had locked up in his desk. He then went on to tell me that he got such a shock when he had seen the similarity between my sketches and his secret blueprints that he had nearly had a heart attack.

'Well, I might have an explanation, Sir,' I said thinking furiously how this coincidence could have happened, 'you remember how I had what you called my 'funny feelings' about the pilot that wanted to kill himself?'

He nodded slowly, and I continued, 'Well, it's a bit like that. I seem to pick up other people's thoughts, but how I manage to do that when I'm fast asleep, I have no idea. Is it possible that I could have 'tuned-in' to your thoughts somehow?'

Doctor Du Caine asked me to try and remember which nights I'd had these dreams.

I thought for a bit and replied, 'It was last Tuesday and Thursday.'

'You seem very sure,' the doctor remarked.

'I remember, because we always have cheese on toast for supper on those nights, and cheese seems to make me dream more than usual,' I told him.

The doctor continued to stare at me intently, and then said that those were the two nights that he and some colleagues had stayed up past midnight discussing the latest radar systems and a new prototype pressure suit to enable the pilots to overcome G-force.

'The blueprints for both these new innovations were locked up in my desk for security, and if I was to show them to you, which I can't, you would understand why I got into such a flap. Your drawings look almost identical. I can't think how, but somehow you must have picked up on my thoughts while we were discussing these matters. I can think of no other explanation unless—' the doctor paused for a moment to think, and then he turned to me and asked, 'Have you ever heard of ESP Mary?'

'Yes, Sir, I was told about Extra Sensory Perception by Surgeon Commander Timpston, when I was at HMS Daedalus,' I replied.

'Why did he discuss ESP with you? It's hardly an everyday conversation,' the doctor asked, now appearing to be genuinely interested and not so cross anymore.

'Well, as I had been picking up other people's stressful thoughts, the Surgeon Commander lent me some books, so that I could try to understand why I had this ability, but I still haven't worked it out,' I told him.

Doctor Du Caine then sighed, 'Well I have to admit that I have been extremely stressed and tired lately, so I suppose it is just possible that you picked that up, but I don't pretend to understand this either. However, I do believe you are innocent of any wrongdoing and I am sorry that I jumped down your throat, but please understand why I had to. Security has to be my main concern at all times.'

'Perhaps I had better refrain from doing any drawings for a while,' I suggested.

'Well, just stick to drawing flowers until after the war, will you Mary?' Doctor Du Caine said, now smiling at me.

A few days later Doctor Du Caine asked me to stay behind after work, and told me that he wanted to do an experiment on me to see if I could pick up his thoughts while he was in his office, and I was sitting in the decompression chamber on my own. He gave me a pencil and a pad of paper and told me to just sketch anything that came into my head during that time.

For the first ten minutes I couldn't think of anything to draw so I just sat there and tried to think about what else I was going to be doing that week. I then suddenly remembered I was due to go bird-watching with CPO McPhie and his young son the following evening, and that I had forgotten to ask him to bring a spare pair of binoculars for me to use, so I started to draw some binoculars as a reminder, and then I remembered that I needed to buy some more coffee for our office, so I drew a can of Nescafe. After that I drew a few other doodles just to pass the time away, and then suddenly for no apparent reason, I began to feel really agitated and began to draw pieces of paper, similar to the one that I was using, falling through the sky. I then drew a picture of a telephone and a man with an angry expression on his face sitting at a desk with an inkpot in his hand, but had no idea why I had felt compelled to draw any of these images. Finally I drew a calendar and put a ring around 21 September. A few minutes later Doctor Du Caine joined me in the decompression chamber to see what I had been drawing.

'Extraordinary,' he chuckled, 'quite extraordinary,' and then he put crosses against the binoculars, the coffee and my doodles, and then ticks against everything else, so I asked him why he had done that.

'Well, when the phone rang it gave me such a shock that I dropped a pile of medical reports on the floor. I was so angry that I swore like a navvy to whoever was on the other end of the phone, and then told them that I was too busy to talk, before I slammed the receiver down,' the doctor recounted, 'A few minutes later someone came barging into the room without knocking to tell me that I had filled in a form incorrectly, so I told him to go away, and in no uncertain terms too. In fact I was so angry that I picked up my inkpot and was just about to throw it at him when I came to my senses and didn't, thank goodness.'

I was speechless and Doctor Du Caine looked at me intently. 'You seem to have read my thoughts exactly. I know it's not exactly a proper scientific test, but you definitely have some sort of telepathic skill, Mary,' the doctor insisted. 'You even circled the date of my wife's birthday!'

'What?' I said astonished.

'The twenty-first of September is my wife's birthday,' he repeated. 'Why did you choose that particular date?'

'I have absolutely no idea at all,' I replied, and that made us both burst out laughing.

That night when I got back to my billet, Hazel begged me to be a good sport and make up the numbers the following Saturday for a dance at the local hotel in Campbeltown.

'It will be fun, Mary,' she promised, 'and you won't be expected to pay for a thing, as we have been invited as the guests of a group of Officers.'

I didn't really want to go, but as I had turned her down so many times before I felt that I couldn't refuse her yet again, so reluctantly agreed to go.

'There will be eight of us altogether, so I guarantee that you will be properly chaperoned,' she teased.

On Saturday evening Hazel and I washed our hair and got dressed up in our pretty afternoon dresses. We then sat in the Ugadale lounge while we waited to be picked up. It wasn't long before we heard the sound of a car's horn honking, and then two cars pulled up outside the hotel drive with a screech of brakes.

It didn't take us long to get to Campbeltown, and when we got to the dance hall, I soon relaxed and started to enjoy myself more than I thought I would. I danced with all the Officers in turn, and they behaved like perfect gentlemen, all except for one called Rodney, who kept trying to hold me close to him, which was very annoying.

'Stop holding me so close, Rodney, and dance properly, or I will go back to our table,' I told him curtly.

I thought this firm but polite warning would work but Rodney, who was now a bit drunk and didn't seem to care what he said or did, just laughed at me.

'Stop behaving like a silly virgin,' he said, now pushing his body even closer to me.

'I don't want you to hold me so close Rodney, because I already have a boyfriend and I only came along tonight to make up the numbers, not to be manhandled by you.'

'Do you sleep with your boyfriend?' Rodney asked with his mouth now close to my ear.

I went scarlet and pulled away from him immediately, 'I most certainly do not,' I replied indignantly, 'I'm not that kind of a girl.'

I then started to walk back towards the table, but Rodney was not going to let me get away so easily. He caught hold of my hand and swung me back into his arms.

'What you need is to be taught by an older man who knows what he's doing, otherwise you'll be frigid on your wedding night,' he whispered menacingly.

I looked frantically around the dance floor for Hazel and saw that she was now dancing cheek to cheek with one of the Officers called Mack, so couldn't get her attention.

'Excuse me,' I said to Rodney, as politely as I could and made a dash for the Ladies. I didn't want to make a big fuss and spoil Hazel's evening, so I decided that I'd just hide there until it was time to leave.

When I heard the music stop I went to find Hazel and begged her to allow me to sit in the front seat of the car next to Mack on the way back.

'Why?' she asked. 'Do you feel car-sick in the back?'

'No, it's not that, Hazel. It's Rodney, he keeps saying disgusting things to me and trying to grope me, I don't like him, he's horrible.'

She laughed and told me not to be silly, and then climbed into the front passenger seat, so that I was forced to sit in the back with Rodney, who kept touching my knee the whole way back, and at one point he even tried to put his hand underneath my dress. He is disgusting, I thought, what on earth is the matter with him? I tried to hold my dress tightly around my knees, so that it made it impossible for his hand to wander, but despite my obvious distress, he still seemed to think it was a great joke.

I was immensely relieved when the car drew up outside the Ugadale, and was even more thankful that, with only two minutes to spare before our late passes expired, there was no time to say more than a quick 'thank you and goodbye.'

While Hazel and I were undressing that night, I told her that I'd rather die than go anywhere near Rodney again.

She just laughed and said, 'Boys will be boys! You should take it as a compliment that he fancies you.'

'Well I don't think it's a compliment, and I'm upset,' I said firmly before going to bathroom.

As I lay in bed that night I realised that Hazel and I had very different ideas about men, so I decided that I would not go out on the town with her again.

The next day I decided to make the most of the good weather and go for a bike ride with Veronica. When I told her about Rodney's bad behaviour, she was shocked and asked me if I was going to report him.

'What's the point? He is an Officer and I am just a lowly Wren, so nobody will believe me,' I said, feeling a bit sorry for myself, 'Oh well, hopefully I won't see him again.'

That evening after high tea Hazel suggested that, as it was still warm and sunny, we should go for a walk along the dunes to look at the sea. I agreed to go, as I needed some fresh air. When we got to the dunes, Mack suddenly appeared over the top of a dune waving at us. Hazel had obviously pre-arranged to meet him, but then to my utter horror, I then saw that he had brought Rodney with him.

'Hazel, how could you? You know I detest that man after his behaviour the other night.' I snapped.

'He begged me to bring you here Mary, he wants to put things right between you,' Hazel confessed. 'He was really taken with you and I think he just wants to apologise.'

I was furious, but before I had a chance to turn around and go back to the airfield, the two men were standing by our side. The moment Rodney saw me he began to laugh and shouted out loudly, 'I knew you couldn't resist me!'

It was obviously supposed to be a joke, so I did my best to take it as one and decided to give him a second chance, thinking that perhaps he had just been drinking too much the night before and really was sorry for his actions.

As the four of us walked towards to the sea, with Hazel and Mack leading the way, Rodney said, 'Hazel told me that you like going on bicycle rides, where do you go?' He was obviously making an effort to be friendly, so I told him how I had seen some seals on one of my rides. We were so busy chatting that I hadn't noticed that Hazel and Mack had now disappeared from view, and must have gone behind one of the dunes. Suddenly without any warning, Rodney tried to kiss me on the mouth. It was then I realised with dismay that I had been too trusting and that he only had one thing on his mind. He then started to grope me and touched my breasts.

'Help!' I screamed, 'Hazel, where are you?'

'Leave them alone, you silly girl,' Rodney said nastily, 'they're off having a cuddle just like you and I should be doing.'

'Don't touch me!' I shouted, as he tried to force me down onto the sand and put one of his hands under my blouse. I pushed him as hard as I could and when he lost his balance for a moment, I took off like a bullet and ran as fast as I could.

When I got back to the airfield, I was relieved to see that one of the drivers, who I knew quite well, was standing by his lorry, so I asked him if he'd mind if I sat in the back until it was time for him to leave. He gave me an enquiring look and scratched his head. 'I don't see why not, but we're not leaving for another half an hour, so why don't you wait in the NAAFI?'

'I would rather stay here,' I said quietly, 'if that's all right with you?'

Just before the lorry was about to leave, Hazel turned up with her hair all over the place and her shirt hanging loose outside her skirt. She laughed when she saw me and said, 'Where did you get to? You are a dark horse. I couldn't see you anywhere, perhaps you know somewhere that I haven't found yet deep in the dunes?'

I was really angry with Hazel for setting me up with Rodney, but decided that it wasn't worth spoiling our friendship over, so simply said that I had got cold and decided to come back early.

The following day, Rose wasn't feeling well, so I told her that, as there was only one pilot to re-test in the morning, I would do it for her.

When I arrived at the Sick Bay on Saturday morning, I glanced at the form and saw that I was re-testing a Lieutenant Farland, so went to the testing room to get everything ready for him. I switched on the lamp on the small table that we used for giving our lecture and then turned off the main light, so that when he arrived his eyes would adapt to the dark quicker. A few minutes later I heard someone enter the room and when I looked up I couldn't believe my eyes: it was Rodney.

'Go away!' I said firmly, 'I am expecting Lieutenant Farland for a re-test any minute.'

'That's me,' he said chuckling, 'ready and able!' He then closed the door and started to walk slowly towards me, 'Why did you rush off like a frightened rabbit last night? Are you scared of me, or are you frightened of all men?'

'It's you Rodney, I'm frightened of you, the way you behave, now go away and leave me alone,' I scolded.

'But what about my re-test?' he asked, grinning at me.

There was no way I was going to sit in the dark with this horrid man, so I told him, 'The re-test is off, so you will have to come back on Monday when the other tester is here with me.'

'Damn the bloody re-test, Mary. I only booked this one hoping I would get to see you again,' and then he added menacingly, 'on your own.'

'I have already told you that I am in love with another man, Rodney, so why can't you accept that and leave me alone?'

'I can't. You are driving me crazy,' he said with a glazed look in his eyes.

'I am sorry that you feel like that, but it's not my fault and I have made it quite clear from the start that I am not interested or available, so please leave me in peace and stop pestering me,' I pleaded.

'Just give yourself to me once and then I will go away,' he said desperately.

I was starting to get really frightened, so began to slowly walk towards the door hoping that when I got there I could run away, but he must have read my thoughts, and got to the door first. Then he turned the key in the lock and put it in his pocket.

'Open the door, Rodney! This isn't funny. I am going to report you,' I yelled.

This made him angry and he grabbed my shirt and began to pull it out, tearing some of the buttons off in the process. He then pushed me against a wall, trapping my body with his before putting his hand under my shirt, trying to pull down my brassiere. I screamed, but knew it was pointless, because the walls were made of solid concrete.

I suddenly remembered the panic button, which was situated on the wall near our table, with the lamp on it. If only I could reach it someone would come to my rescue.

Rodney was obviously much stronger than me, so I knew that somehow I would have to trick him into letting go of me to win enough time to get to the bell, so I made the decision to stop struggling and went limp in his arms, pretending to finally give in.

'Aha! I knew you'd surrender eventually,' he smirked, and then he let go of me and started to take his jacket off, so I immediately took my chance and hurried to the table to turn off the lamp. We were now in complete darkness.

I tried to locate the button, but when I couldn't find it, I started to panic.

'Where are you, my little blonde bombshell?' Rodney called out, and then I heard him knock over one of the chairs and curse. Thankfully, I then saw the faint red glow of the bulb of the panic button and put my finger on it and kept it there.

'What the hell is that?' Rodney said crossly. 'Is that the fire alarm?'

I heard someone put the spare key in the lock and then the door was opened and the main light was turned on.

Rodney was momentarily blinded by the light and put his hands to his eyes. He made quite a spectacle, as his trousers were now around his ankles.

I then saw Surgeon Commander Tapps and the Chief SBA standing in the doorway looking in disbelief at the sight before them.

'What's going on in here, Lieutenant Farland?' the Commander said although it was pretty obvious what Rodney's intentions had been.

As I looked down at my shirt, I could see that it was ripped and hanging open to leave one of my breasts exposed. I began to tremble uncontrollably and then my legs gave way, but fortunately the Chief SBA caught me just in time and led me gently to a chair.

Doctor Du Caine came to see what was going on and seeing my distress immediately took off his white coat and put it around my shoulders.

The two doctors looked at one another gravely, and then I heard Surgeon Commander Tapps yell, 'Tidy yourself up Farland, and then report to my office immediately.'

Rodney silently tucked his shirt into his trousers, put on his jacket, and left the room without saying another word. I was so relieved that I burst into tears. The SBA knelt down beside me and whispered, 'There, there Lassie, it's all over now.'

Before leaving, Doctor Du Caine told the Chief to take me to the Accident Room, wrap me in a blanket and give me some brandy, while he made arrangements for a Wren Officer to attend to my clothing.

As we got up to leave, Commander Tapps said, 'I don't want one word said about this incident until I've had time to think about it and make out a formal report.'

'Yes Sir,' I whispered and then followed the Chief to the Accident Room where he found some safety pins for me to re-attach the loose strap of my brassiere. As he helped me to pin the front of my shirt together he said, 'You can wear my spare shirt, it's clean I promise.'

'It's okay, Chief, it doesn't matter. I've got another one in the office in case I spill ink on the one I'm wearing,' I replied, trying to smile, but bursting into tears again instead.

'Take a few more sips of that brandy, Lassie,' he said kindly.

By the time the Third Officer Wren arrived, I was feeling quite light headed from the amount of neat brandy I had been drinking, and I hoped that I wasn't slurring my words when I asked her if she would be kind enough to collect a clean shirt from the cupboard in my office. She returned a few minutes later and told the Chief that she would look after me now, so he could go back to his duties.

As I put on my clean shirt she must have noticed the scratches on my chest and said gently, 'I'm afraid I'll have to ask a doctor to examine you; it's the rules and regulations.'

'He didn't have time to do anything really bad to me; I managed to reach the emergency bell before he had a chance,' I told her.

'I'm afraid that under the circumstances you may well be asked to make a charge against the Officer who molested you,' she informed me.

I looked up, startled 'Will that mean he could be sent to prison?'

'I'm not quite sure, but he could possibly be court marshalled and lose his commission,' she told me.

A female doctor now entered the room and explained that she was a gynaecological specialist. She told me that she would need to check to see if I had any other bruises in addition to those that she could see, and then in a very kind and reassuring way offered, 'And while I'm at it, let's just make sure that everything down below is unharmed.'

The Third Officer Wren gave me a smile and left me alone with the doctor who then examined me.

Once she was satisfied that I was still 'intact' and that there were no other scratches or bruises other than those that could be seen on my upper body, she told me that I could get dressed again, and advised me to try and put the whole unpleasant business out of my mind.

I thanked her for being so kind, and as she left, the Third Officer returned to tell me that Commander Tapps would like a quick word with me if I was up to it.

As I entered his office, the Commander looked up from his desk and asked me whether I was feeling better. When I told him that I was, he said that he now understood why it was so important to have a panic button fitted in the testing room.

'Lieutenant Farland has behaved quite disgracefully. Do you want to make a formal charge?' he asked.

'Not really, Sir,' I replied, 'because if I do, sooner or later someone will get to hear about it, and that would be terribly embarrassing for me.'

'Yes, I can appreciate that,' he said in an understanding way, 'but sexual harassment is a very serious offence.'

When I didn't say anything, he then continued, 'Farland's squadron are flying out of Landrail in two days time to join their carrier, and as he is such a good pilot, they can't really do without him, so if you aren't going to press charges then I won't force you to, but I promise you that I will put the fear of God into him, so that he'll never do anything like this to you, or anyone else, ever again.'

I told the Commander that I would leave it to him, as all I really wanted to do now was have a hot bath and to try to forget about this frightening incident, as quickly as possible. He then told me to take the rest of the day off.

On Monday morning the weather was fine but by midday it was so foul that I thought that nobody would be expected to fly for the rest of the day. There was low cloud and a damp, dense mist but apparently, Commander Flying had ordered one of the squadrons fly to Ireland earlier that day, and then after refuelling there, they were supposed return to Landrail by a different route over the Mull of Kintyre. But as the mist got thicker and thicker we started to worry about the pilots; it was clear that any aircraft still in the sky were now in danger. Flares were lit all along the runway to help guide the planes in when they landed.

I tried to imagine what it must be like for those poor pilots who would be frantically looking at their instruments to tell them where they were, and at the same time, straining their eyes to search below for familiar landmarks. I knew that all the pilots had practised landing in simulated mist or fog situations before, but this was a real pea-soup fog, and I wondered how they could possibly know where the sky and sea met. I then wondered whether the NV tests I had given these young men would be any use to them in this situation, and decided to ask them when they got back.

I remembered that Duncan had told me that it was almost impossible to make the right decisions when visibility was nil and you begin to panic, so with this in mind, I began to pray for them all.

Thinking I should offer to do something useful, I went in search of the SBAs to offer my services if a plane had to crash-land on the runway. When I arrived at the Dispensary, I was surprised to see that it was deserted. Glancing down the corridor towards the main doors, I realised why: the SBAs and doctors were busy loading First Aid equipment and several stretchers into ambulances. I felt my stomach tighten with apprehension.

Doctor Du Caine noticed me hovering near the door and asked me to ring the electrical department to ask Chief Sparks to bring as many spare torches and Very lights he could find, so I hurried to the nearest telephone to make the call. The very moment I hung up, an alarm bell rang in the Accident Room. This was the signal to alert the medical team that a plane had been spotted trying to land.

When I went outside I saw two ambulances disappear into the mist, and could only just make out a Rating waving barely-visible lamps in front of each vehicle in an attempt to guide the ambulance drivers along towards the runaway. I then heard the sound of a spluttering plane overhead and hoped that the pilot would land safely. I waited for a few minutes, and when there was no sickening boom of an aircraft crashing to the ground, I felt strangely relieved.

Just as I went back inside, the telephone rang, but before I could get to it one of the Wren Writer's answered it. After she hung up, she told me that a plane had crashed into the sea, and asked me if I would go to the Control Tower to tell Commander Flying what had happened, as quickly as possible, so that he could call the coastguard. They would then send the local lifeboat out to try and locate the surviving crew.

When I went outside, I saw a naval messenger getting on a motorbike, so I asked him if he would go to the control tower for me, as it would save time. He readily agreed, telling me that his brother was in one of the planes that hadn't come back yet. When I went back inside the building, I told the Wren Writer that I had asked a Rating to deliver the message, and she smiled back at me, saying that two planes had just managed to land successfully between the flares.

An hour later, when none of the other planes had returned, we had to accept that our worst fears had been realised.

CHAPTER 14

1944

The recent loss of their friends in the fog must have preyed heavily on the minds of the pilots, as they practised their 'circuits and bumps' on the runway, which had now been marked out to represent the same size area that they would have to land on the new and smaller Escort carriers. Landing on the real thing would be difficult when the ship was pitching and rolling, so it was vital that they got it right here first. They also had to practise formation flying, dog fights and various other exercises designed to increase their familiarity with their planes capabilities. The pilots did all this without complaining, but it was obvious to everyone that their morale was low, so the Station Captain decided that he would call a meeting with Commander Flying and some of his other colleagues to discuss the situation. In the end it was Doctor Du Caine who came up with a possible and apparently popular solution. A Pin-up girl on the runway!

'I told them we should find a wee lassie, that was preferably ample in the bosom-department, and give her some 'paddles' to guide the planes in as they land, and for some inexplicable reason, I thought of you!' he told me after the meeting.

I was shocked at first, and then rather offended by his remark, but he had said it with such a cheeky grin, that in the end I just laughed and said, 'So what am I expected to do?'

It was an outrageous idea, but as none of them could think of a better solution, it was now the doctor's task to persuade me to 'do my bit' to boost morale. I was more than a little hesitant, but he must have sensed it, and made a last-ditch attempt by appealing to my naivety. 'You know, Mary, I do believe the ultra violet rays would do you good. It can't be healthy for you to be continually cooped up in that Testing Room every day and I think it would do you good to be out in the fresh air.'

Oh well, if that's what it takes to boost the pilots' morale then so be it, I thought. The only problem was, that I had never 'batted in' a plane before.

When Commander Flying heard that I had agreed to take on this role, he promised to train me himself, but told me that the Admiralty must never know about it.

The next day, the Duty Officer took me over to see the Chippy, who was then ordered to make a box-sized plinth for me to stand on.

'I'll leave it to you to work out how high and wide it should be,' the Duty Officer told the Chippy, 'but for goodness sake please make sure that it's heavy enough not to tip over, just as she starts waving the 'paddles' around!'

I was then summoned to the runway for my first lesson with Commander Flying. He was a patient teacher and explained exactly how I had to move the 'paddles' so that the pilots knew whether or not it was safe to land. He taught me how to do a 'wave-off', which was the order to abort the landing and go around for another attempt and then he showed me 'the cut', making a slashing motion at his throat, which meant that the pilot must reduce power and land his plane.

'There is no room for error,' he warned, 'and it is vital that you make the exact same signals the pilots are used to seeing on their aircraft carriers.'

Commander Flying told me to familiarise myself with the different shapes of the aircraft, so that I could tell one from the other. He then handed me over to the Duty Officer, who assured me that I would never be out of sight, so not to worry too much.

On my first day of 'batting in' aircraft, I felt a bit nervous but soon got the hang of it and fortunately waved my 'paddles' correctly, so that all the pilots landed safely.

I have to admit it was also heaven being out on the runway during what was an unexpectedly hot spell. I enjoyed the cool breeze that blew in from the sea, loved the sensation of the wind catching my curls, and was delighted by the change to my complexion; a healthy sun-kissed glow.

During their training, all the pilots had been taught to never, ever, play the fool when doing their 'circuits and bumps' but once it got around that the new Runway Control Officer was a shapely Wren, the pilots began to bet with one another as to who could land closest to her. My bosoms had apparently provoked quite a lot of rowdy laughter and schoolboy remarks at the time, as the pilots were using their aircraft rather like darts, aiming for a double bull's eye. I was reliably informed that morale had improved enormously lately!

Everything went well for about ten days until one silly young pilot decided to show off, waggling the wings of his aircraft as he came in to land, and not realising that another aircraft was still on the runway. I didn't have time to call for help or use the special code for emergencies, so I frantically waved at him to go round again, until, thank heavens, he noticed the other plane and did what he was told. When the Duty Officer realised that there had nearly been an incident, he came running out to see if I was all right.

'I'm sorry Sir, but I didn't have time to call you, so I just indicated to the pilot that he had to obey my command and circle again.'

The Duty Officer asked me if I knew which type of aircraft had been at fault and whether I knew the pilot.

'You won't tick him off too hard, will you Sir?' I asked him. 'He is still very young and I expect he had a bet on with one of the other Officers that he could frighten me off my box.'

It didn't take long before I became the 'Pin-up' that Doctor Du Cane had predicted I would become. A young Officer called Jasper Cooke, who had been an art student before the war, drew a cartoon of me with my 'paddles' batting-in a plane. He had depicted me standing on a box, that looked more like the plinth of a Roman statue, and of course, he had also over-emphasised my breasts and curves in general. One of his friends liked the cartoon so much that he'd asked if he could buy it, but Cooke had a much better idea and made numerous copies of his drawing, which he then sold for half a crown each, and by the end of the week, he had earned enough cash to buy himself a bottle of malt whisky.

I went into Campbeltown the following Saturday to do some shopping, and when he dropped me off, the van driver told me to make sure I was standing at the designated pick up spot at exactly five to five that afternoon, as he had to pick up a VIP Officer from the ferry terminal at five and then take him back to the airfield before taking me back to my billet. I made sure that I was ready on time and it was just as well that I had, because when we arrived at the quay, we saw that the ferry had arrived early and the passengers were already starting to disembark.

A tall, thin man walked up to us carrying a large suitcase, and handed it to the driver to stow for him on the back seat, next to me. However, I could see that there wasn't going to be enough room for his luggage, and me, and all my shopping bags too, so I offered to take the bus back, but our VIP passenger, who introduced himself as Commander Jack Kit, insisted that, as we would only be travelling a short distance to the airfield, he would be happy to share the front seat. As I was sitting in the middle seat, my legs kept getting in the way of the gearstick, which was a bit awkward for the driver. The road was full of potholes, and I kept sliding to the floor, so the Commander kindly offered me his arm to steady myself.

'Thank you, Sir,' I said, apologising every time I gripped his arm when we went over a pothole. The Commander then put his arm behind my shoulders, so that he could stop me falling forward.

At the next corner a lorry tried to squeeze past us and the driver had to swerve to avoid hitting it. As I lurched forward, I felt the Commander's arm slip from my shoulders and grip my waist, and as he did so, his hand accidentally touched my breast. I flinched, suddenly remembering Rodney's unwanted advances, but managed to regain my composure quickly, as soon as I saw the Commander's face. He was obviously more embarrassed than I was.

As we got closer to the airfield, I spotted a buzzard out of the window, 'Oh, Sir, do look!' I exclaimed. The Commander smiled and told me that he loved birds, so I suggested that he should get in touch with CPO McPhie and ask him to take him out bird watching one evening on the dunes.

Two days later, Commander Kit turned up at the Sick Bay, just as I was finishing for the day, to ask me if I would introduce him to CPO McPhie personally, so that he could organise a time to go bird-watching with him. The two men got on like a house on fire straight away and were soon talking about bird species that I had never heard of before. About twenty minutes later, the Commander looked at his watch and said that he had to get back to the wardroom, and as I wanted to go to the Wren's NAAFI, I said I'd walk with him back to the airfield.

Commander Kit told me that he had been working with Commander Flying in the control tower earlier that day, and had seen a young girl standing on a box on the runway batting-in planes, which he had thought was highly unusual. Commander Flying had then explained to him about the recent tragedy and why they had chosen a temporary female Runway Control Officer to boost morale.

Commander Kit then looked at me and said, 'The girl looked remarkably like you, but obviously it couldn't have been, as you would have been busy doing NV tests wouldn't you?'

'Actually, it was me,' I confessed, 'but nobody is supposed to know about it, as the role is strictly unofficial.'

'Don't worry, Mum's the word,' Commander Kit said with a chuckle, 'actually I knew it was you already, as Commander Flying told me and made me promise to keep it under my hat!'

When we reached the NAAFI, I saluted him and said goodbye. Commander Kit hesitated for a moment and then asked, 'When I go bird watching with CPO McPhie would you like to come along too?'

'I'd love to,' I replied, and then we went our separate ways.

On the following Friday morning CPO McPhie left me a note saying that he was taking the Commander bird watching that evening, so I should meet them at six o'clock by the gate that led to the dunes. After work, I put on some long navy-blue trousers and a pullover, and went to meet them. CPO McPhie had brought along his son, so there were now four of us.

As we walked across the dunes, every now and then the Commander would give me his arm to steady me, just as my father had done when I was a child.

'Over there!' CPO McPhie whispered.

We all lay down on our stomachs amongst the rather prickly tufts of grass on the dunes. Commander Kit offered me his binoculars to look through and I spotted some oystercatchers on the shoreline. Over the next hour, we spotted a variety of sea and shore birds and then as the sun began to go down, I whispered to my companions that I had to go or I would miss my transport.

The next day, I was back on the runway, batting-in four planes that were practising circuits and bumps, when I suddenly noticed an unexpected fifth plane approaching the airfield. I wondered whether it was in trouble and needed to make an emergency landing, so I decided that the best course of action was to treat it as a potential emergency anyway and give it priority over the other aircraft. This meant that I had to signal the four planes to circle again and again until given permission to land after the fifth plane had landed safely. I was about to signal to the Duty Officer to alert him of the problem, but I could see that he had his feet up and was enjoying a cigarette, completely oblivious to the situation, so feeling confident that I had everything under control, I decided to bat-in the fifth plane without bothering him.

I looked along the runway to check that it was clear for the fifth plane to land and couldn't believe my eyes when I saw a man in uniform walking slowly towards me. Surely nobody would be stupid enough to walk on the runway while aircraft were trying to land. I wondered who it could be and to my surprise, saw that it was Commander Kit. And then to my astonishment, he walked right up to me and then knelt down on one knee at the foot of my box, seemingly oblivious to the plane trying to land, and said, 'My dear Mary, would you do me the honour of marrying me?'

I couldn't believe my ears. I had only just met this man. Was he mad?

Suddenly the fifth plane began its descent, so I waved him down and then frantically waved at all the other planes to keep circling.

Meanwhile, the Duty Officer must have finally seen what was going on, and was now running towards us at full speed. As he got closer, he looked at Commander Kit who was still on one knee waiting for my reply, and shouted, 'Sir, please leave the runway at once. You are putting the planes in danger.' He then took Commander Kit by the arm and all but frog-marched him towards his hut.

My legs were now shaking, not just because of the potential emergency situation, but also because of the unexpected proposal. When I had batted-in all five planes safely, my legs finally gave way beneath me and I sat down on my box with my head in my hands and wondered what on earth I might have said or done to give the poor Commander the idea that I might consider marrying him after such a short acquaintance.

Commander Flying decided to walk over to see if I was all right, and said, 'Well done Mary, you did well to keep your head and get those planes down safely. I witnessed the whole thing from the control tower, but didn't want to interfere in case I made things worse.' He then patted me on the back and said, 'You're the best Temporary Acting Runway Officer we have ever had, or ever likely to have again, but we really can't have our chaps proposing to you while you are on duty, can we my dear, so I think its time to send you back to your NV testing duties, don't you?'

It was only then that I saw the funny side of the whole situation and began to giggle. Commander Flying laughed too and said, 'Commander Kit has obviously spent too much time in the laboratory and not enough time living in the real world. Meeting a pretty girl like you must have put his brain in overload poor chap!'

A week after this incident, I was told to go and collect a registered parcel from the naval postal depot. It was quite heavy, so I thought my mother must have sent me an extra pair of walking shoes or something like that. When I opened the parcel, it contained an old fashioned wooden box. I slowly opened the lid and looked inside and then screamed when I saw its contents and slammed the lid down again quickly. It was like looking inside a treasure trove or Aladdin's cave, as it was full of rings, necklaces, broaches and clasps, many of which had precious stones arranged in old gold settings. They must be worth a fortune, I thought. I then saw that there was a note tucked inside the lid from Commander Kit.

'Although you didn't say yes, you didn't say no either. So if you say yes now, all these jewels will be your engagement present.'

I read it again and then burst into tears, it was all too much. Surgeon Commander Tapps, who had been next door, must have heard my sobs, as he came rushing in to see why I was crying.

'Good God, girl!' he gasped, 'what the hell are you doing with all those precious things in a place like this? Has someone left you the crown jewels?'

'Oh, Sir, they are not mine, they are a present and I don't know what to do,' I sobbed, as he pulled up a chair and sat next to me.

'I wouldn't mind taking this for my wife!' he chuckled, as he lifted out a diamond and opal brooch. He then asked me if he could read the note, so I handed it to him.

'Now tell me from the beginning where you first met Commander Kit and maybe I can make some sense of how this situation has arisen.' he said in a fatherly manner.

I explained how we had met and how I had to share the front seat of the van with him and then gone bird watching a few days later, but assured him that I had not said or done anything to give Commander Kit the impression that I would be interested in him romantically.

Commander Tapps thought for a few moments and then suggested that I contact my father to tell him what had occurred, and then ask him talk to our family solicitor to get his advice about what you should do with this box and its contents.

'Meanwhile, can I suggest that I lock it up in my safe until you hear from him?' he offered.

'That sounds sensible, Sir, as I wouldn't feel comfortable having them in my billet,' I replied gratefully.

'You do seem to attract some rather odd admirers don't you, young lady?'

'Yes, it does look that way doesn't it, Sir? But I just don't understand why. What's wrong with me?'

'It's not you, Mary, it's them!' he said as I handed him the jewellery box for safekeeping.

I took the Commander's advice and spoke to my father that night. A few days later, I rang him again and he told me that he had been advised by his solicitor to contact the Admiralty to find out the name of Commander Kit's family's solicitors, and then the two firms of lawyers could work out the best way of returning the jewels. A week later, I received a letter from my father instructing me to take the jewellery to a retired solicitor who lived in Campbeltown, who had offered to act as a go-between for the two legal firms to ensure that the precious box was returned to the Kit family. He then suggested that I write a short, but kind, letter to Commander Kit to thank him for his proposal and explain in very clear terms that I had already given my heart to another and, therefore, I was returning the jewels.

Two weeks later, Commander Kit sent me two lovely matching blue leather-bound books with gold-edged pages; one was a Bible and the other a Book of Common Prayer. He had also enclosed a letter that read: 'I realise that you are still very young and not ready for marriage yet, but if you ever change your mind, I will be waiting. Please accept the enclosed books from me to show you that my intentions have always been honourable.'

Tears tumbled down my cheeks. I felt sorry for this poor, lonely man who was obviously still in love with me. I couldn't begin to understand why such an intelligent man could be so unbalanced and behave in such an obsessive and irrational way, but I felt compassion for him nonetheless.

One evening, Hazel came back from work and told me that she been told Duncan's squadron would be flying into HMS Landrail any day now, and that most of the pilots would be given extended leave to recover from what had been a very difficult tour of operations. I was so excited at the thought of seeing Duncan again that everything else that had happened over the previous few weeks didn't seem to matter anymore.

When Duncan's squadron did eventually arrive, I discovered that they were to be segregated for a few days from the rest of the airfield until they had completed their reports, which meant that it was impossible for us to meet straightaway. However, he was able to get a note to me at the Sick Bay to let me know that he was alive and well, and that he would be in touch as soon as he could.

Three days later I found another note from Duncan asking me to put in a request for leave for the following week, as he thought it was time for him to meet my family. He also asked me to get a late pass for the following evening, as he wanted to take me out for dinner in Campbeltown. He told me to be ready at seven o'clock outside the Ugadale, as was going to borrow a car from one of his fellow Officer's.

As I waited for him in front of the hotel to arrive, I could hear a car making strange banging and spluttering noises, a mile away. I had told the other girls at my billet that my boyfriend was taking me out for dinner, so they were now leaning out of their windows to get a good look at him. When Duncan got out of the car he came straight up to me and gave me a passionate kiss, which drew cheers and applause from my friends. I was desperately embarrassed, but Duncan just took it all in his stride, smiled at me, and then gave the girls a mock salute, which made them all laugh and scream at the top of their voices. His 'heartthrob' status is obviously still intact, I thought smiling to myself.

Duncan and I then set off in the 'old banger', as he called it, and headed towards Campbeltown.

'How I've longed to see your lovely face again,' Duncan said looking at me more than the road.

'I would prefer it if you keep your eyes on the road!' I laughed, 'at least until we have arrived safely.'

When we pulled into the hotel car park in Campbeltown, Duncan told me that he wanted to telephone my father that night, so he was going to ask the hotel manager if he could use this private phone. The manager agreed, and I got through to my father almost immediately.

I introduced Duncan to my father over the phone and then handed it to him. The two men chatted for a while and then Duncan asked if it would be convenient to meet up the following weekend in Woking. I overheard my father telling him that my mother and Aunt Beth were away in Harrogate at a Spa Hotel and up their necks in mud baths, so why didn't we all arrange to meet up there instead. I took the phone from Duncan and asked my father if he thought the hotel would be able to accommodate all of us at the same time.

'I hope so,' my father said, 'as I could do with a mud bath myself! I'll ring your mother and ask her to book us all in,' He then told me to call him back at the same time the following night, so that we could confirm dates, times and so on. Duncan and I then made our way to the hotel dining room and enjoyed the best meal either of us had eaten in a long time.

On the way back to the Ugadale, Duncan stopped the car in a quiet lane, so that we could sit and chat to each other until it was time for me to return to my billet. We whispered sweet nothings to each other, and then Duncan gently kissed me.

When he finally dropped me off, I noticed some of the curtains being pulled back and then saw several girls peeping out to get a glimpse of us. Duncan, ever the showman, blew one or two kisses up to the windows, which made me giggle. When I finally let myself in and went upstairs, I then had to field off a lot of questions about my 'handsome boyfriend', before finally getting to bed. I was just about to drop off to sleep when Hazel returned from her night out, and begged me to recount the whole of my evening, and wouldn't let me go back to sleep until I had.

The next day, I received a telegram from my mother, which read, 'Come to Harrogate soonest. Stop. What fun! Stop.'

That evening, Duncan suggested that we drive to the sand dunes and then go for a walk. When we got there, Duncan stopped the car and took both my hands in his, 'I love you, Mary, and I want to marry you, but before I ask your father's permission, I want to be sure that you feel the same way about me. Do you love me Mary?'

'Oh Duncan,' I said, 'of course I do, I love you with all my heart, and if you asked me to marry you right now, the answer would be yes.'

Duncan smiled and then kissed me passionately. After a few minutes he stopped and said, 'I think we had better stop now, as I am having trouble controlling myself. I think it would be a good idea if we went for a brisk walk on the dunes to cool off!'

I laughed, as I knew it must be hard for him to behave like a gentleman when it was obvious that he wanted to be anything but.

As soon as we were out of the car Duncan shouted, 'Race you to the sea,' and then we both ran as fast as we could to the shore. He got there first and immediately threw off his shoes, rolled up his trousers and ran into the sea up to his knees, but before I had a chance to follow, I heard him scream like a girl in a high pitched voice, 'Its bloody freezing!' We both doubled up laughing and Duncan nearly fell over, as he ran back out of the sea and into my arms. We kissed again and then he took my hand in his and we walked along the sand for a while, making plans for our leave.

First thing in the morning, I went to see Commander Tapps to ask him if I could take two weeks leave, starting on Wednesday. He was a bit surprised that I wanted to go so suddenly, but when I explained that Duncan might only have a few days off before being recalled to his ship, and that we needed to take this opportunity for him to meet my family, he immediately said that he had no objection, as long as Rose was happy to do my duties while I was away, which thankfully she was.

A few days later, I met Duncan at the quay to get the ferry to the mainland, and he told me that Commander Flying had introduced himself to him at the Officers mess the night before, and told him that he should get married as soon as possible, as I was becoming a flight hazard. When Duncan had asked him what he meant by that, Commander Flying had chuckled and said, 'Mary is a ripe cherry waiting to be picked and there have been a few incidents with some of our chaps wanting to do the picking, so you had better hurry up old man and get that lovely girl of yours down the aisle!'

Duncan asked me to explain what incidents they had been referring to, so I told him that as it was quite a long story I would tell him later.

When we got to Perth that evening, Duncan's parents gave me a warm welcome, as if I was already part of their family. As Ruth hugged me, she told me that her husband, John, had been calling her 'Bumble' ever since my last visit. I laughed and then apologised, but she said that she rather liked her new nickname.

Ruth took me up to the spare room, which Janet and her husband had been staying in on my first visit, while Duncan went into his old bedroom to unpack.

'Where, may I ask, have my doggy curtains gone?' we heard Duncan yell, which made Ruth and I laugh.

We had a lovely meal together and then, after saying goodnight to everyone, I went upstairs to my room. Just as I had got into bed, there was a knock on the door. It was Duncan, to ask if there was anything else I needed.

'A kiss goodnight,' I asked, putting out my arms.

'I am not sure if that would be wise my love,' Duncan said. 'If I get too close to the bed I will want to climb in with you!'

'What would your mother and father think?' I laughed.

'Exactly!' he replied, and then blew me two kisses from the door before shutting it quietly.

I lay in the darkness for a while wondering which room we would sleep in when we were married and what it would be like sharing a bed with Duncan. The thought made me giggle; at least I wouldn't have cold feet!

The following morning, Duncan and I were both up bright and early and decided that we'd walk together into town, so that he could introduce me to the parents of one of his school friends who owned a jewellers shop. We looked together at some engagement rings but decided that we would wait until we were officially engaged before buying one. We then went to McEwans department store, so that I could buy a suitable dress to wear in the evenings at the rather smart Spa Hotel, where we would be staying with my parents.

The next day Duncan and I said goodbye to his parents and on our long journey to Harrogate, I finally told Duncan all about my ordeal with Rodney and Commander Kit's proposal on the runway. He was not amused by either incident, and told me that he would have gladly hit Rodney if he had been there, and as for the lovesick Commander, he shook his head in disbelief and told me that he was just grateful that a terrible accident hadn't occurred.

When we finally arrived at Harrogate, I still felt excited at seeing my parents again, but I noticed that Duncan was becoming more and more nervous at the prospect of meeting them.

'You are not having second thoughts are you, Duncan?' I asked, smiling at him.

'No, not at all, but I am a bit worried that your parents might think I am not good enough for you.'

'You are the best man I know and that should be more than enough for my father,' I told him honestly.

Duncan and I took a taxi from the station to the hotel, and while we were signing the register Aunt Beth came joyfully up to us to let us know that she and my mother were in the bar having a sherry before dinner, so we should join them as soon as we were ready.

When we entered the bar, my mother immediately stood up and gave me a hug before telling me that my father wouldn't get here until the following day. She then shook hands with Duncan, who made a courteous bow like an old fashioned knight, which made my mother smile, and I knew then that he had already charmed her. As for Aunt Beth, she just stared at Duncan's hair and remarked, 'I have only seen that fabulous colour once before in my life and that was on a red setter!'

After another round of drinks, we all went into the dining room and had an enjoyable meal together. Duncan apologised for giving so little warning of our visit, and said that he hoped he wasn't putting them out too much by turning up suddenly while they were having their holiday, 'The trouble is that I have to be back on board my carrier soon, and then I doubt if I will get leave again for a month or so, and that's why I wanted to meet you now.'

I could see that my mother's brain was working overtime, as she listened to Duncan talk. I bet she is making a mental list of his attributes and faults, I thought. Good manners, not too broad a Scottish accent, well maintained hands and nails, clean hair, which yes, she had to admit was a remarkable colour! All we needed now was to get my father's approval.

When it was time for us to go to bed, my mother apologised that Duncan's room was on the upper floor. She told him that it was the only free single room left in the hotel. I would have my own room until my father arrived and then Aunt Beth, who was sharing a room with my mother, would move in with me.

Before going upstairs Duncan suggested that he and I meet for breakfast and then spend the day at Fountains Abbey, while my mother and aunt were having their spa treatments. As my father wasn't expected until after lunch, it seemed like a good plan.

In the morning, I was delighted to see that Duncan was looking relaxed and was now wearing a pair of cord trousers and a tweed jacket, which looked far more comfortable than his uniform. I teased him, telling him that he looked every inch the English county gentleman: 'Do you mind?' he said, 'I think that what you meant to say was that I look every inch the Scottish gentleman!'

As we walked around the rather magnificent Abbey ruins, Duncan told me that it was founded in 1132, which made me think he was terribly clever until I saw the same notice board that he must have seen moments before, which gave the date and a potted history of the ruins. It was awe inspiring being in such an ancient place and I tried to imagine what it must have been like when the monks had lived there. According to the information on the board, the Abbey had been one of the richest religious houses in England before Henry VIII had put a stop to its power during the dissolution of the monasteries in the 16th century.

As we walked though where the cloisters had once been, I suddenly started to shiver uncontrollably despite it being a warm day, and called out to Duncan, 'Something feels very wrong. I need to get out of here.'

'What's the matter darling?' Duncan asked. 'Are you feeling unwell?'

'It's not me, it's the oppressive atmosphere here,' I told him. 'I need to get out of these ruins right now, as the feeling of hopelessness is overpowering.'

'I am sorry, darling, we can go right now if you want,' Duncan said kindly, taking my hand in his. 'My goodness you are freezing,' He then took off his jacket to put around my shoulders and led me back into the sunlight.

'What just happened, Mary?' Duncan asked. 'Try to explain it to me.'

'It's hard to put into words, but I suddenly felt as though I was surrounded by people who were terribly unhappy,' I explained. 'Maybe I sensed what the monks were feeling at the time of the dissolution of the monasteries; I know that doesn't make any sense, but I felt this terror and it was horrible.'

'Have you had feelings like this before?' Duncan asked.

'Yes, a few times, but nothing as strong as this and I have never felt such a terrible feeling of utter misery going through my whole body like that ever.'

'I have heard of other people having similar experiences in one of the castles in Scotland, where there had been a terrible battle, but I don't know enough about the history of this place to offer any suggestions. Do you want to find out what might have happened here?' he suggested.

'No, I just want to get away,' I said quietly.

Duncan suggested that we go back to Harrogate, as he wanted to buy some postcards, and as it was nearly time for lunch he wanted to find a pub that served 'proper Yorkshire puddings'. Determined not to spoil our day together I decided to put the unpleasant experience out of my mind and by the time we arrived in Harrogate I was back to my usual happy self. We soon found a shop to buy some postcards. Duncan bought two and I bought ten, which he told me was extravagant.

'How can sending a postcard to people that I love be considered extravagant? Think how pleased they will be to know that I was thinking about them when they receive the cards,' I told him.

'I hadn't thought of it like that,' Duncan chuckled. 'I suppose I am a just being a bit careful with my pennies.'

'Careful?' I giggled, 'I think you mean Canny!'

Duncan laughed and said, 'That may well be true, Mary, but don't forget that once we are married, we will have to consider every penny we spend carefully because I won't have any income after the war, at least not until I have qualified as a Forester and can start earning a salary.'

'Don't worry about that, I can find a job while you are at university and then we will be fine,' I reassured him.

'Let's not talk about that now, my tummy is rumbling, and I want to find the biggest Yorkshire pudding in Harrogate!' Duncan said, quickening his pace.

The Yorkshire air had made us both very hungry and it didn't take us long to find a pub claiming to serve the best puddings in Yorkshire. As it was wartime, the pudding was filled with sausage, rather than beef, and served with a handful of chips.

After lunch we slowly made our way back to the hotel, and when we got there I was delighted to see that my father was sitting in the lounge having a cup of tea on his own. I ran to him and gave him a hug and then introduced him to Duncan. As the men shook hands I went to order some tea for us, and on my return, I was relieved to see that they were laughing and obviously getting on well together.

After tea, I told the men that I wanted to have a bath and get changed, and would meet them at six for a drink in the bar. Just as I was leaving, I overheard my father say to Duncan, 'Feel like a turn around the garden?'

When I got to my room, Aunt Beth had already moved into my room and was sitting with her legs up on the spare bed manicuring her nails. She asked me what we had been doing all day, and then she told me about the lovely massage followed by a mud bath that she and my mother had enjoyed that day.

After a long soak, I changed into the new dress that I had bought in Perth and then we both went down to the lounge bar to join my parents, who appeared to be happily chatting away to Duncan. When he saw me he came straight over and took my hand in his. I could see that all the tension had now gone from his face and he looked several years younger than he had that morning. The big smile on his face alone told me that my father must have agreed for us to marry.

'Can I presume that Daddy approves of my choice of future husband?' I asked.

'Yes he does thank goodness,' Duncan replied, 'now all I have to do is ask you if you will be my wife.'

'Oh Duncan, yes please,' I sighed.

'This isn't how or where I wanted to propose to you at all,' Duncan said softly looking deeply into my eyes, 'so please know that I will do it properly when we are on our own and back in Scotland.'

My father had arranged for us to sit at a quiet table together for dinner and when the wine waiter came over to show him a bottle of what I suspected was very expensive champagne, I knew all was well. I immediately flung my arms around my father's neck and announced, 'Daddy I am so happy. Does this mean you have given us your blessing to get married?'

'Whatever gave you that idea young lady? I drink champagne every night, don't I, darling?' my father joked, looking at my mother. Everybody laughed, and then Aunt Beth asked whether we had decided on a date for the wedding yet.

There was a moment's silence until Duncan replied apprehensively, 'Ah, well now, that could be a slight problem as my next leave is at the end of next month, and I won't get any more leave after that for at least another six months, so we will either have to get married by special licence, as soon as we can arrange it or, if we want a church wedding, we will have to wait until sometime next year which I don't really want to do because of the war.'

My father then said that although he would have preferred us to wait until the following year, he could understand why we might like to get married straightaway, and he had no real objection. My mother then pulled out her diary and told us that she would talk to the vicar and ask him if he would be willing to call the bans at once, as she really wanted me to have a church wedding if it was at all possible. We agreed to wait until my mother had spoken to the vicar before making any further plans.

When it was time for bed, I kissed Duncan goodnight and then made my way to my parent's room. My mother tactfully removed herself, saying she needed to have a word with Aunt Beth for a moment, leaving me alone with my father. He told me to sit down, as he needed to talk to me seriously.

'I don't want to frighten you, my darling, but what happened to me could possibly happen to Duncan. He could be badly wounded, although hopefully he will never be gassed, but have you ever thought that he could end up as one of McIndoe's guinea pigs and that he could be so badly burned that you won't recognise him?'

I told him that Duncan and I had already discussed the possibility, and had promised one another to be absolutely honest if and when that time came, 'If it is that terrible he will need me even more,' I whispered. 'He will always be Duncan to me, no matter what he looks like.'

'He might also become a Prisoner of War and then you might be on your own for years; are you quite sure you could be faithful and wait for him? I am ashamed to ask you this, Mary, but in the last war many wives took lovers when their husbands were away, and some husbands had mistresses, and there is no doubt that if you did that, you would break Duncan's heart.'

I must have looked horrified. 'Such a thing would never enter my thoughts, Daddy,' I protested.

'It might not enter your thoughts, my dear, but there are men who would do their best to seduce a married woman when the husband is away.' I assured my father that I would never be interested in any other man than Duncan.

'Now, about finance,' he went on, changing the subject suddenly. 'It doesn't concern me that Duncan has very little capital at the moment, as he seems set for a good career once the war is over. I know that he feels nervous about his financial situation. I went through similar fears when I proposed to your mother. Anyway, my dear, I know you will make a lovely wife, and one day, a very good mother too.'

'Thank you, Daddy,' I said as I flung my arms around my father's neck.

'There is one more thing,' my father said very solemnly, now holding me tight. 'Horrible though it sounds, it is wartime and I wonder have you faced up to the fact that you could find yourself a widow?' Poor Daddy, I thought, he had obviously forced himself to say this to me even though it was hard for him to do so.

'Yes, Daddy, I have thought about it and I expect I will make an awful fuss if Duncan is killed, as it would be agony, but I know you, Mummy and Aunt Beth will always be there for me, just as you were before, when Henry and then Charles died. And I know Duncan's family would all support me too,' I added solemnly, 'so I hope that if I lost my life in an air raid you would be there for Duncan too.'

On that sombre note, I kissed my father goodnight and went to my room. Aunt Beth was already in bed, but she was sitting up waiting for me.

'Now, Mary, I have been giving your wedding dress some thought and have decided that I should try to find you something suitable in London when I get home,' and then she added, 'I am going to hunt around the theatrical shops to look for something that doesn't require coupons.'

As I started putting on my hideous Wren pyjamas, Aunt Beth looked horrified and said, 'You can't possibly go on your honeymoon in those, or you will never have any babies!'

'Aunt Beth!' I shrieked, a bit shocked, and we both giggled helplessly.

The following day we all had breakfast together, and then after saying our goodbyes to my family, Duncan and I headed back to Scotland.

When we arrived back in Perth, 'Bumble and Father John' greeted us both warmly and were pleased to hear that my father approved of their son, and, although they were initially a bit concerned about our decision to get married so quickly, they agreed to fit in with whatever my parents could arrange.

The next morning Duncan decided to take me to Dunkeld, as he wanted to show me the hotel where he thought we could spend our honeymoon.

He said that it was the most beautiful place on earth, as it was surrounded by many trees, and the leaves would all turn magnificent colours in the Autumn, which is when we would be there. He told me that he had helped plant many of the trees there when he had done his early forestry training, so he had a real affinity with the place. He then explained how important trees were for the wellbeing of our world and that he wanted to join the Forestry Commission after the war to help protect our forests for the future.

When we arrived in Dunkeld, we made our way straight to the hotel, and Duncan told the manager that we were getting married soon, so we wanted to look at the rooms to choose one for our honeymoon. The manager showed us the honeymoon suite, which had its own bathroom, but was rather expensive, and then showed us another very pretty bedroom, which although was a lot less expensive, the bathroom was down a long corridor. Duncan told him we would wait until our wedding date was confirmed before letting him know which room we would like to take.

After lunch, Duncan suggested that we go for a walk in the nearby forest, and on the way back, we could look at the ruins of Old Dunkeld Cathedral. As we walked through the forest, he told me the names of the various trees and pointed out the different shapes of the leaves, bark and cones. He then explained how the trees regenerated themselves, which I found fascinating, but when he then began to talk about the various mosses and fungi in the forest, I started yawning, which he rightly took as a sign to stop talking and start kissing.

At the ruined Cathedral, we entered through the original entrance and walked up to where Duncan said he thought the altar must have been. He then took my hand in his and with a huge grin on his face he said, 'There is something I have been meaning to ask you, Mary.'

'Oh is there, Duncan? What's that?' I said. He then went down on one knee and said, 'Mary Arden, will you do me the honour of becoming my wife?'

'Most men ask that question before they go with their intended to look at rooms for their honeymoon!' I said laughing.

'I was waiting until I could bring you here to propose to you, as I think this is a very spiritual place and I want this moment to be special: So, Mary, will you marry me?

'Yes, I will,' I said kneeling down next to him, so that I could kiss him.

Just then the sun appeared from behind a cloud and shone on the exact spot where we were kneeling, and for a moment, it felt as if we had been blessed from above. It was very romantic, but as we began walking back to the hotel for lunch, the spell was soon broken when Duncan squeezed my hand and said, 'I don't know why I agreed to us getting married in a church, it would have been much quicker if we'd had a special licence and then we could go straight to bed now!'

I hit him playfully on his arm and told him that he would have to wait, as I was intending to wear white at our wedding.

Over lunch we discussed our wedding plans and both agreed that we would prefer a quiet ceremony with just family and a few friends. Duncan was concerned that my mother might want a big reception to make up for the small village wedding, but I assured him that this wouldn't happen because my father would consider it inappropriate to hold anything too lavish during wartime.

That evening Father John produced a good bottle of wine to celebrate our engagement, and then inevitably the conversation turned back to our wedding. My future father-in-law suggested that, to save the risk of any of their family getting caught up in the bombing, perhaps it would be wise if only their immediate family attended the wedding in England, and then we could have a second reception in Scotland after our honeymoon. We all agreed that was a good idea.

Later that evening Duncan rang his elder sister Janet to tell her about the wedding plans. She announced that she had only just found out she was pregnant, and hoped that we would understand if they didn't travel to England for the wedding, but they would love to attend the Scottish reception, and that she would be happy to help organise it. Duncan then handed the phone to his mother, who shrieked with delight at the news that she was going to become a grandmother.

Both Duncan's parents were overjoyed by the happy news, but I noticed that Celia, after congratulating her sister on the phone, looked rather sad. I thought that perhaps she was still grieving for her fiancé, and that this news might be making her think about the children she would never be able to have with him. I felt very sad for her and hoped that one day she would find someone else.

The following day, Bumble showed me a beautiful sapphire and diamond ring that had been in the family a long time, and asked me if I would prefer this one as an engagement ring to the opal ring they had showed me previously. I told her that I really loved it, and although it was a little loose when I tried it on, I felt sure that it could be made a bit smaller to fit my finger. Later that day Duncan took me to the jeweller to arranged to have the ring re-sized, and while we were there, he asked whether he had any wedding rings to match the gold setting of the sapphire ring. The jeweller explained that it would have to be a second-hand ring, because a new one would be a different shade of gold. He then pulled out a tray of gold rings and Duncan picked one up that had little decorative scrolls all around the edge and was a perfect colour match. The jeweller measured my finger and told us that he would clean both rings and put them in a special box for us. Duncan then explained that we had to leave the next day, but that his father would come and collect them when they were ready.

Duncan took my hand in his and confessed that he was a bit concerned that, as I would be returning to work without an engagement ring, nobody would believe that I was engaged, so he asked me if I would wear the opal ring as my engagement ring until we were married.

'Is that to ward off all the other men?' I teased.

'Absolutely!' he chuckled, 'I can't risk another chap kneeling down on the runway to propose to you!' He then slipped the ring onto my finger and I was so happy that I burst into tears. Poor Duncan thought that he had pushed the ring on too hard and had hurt me, so asked me if I was all right.

'Yes, I am fine, but I always cry when I am happy,' I warned him.

'Make note to self, bring clean handkerchief to wedding!' Duncan joked, so I reminded him that it was only because he had been carrying a clean handkerchief that we met in the first place.

'I could hardly forget that night, Mary, because that was when I first fell in love with you,' Duncan confessed.

'Love at first sight?' I asked incredulously, 'You haven't told me that before.'

'That's because I have been too busy falling in love with you every day since.'

'Oh Duncan, you romantic fool!' I sighed, and we both began to laugh.

Later that evening when Celia and I were laying the table for supper she lowered her voice and confided that she had recently met an army officer called Anthony at a dance in Perth; he had asked her out for dinner the following week. She admitted that she was a bit nervous, but also rather excited, as it was the first man she had felt drawn too since her fiancé had been killed. I asked her whether she still missed him.

'I always will, but it's lonely on my own, and I must admit that I had rather given up hope of meeting someone else, but now, perhaps—,' she then put her fingers to her lips and whispered, 'please don't say anything about it yet.' I instinctively put my arm around, her and gave her a hug.

Early the following day, Duncan's father took us back to the station to get the train to Glasgow, which was the first-leg of our journey back to Machrihanish. When I kissed Father John goodbye, he made me promise that I would call him as soon as the date was confirmed.

On the long journey back we discussed the wedding plans again and Duncan told me that he was going to ask his cousin Ian to be his best man, and I told him that I wanted my cousin Jane as my Maid of Honour.

When we boarded the ferry for Campbeltown we had to act like strangers, because we were both wearing our naval uniforms and Officers and Other Ranks were not allowed to be too familiar with each other, even if they were now engaged. When we disembarked, Duncan saluted formally instead of kissing me goodbye. I nearly started laughing before remembering that as he was my superior in rank I had to salute him back. The next minute a car pulled up beside Duncan and the driver got out and opened the back door for him; Duncan got into the back seat like Lord Muck while the driver put his suitcase in the boot and then they drove off leaving me on my own. In contrast, my transport was an old naval lorry and I had struggle with my own luggage. Welcome back to the real world Mary, I thought.

As soon as I went into my bedroom, Hazel noticed my left hand and screamed, 'Wow! That's a beautiful ring, Mary, congratulations.'

'This is just temporary, you wait until you see the ring that Duncan is having re-sized for me,' I told her excitedly.

'Tell me all about your engagement? Did Duncan get down on one knee; was he romantic and did you... well you know?' Hazel asked.

'Certainly not! I have told you before I am waiting until I am married,' I said rather primly.

Hazel just laughed and told me that she was really happy for me even if I was determined to remain the last virgin left in Britain.

At lunchtime the following day, Duncan left a message for me at the Sick Bay to say that I should meet him by the wooden gate leading to the dunes at six o'clock that evening. He was already waiting for me when I arrived and he told me that we could only have an hour together before he had to return for a briefing, as his squadron were leaving first thing in the morning. We sat on a clump of grass and cuddled each other while we worked out the best way to keep in touch, which was via his parents, who would act as go-betweens as we had done before.

'I will telephone them whenever it's possible,' Duncan promised, 'and you must call them regularly to keep them updated with the plans for our wedding, particularly the day your mother is able to book the church for us,' Duncan said, 'that way I can ask for special leave around that date.'

The hour went by far too quickly, but at least we were alone and had the chance to kiss each other goodbye.

After Duncan's squadron had flown out, I sat down and wrote to Daddy-T to explain that I was getting married in about a month's time to a Fleet Air Arm pilot, so wanted some more leave, even though I had just taken some. Before signing off I asked him if he would be able to put in a good word for me with Commander Tapps, so that he would allow me to have enough time off to have a honeymoon.

Three days later I was summoned to Commander Tapps' office and informed by his Writer that Surgeon Captain Timpston was on the phone asking for me.

'Now listen carefully, Mary,' he boomed down the line, 'I am letting Lydia have some much needed leave, so I want you to come back to HMS Daedalus for a few weeks to cover for her, and that will then allow you to have your weekends free to organise your wedding and take compassionate leave for your honeymoon. How does that sound?'

'Oh Daddy-T, you are a lovely man!' I replied, and then seeing Commander Tapps and the Writer looking at me with astonishment, added more formally, 'I mean thank you very much, Sir.'

'Well before you get too excited, I have something else to tell you,' he continued, 'When you get back from your honeymoon, I will be posting you to Northern Ireland.'

I rushed back to the office to tell Rose that I would be leaving soon, and naturally she wasn't very happy about it, until I told her the reason why I was going and then she said how thrilled she was for me. My friend Veronica shrieked with delight as soon as I told her about my engagement but then became quite tearful when I had said that I was going to be re-posted to Ireland after my wedding. She made me promise to stay in touch, saying that she considered me a lifelong friend and would be very cross with me if I didn't write to her at least once a month and get in touch with her as soon as the war was over.

As I would be spending a few days with my family in Woking, before heading on to Lee-on-Solent, I made my way to see CPO McPhee about getting all my luggage and bicycle back home.

'Leave it all to me,' Chief said with a wink. 'I usually only organise luggage relocation for Officers, not Leading Wrens, but as you are my bird-watching protégé I will make an exception this time!'

That same evening I rang my parents to tell them that I would be home in a week's time. My mother then confirmed that she had been able to get the banns read and that the local church was going to be available either on the last Saturday of September or the first one in October, so would I let Duncan know as soon as possible so that we could lock-in on one of those dates.

I wasted no time in ringing Duncan's parents to let them know the two available dates to pass on to Duncan, and that he would have to make a choice as quickly as he could. Father John said he would send a telegram via the Admiralty, which I thought was a brilliant idea. I then told him that I wouldn't have time to stop off in Perth to see them on the way home, so 'please do not to forget to bring the rings!'

A few days before I was due to leave Landrail, Petty Officer Brown, who was in charge of our billet, called all the girls together before we went to bed and made us promise not to repeat what we were about to hear.

'A very brave woman,' she began, 'whose name I can't tell you, is being dropped by parachute from one of our planes behind enemy lines tomorrow night and she will need somewhere quiet to sleep during the day from about after lunchtime until nine o'clock in the evening.'

We all looked at one another astounded but said nothing.

'It has been decided that the Ugadale is the most suitable place for her to stay before her mission, so it is vitally important that the house is as quiet as possible during the time she is here,' PO Brown continued. 'Therefore it would be helpful if most of you would be willing to stay at the airbase until nine tomorrow evening. Now I know that it is Saturday and that a lot of you like to return here in the afternoon to rest, but I can't emphasize enough how important it is that this woman has a chance to sleep before she goes.'

One of the girls said, 'What are we all going to do holed-up at the airbase on a Saturday evening?'

PO Brown smiled and then said that a film showing had been arranged at the Entertainment hut after high tea, 'I am afraid it is only a Western, as that was all that could be arranged at short notice.'

I told Veronica that I wasn't keen on seeing a Western, and she said that neither was she, so we asked the PO if it was all right if we came back to the Ugadale after high tea, if we promised to be as quiet as mice. She agreed that we could but told us that we would have to walk back across the dunes, as there wouldn't be any transport before nine. A girl called Helen overheard us and asked if she could join us, as she didn't want to see the film either and didn't want to walk back across the dunes alone.

PO Brown then explained that we would have to let ourselves in through the back door before handing Veronica a key and telling her to replace it in her office once we had let ourselves in and re-locked the door. 'I know it sounds a bit cloak and dagger but I am sure you can appreciate that security is vital.'

After work the next day, Veronica and I waited by the gate to the dunes for Helen to join us and then the three of us headed back to our billet very slowly, chatting happily about what our plans were after the war was over. When we arrived back at the Ugadale we all stopped talking and walked very quietly to the back door. Veronica then opened the door to let us in and then locked it behind her, as silently as she could.

The hotel was mysteriously quiet and none of us had any idea of how to get back to the main part of the hotel, as this was a part of the hotel we had never ventured into before. There were several doors in front of us but none of us knew which one we should use, so seeing that one of them was already slightly ajar, I pushed it open to see where it led. To my amazement the door opened into a large area, that had a row of six washbasins fixed to one of the walls but there weren't any taps, which I thought was a bit odd. I was quite thirsty after our walk and wondered how on earth I could pour myself a drink of water if there were no taps, so beckoned to Veronica and Helen to come and have a look.

'I was just going to have a drink of water but can't see any taps so can't work out where the water comes from, can you?' I whispered.

'You wouldn't want to drink out of them, Mary. They are urinals!' she said as Helen snorted trying to stifle a laugh.

'What are they meant for?' I asked innocently, as I had never seen one before.

Helen then walked up to one of the urinals and gave a demonstration, 'you silly cow, this is where the men have a pee!'

Veronica now shook with laughter and had to stuff her handkerchief in her mouth, so that she didn't make any noise that might wake the mysterious sleeping woman.

The following week, I took the long journey back to Woking and it felt wonderful to be home again. My father told me that they had seen Archie McIndoe recently, and when they had told him that I was about to get married, he had reminded them that if it hadn't been for him suggesting that I join the Wrens, I would still be a spinster! We all laughed; it seemed like such an age since I had become a Wren.

I phoned Duncan's parents the next day to tell them that I had got home safely and that the Banns were already being called. They said that Duncan had been in touch and that the last Saturday in September was fine with him. Bumble asked me to thank my parents for offering to put them up and to tell them that she and Duncan's father were very much looking forward to finally meeting them.

That night I went to bed early, worn out from all the travelling, and fell asleep as soon as my head hit the pillow. I woke up the following morning to discover that Aunt Beth had just arrived with two suitcases full of clothes that she had found in one of the smarter second-hand shops in London that sold clothes without coupons.

'These will be perfect for your honeymoon darling,' Aunt Beth declared as she began to lift out garment after garment from the suitcases, 'they just need the odd stitch here and there to make them fit.'

My mother said that one of her bridge friend's had offered to lend me the dress her daughter had been married in to save buying a new one, thus saving precious coupons. Aunt Beth then suggested that I try it on right now, so I slipped it over my head and looked at myself in the mirror. I thought it looked rather dull, but Aunt Beth was cooing over it and saying that it was superbly cut and would show off my figure, 'Don't worry my dear,' she reassured me as ever, 'once I have worked my magic on it and made a pretty veil you will love it, I promise you.'

I wasn't convinced, but trusted my Aunt's good taste in clothes, as she had never let me down in the past.

My mother then got in on the act and soon the two sisters were arranging my entire trousseau for me, without consulting me at all. It was decided on my behalf that apart from my wedding dress and veil, I would need three different nightgowns, two matching petticoats and knickers, four pairs of stockings and an assortment of other clothes that would not have been out of place on a cruise ship. I tried to point out that Duncan and I would be staying at a tiny country hotel for our honeymoon and not the Ritz, but it seemed to fall on deaf ears.

Later that evening I mentioned to my father that I felt a bit ashamed that we were spending so much money on my clothes when there was still a war on.

'Don't think about that too much, Mary, darling. Just enjoy watching your mother and her sister have so much fun organising your wedding for you. I haven't seen your mother so relaxed and happy like this for ages, and it makes me feel good to see her this way, especially with Peter away in Burma.'

'Oh, I'm sorry Daddy, I hadn't thought of that. You must both miss him terribly, I know I do,' I replied, hugging my father.

The following morning my bicycle and the rest of my belongings from Scotland were delivered. It was only two days until I was due to leave, so now I tried to forget all about the wedding and start sorting my clothes suitable to wear in Ireland.

I decided to go for a bicycle ride that evening and as I went past the entrance to the Derwents' drive, I felt sad that none of the boys would be around, as they were all away fighting somewhere.

I just hoped that they were all still alive.

CHAPTER 15

1944

As I boarded the train in Woking to start my journey back to Lee-on-Solent, I had a flashback to the first time I had taken this same trip two years previously. I couldn't believe all the places I had been to in that time. But when I arrived at HMS Daedalus it felt as if I had never been away.

I handed in my pass at the guardroom and went straight to the Billeting Office, where I was told that I would have to sleep in a Nissen hut with four other Wrens. It didn't take long to unpack the few things that I had brought with me and then I went straight to the Special Eye unit to report to Daddy-T, who welcomed me like a long lost daughter.

It felt strange being in my old office without Lydia, and I wished she wasn't away on leave, as it would be a bit lonely working there on my own. However, once I had arranged all the tests for the coming week, I soon got back into the routine and started to make myself at home. It turned out to be a busy week and before I knew it, I was back on the train again to go home for the weekend.

On the Saturday morning my mother took me to Old Woking church to meet the vicar, who would be conducting our wedding service and to talk to the organist to arrange the music. When we returned home, Aunt Beth had arrived. When she showed me what she had done to my wedding dress, I hardly recognised it, as instead of the boring garment I had seen only a week before, my clever Aunt had now transformed it into something fit for a Princess.

'This is only the beginning,' Aunt Beth beamed, 'wait until you see the veil I'm going to create for you.'

For the first time, I started to get really excited at the thought of walking up the aisle and now missed Duncan more than ever. For the rest of the weekend we discussed the choice of flowers, which hairdresser to use, who would go in which car, which guest would sleep in what room; and most importantly, what food we could provide in wartime for the wedding feast.

My second week at Daedalus was just as busy as the previous one, but thankfully it was all fairly easy and there were no problems with any of the tests. When I got home to Woking that Friday evening, there was a letter from Duncan waiting for me, which confirmed the dates of his arrival and our honeymoon arrangements.

Most of the weekend was taken up with last-minute fittings for my trousseau and I was pleasantly surprised to discover that Aunt Beth had dyed an old pair of my slippers a lovely copper colour, which she told me would match the autumn colours of the flowers my mother had ordered for the church.

At the end of my third week at Daedalus, Daddy-T came to the NVT office to say goodbye and to wish me good luck. He gave me a box of silver teaspoons, as a wedding present from his wife and himself.

'Before you leave, I just wanted to tell you what will be expected of you in Northern Ireland,' Daddy-T said. 'First you will be posted to HMS Gannet in Belfast, and then you will have to juggle your work between there and HMS Shrike, which is near Londonderry. You will be on your own to start with and it will be up to you to arrange how long you stay at each base, which will rather depend on how many pilots there are at each place who still haven't been tested.'

I said goodbye to Daddy-T, and then went into the NVT office to write a short note to Lydia, telling her how grateful I was for her friendship when I first joined the Wrens and that I hoped that we would meet up again after the war.

When I arrived back at Woking that evening, my mother and Aunt Beth were sitting quietly in the drawing room enjoying a drink. I thanked them for all their efforts and told them it was now my turn to help with anything that still needed to be done. Aunt Beth immediately quipped, 'Well you can top this glass up for a start!'

My mother told me that Pansy would be coming every day to help make the beds and clean the house while we had guests, and as Agnes had taken a week's leave from her job at the 'munitions' factory to resume her work as our parlour maid, we had enough help in the house. However, Mrs Green would be very busy in the kitchen with all the extra mouths to feed, so she suggested that I could make myself useful by chopping up vegetables.

The next morning Jane arrived with two bulging suitcases. We were both excited to see each other again, as we hadn't been able to for more than a year, and even though we had written to each other often, we still had a lot of catching up to do. As she unpacked, I thought that I had better start thinking about what clothes I was going to take on my honeymoon, and asked Jane about what I should wear in bed.

'Nothing you silly cow, that's the whole point!' Jane shrieked, 'you are so naïve, Mary, surely you know what goes on by now, or I should say in!'

'Jane!' I exclaimed, 'you haven't have you?'

'Certainly not!' she said, 'but Bridget has, and she told me all about it, in some detail I might add.'

'Well, you had better spill the beans then, as I haven't a clue what I am supposed to do,' I tittered.

'I wonder if a man's willy floats in the bath, or sinks?' Jane asked.

'I'll send you a postcard when I find out,' I promised. 'No, seriously Jane, you are going to have to tell me everything Bridget told you, as I feel a bit embarrassed still not knowing anything about the birds and the bees at my age.'

So she told me all that Bridget had told her but I didn't believe half of what she said, and hoped the other half wasn't true, especially when she reminded me that a man's willy was like a chipolata to start with and then turned into a German sausage!

After lunch Jane and I walked across the park to see Kay, and to check whether the pageboy clothes for Richard had been delivered. Kay said that she thought her son would think they were a bit sissy but was sure that she could persuade him to put up with looking like a girl for a day by bribing him with a Mars bar. However, trying to get Julie to dress more like a girl than a boy was going to be much more difficult, as my goddaughter was such a tomboy and hated wearing dresses.

After breakfast the next day, my father went to collect William from Charterhouse, where he was boarding. When they got home, I was amazed to see how tall and broad shouldered William had become since I last saw him.

'What's for lunch?' he said as soon as he walked in the front door, which made me laugh. He may have got bigger but he was still the same little brother I knew and loved.

After lunch William told me that although he was pleased to have been asked to be Head usher, he wished our brother Peter could have been here to do it. I did too as I missed my big brother and wondered where he was right now.

My mother asked William if he would work out a bath rota, so that our houseguests wouldn't have to form a queue all along the landing to the bathrooms. When I checked his list a bit later I noticed that he hadn't put his own name down so asked him why, and he said, 'I had a shower after games yesterday and that will do until I go back to school on Monday!' I decided that if necessary, I would have to force my smelly little brother to have a bath the night before the wedding.

Agnes was just about to serve the soup that evening, when we heard the front door bell ring. My father asked her if she would see who was at the door while he attended to the soup. A few moments later she threw the dining room door open with a huge smile on her face and announced, 'Lieutenant-Commander Ogal-Bee is here.'

I looked up from my soup and saw Duncan standing in the doorway. He was wearing his naval uniform, but it now had an extra half-stripe between the two wavy gold stripes, so I realised that he must have been promoted since I had last seen him. He apologised for arriving a day early and explained that his squadron had returned earlier than expected and that when he had gone home he had discovered that his parents were not at home, but were staying with his sister Janet. He had tried to telephone us several times but that the phone was always engaged, so he thought he might as well come straight here. My father stood up and shook his hand and said, 'this is your second home now Duncan, so you are always welcome here at any time.'

I leapt up from the table and gave Duncan a hug but when he leant in for a kiss I only gave the poor man a peck on the cheek, as I felt a bit embarrassed kissing him with everyone now looking at us.

While my father introduced Duncan to William and Jane, Agnes quickly laid another place at the table and then hurried into the kitchen to warn Mrs Green that there was one extra for dinner. During the meal, my mother apologised that there was more bread than pork in the sausages but Duncan politely replied that after a month's Navy rations they tasted delicious. Jane said nothing and simply stared at Duncan in awe but William kept petering him with endless questions, like what it was like to shoot down enemy planes and if he had he ever landed in the sea.

After dinner, my mother suggested that I take Duncan to look at all our wedding presents, which were being displayed in the 'big room'. When we got there, I was just about to switch on the light when Duncan pulled me close to his body and began to kiss me passionately. The next minute he was kissing me down my neck and I felt a hand slip inside the front of my dress to feel my bosom. I was unable to resist and for the first time in my life didn't want to. In fact to my surprise I found myself pressing my body closer and closer to his and it was actually Duncan that pulled away first saying, 'I think we had better stop, before I can't.'

It was a good thing that we did, as just at that moment I heard Jane and William's voices in the corridor coming towards us. I quickly did the button up on the front of my dress, while we pretended to be looking at the wedding presents, which were all displayed on our old ping-pong table, which had been elegantly covered with my mother's biggest damask tablecloth.

Jane looked at all our presents with envy and asked where we would put them all, so I explained that my parents had offered to store them in the attic until we had our own home after the war. Among the gifts was a beautiful white china horse, which Charles's parents had sent us, which had made me feel a little sad, but also glad to know that they were happy for me.

When William spotted a new toaster amongst the gifts, he suggested that we make use of it the following morning, as there were too many of us for our old pre-war toaster to cope with on its own. When we agreed that it was a good idea, William picked it up and said that he was going to test it out right now.

'Of course I may have to use more than one slice, just to check that the toast is the right shade of brown, and then taste them to make sure!' he said before disappearing into the kitchen.

'I don't know where he puts it all,' I said. 'We have only just had dinner for goodness sake.'

'I was just the same at his age,' Duncan smiled, about to lean in for another kiss.

Jane cleared her throat, 'Excuse me. Do you mind? I am still here you know!' We all laughed and went back to say goodnight to my parents before going to bed.

As I showed Duncan to the spare bedroom, he whispered, 'Not long now my darling and we will be able to share a bed at last.'

When I got to my room Jane was getting ready for bed and wanted to know all the details of what Duncan and I had been up to just before she had come into the big room, so I said we were just looking at our presents. 'No you weren't!' she giggled, 'I know exactly what you were up to because I saw that your buttons were still undone on your dress. I think Duncan was about to show you his wedding present!'

'Jane!' I gasped pretending to be shocked, 'don't be so vulgar!' We both giggled helplessly as we finished getting undressed and finally went to bed.

While we ate our breakfast, Duncan was called to the phone. When he returned to the dining room he told my father that his cousin and best man, Ian, was on the train from Waterloo and would be arriving in Woking within the hour, a day earlier than expected. My father burst out laughing and said, 'What is it with you Ogilvies, do you always arrive early?'

My father suggested that we take my mother's car to collect Ian, and as we drove to the station Duncan told me that he had chosen Ian to be his best man, because his two best friends, George, who was a six-foot Canadian, and Alastair, an Irishman, who had both shared digs with him, when they were all studying for their BSc in Forestry at Edinburgh University together in 1939, were both away fighting, and he had no idea where they were.

When we drew in at the station car park half an hour later, I saw a man dressed in army uniform waiting by the telephone box. For a split second I thought it was my brother Peter, but soon realised that it wasn't and must be Ian. 'There he is,' Duncan announced leaping out of the car to greet his cousin. I got out of the passenger side to join them. Duncan put his arm around my shoulder and said proudly, 'Ian, this is my Mary. Darling this is my cousin Ian.'

Ian didn't say anything for a moment and just stared at me, which was a little unsettling and then he suddenly flung back his head and started laughing, 'Ah Duncan, I can now see why you couldn't wait until after the war to get married.' He slapped his thighs and tossed his hat in the air and the next minute he was hugging me like a bear, 'Mary my dear welcome to the Clan!' There was something about Ian that I liked straight away. It was like having an instant new brother.

As Duncan lifted his cousin's luggage into the car, I went to pick up Ian's two carrier bags but he warned me that they were very heavy, as they were full of bottles of scotch and wine, which were gifts from his family to ours. I peeped into one of the bags and noticed that it was not only full of bottles but also had some Edinburgh Rock and several packets of shortbread.

When we got back to the house my mother met us at the door and Ian immediately charmed her with his beautiful manners and it didn't take long for the rest of the family to warm to him as well. Ian then produced a ration card and said that he hoped it would help towards feeding him. My mother accepted it gratefully and exclaimed, 'I can now get the extra sugar and butter I need without resorting to the black market.' She then went on to say that as Ian had come a day early she had rung the vicar who had told her that we could come for the wedding rehearsal that afternoon rather than the following day.

When we arrived at the church, Ian, who by now was taking his best man duties very seriously, went straight up to the vicar and shook his hand. This must have made the vicar think that Ian was the groom rather than Duncan and so he patted him on the shoulder and told him not to be nervous. Duncan then explained to the poor man that he was the groom, so it was he who needed the reassurance, not his cousin.

As the vicar went through the wedding service with us, he tried to explain where we should all stand but it was difficult to concentrate as Aunt Beth and the florist kept moving up and down the aisle getting in our way and whispering loudly about where the various flower arrangements should be placed. At one point she even interrupted the proceedings to ask the vicar if there were any autumn leaves in the vicarage garden that she could use, which made us all laugh as it was so typical of my Aunt, as once her creative juices were flowing there was no stopping her.

The vicar remained calm and suggested that we begin all over again, and it was all going smoothly right up to the moment when my father was about to hand me over to Duncan when there was suddenly a strange noise coming from the direction of the church organ. The young organist had obviously just arrived and was warming the organ up before practising the music we had asked him to play at the wedding.

'That sounds a bit like an elephant's bellow,' I could hear Jane whisper behind me.

'More like an elephant's fart!' William sniggered.

'Shh!' my mother reprimanded. 'Remember where you are.'

We all tried to take the rest of the rehearsal a bit more seriously but I was glad when it was over and hoped that it would be a lot more romantic on the day.

As we left the church Duncan took the opportunity to thank everyone for working so hard to make our wedding day special. 'I just hope that my father remembers to bring the rings with him!' he chortled.

I had been worried that Duncan's parents might not get on with mine, as they were so different and had very little in common, but shortly after they arrived our two mothers started comparing notes about the problems of food rationing. When Bumble told my mother about having to queue for nearly an hour just to buy one sausage my mother laughed and told her about having to queue for just as long to buy a piece of unrecognisable fish that had whiskers like a cat. Bumble said that in Scotland it would have been a cat, which made my mother laugh out loud, and then I knew all would be well.

A little later I watched my father show Father John around the garden and was amazed when I saw Duncan's father removed his jacket and start helping old Bullen prune the fruit trees in the orchard with a pair of long-handled clippers that my father had bought recently.

When Celia arrived the following morning, she hardly had time to unpack before Aunt Beth whisked her away in the car to help organise the flowers in the church. As they left, Duncan and Ian returned from Woking where they had been doing some last minute shopping, which included buying a tie for William, as a thank you for taking on the role as head usher. My little brother was thrilled and couldn't wait to try it on, proudly announcing that it was his first 'grown up' tie and wasn't one of his 'boring school ties'.

Duncan beckoned me to follow him into the big room, which was now full of trestle tables covered in white linen cloths and the caterer's china and glasses. He told me to shut my eyes. Thinking he was going to show me a surprise wedding present, I was quite unprepared for what he did next. I felt him gently pull the opal engagement ring off my finger and then slip on another ring. 'All right you can look now,' he said.

I opened my eyes and looked down at the lovely sapphire and diamond ring that we had left to be cleaned and resized with the jewellers in Perth on my finger. It was quite magnificent and sparkled as I moved my hand. 'Oh Duncan, it's beautiful,' and then I started crying.

'Does Mary always cry when she's happy?' Duncan asked as Aunt Beth and Celia came into the room but he couldn't get a sensible answer from either of them because as soon I held up my hand to show off the ring they both started crying too.

My father then came into the room to say that it was time to take Duncan and Ian to the Derwent's house, where they would sleep that night in order not to see the bride until the wedding. It was then that it suddenly hit me: I was getting married in the morning! I had talked about it so much over the past few weeks that I hadn't really taken in the reality of what that meant. This was my last night as a single woman and more importantly as a virgin!

When I woke up the following morning, Jane was fiddling noisily with something on her bedside chair. When I asked her what she was doing she said, 'I am checking the elastic in my knickers in case they fall down when I walk down the aisle!'

After breakfast, Jane and I went back upstairs and shared a bath. We filled it to the brim with bubble foam and half an hour later we both smelled so much of violets that I wondered whether we would make the vicar sneeze. As the hairdressers were due to arrive any minute, my mother told us to put on our petticoats, so that we were 'decent' and then wait for them in her bedroom. We didn't have to wait long as the hairdressers soon arrived and after they had gone we then put on our makeup. Aunt Beth popped her head around the door and said, 'You both look lovely. I just wanted to see how your hair was set, so that I can make a few last minute changes to the headdresses. I will be back later.'

Agnes then appeared with a tray of coffee and told us that my old governess Kay had arrived but that she was worried about her, as she looked rather upset. The reason we soon discovered was because my goddaughter, Julie, had refused to put on her dress. However, Kay had brought it with her just in case she could get her to change her mind later.

Aunt Beth came back into the room to tell me it was time for me to get dressed. She told Jane to go to her room to get ready but asked Kay if she would stay and help her. I put on the wedding dress and then Aunt Beth told me to close my eyes while she put on the veil. I did as she said and then after several minutes of her re-arranging my veil, I heard her whisper, 'it's perfect, you can open your eyes now.'

When I opened my eyes and looked in the mirror, I couldn't believe what I was seeing. Aunt Beth had sewed hundreds of tiny flowers and leaves all over the veil and similar ones onto a tiara-shaped headdress. It completely transformed the whole wedding outfit and I now looked like a maiden in a Pre-Raphaelite painting. The veil was truly magical and I felt so happy that I started to cry but Aunt Beth said, 'Don't you dare, you'll ruin your makeup!'

Just then my mother came in to see if I was nearly ready. When she saw me she burst into tears, 'Oh darling, you look so lovely. I have longed for this day and now it's really happening. I am so happy for you.' She then had to sit down at her dressing table to remove the smudged mascara under her eyes. As she did so she reminded me to be very careful coming down the stairs and told me that she would send Agnes and Pansy to help me, as she didn't want me tripping over the short train at the back of my dress. I then caught my mother's eye in the mirror and noticed that she was staring at my face.

'You look very pale darling. Are you a bit nervous?' she asked gently. I nodded silently. She then came over to me and rubbed a little of her rouge on my cheeks. 'That's better', she said calmly, 'now darling, we are all leaving for the church in a minute but Daddy is waiting for you downstairs, so just try to relax until Agnes comes up to fetch you.'

When everyone had left the room, I took another look at myself in the full-length mirror. I then heard a sigh behind me and as I turned around I saw Jane standing in the doorway looking very pretty in her cream and coffee-coloured long dress with a wide pale-green sash around her waist and slippers that Aunt Beth had dyed to match.

'You look very pretty', I told her.

'I feel sick,' Jane replied.

'I'm the one that supposed to be nervous, Jane, not you!' I joked.

'I've forgotten what I am supposed to do,' June spluttered.

'Don't worry it will be all right on the night, as they say in the theatre!' I said, trying to make her laugh.

'We have to get through the day first,' June giggled, 'Oh, by the way, I completely forgot to tell you that Celia has managed to get your goddaughter to agree to wear her dress.'

'Really, well that's a miracle,' I said genuinely surprised.

'Nothing miraculous about it,' Jane said, 'she bribed her with sweeties!' And then just as she was leaving the room she said, 'See you in Church you beautiful silly cow!'

I was still giggling when there was a knock at the door. Agnes and Pansy had come to take me down to my father. The three of us then slowly descended the stairs. My father was waiting at the bottom, smiling. He took my hand as I reached the last step, and whispered, 'Oh Blossom, What a pretty picture you make.'

It was difficult getting into the back of the wedding car without crushing the flowers on my veil but with my father's and the chauffer's help we managed. Once I had settled in the back seat I could see through the windscreen that the chauffer had decorated the bonnet with white ribbons. He had also placed a single white rose in a small silver vase at the back of the car, which I thought was a lovely gesture. My father got in the back seat beside me and took my hand in his. I was no longer feeling nervous, but he obviously was, as his hand trembled all the way to Old Woking church.

We drove down the back lanes quite slowly as we had time in hand, and my mother had said it was good luck to arrive a few minutes late. William was waiting outside the church entrance and I could see that he was relishing giving all the ushers, who were nearly twice his age, their orders. One of the ushers then turned around and I was delighted to see that it was my cousin, Marcus, who had stitched up my wound when Charles and I had got caught in the Blitz. My thoughts immediately went to Charles and how I nearly married him. I would never forget him and just hoped that if he was looking down on us today that he would be happy for me.

After the chauffer had opened the door for me, I had to be very careful as I climbed out of the back of the car, so as not to tear my veil. Aunt Beth then did some last minute adjustments to it and said, 'It looks even better in the sunlight.' She then led me to a small anteroom just inside the church where Jane, my Maid of Honour, Julie, my flower girl, and Richard, my pageboy were waiting for me. My father waited patiently in the porch, while

Aunt Beth did her final check to ensure that we all looked perfect and then she gave us a thumbs up, just as the organist started playing Elgar's Enigma variations. My father took my arm in his and smiling at me whispered under his breath, 'Onward Christian Soldiers!'

As my father and I began to walk slowly down the aisle, Duncan turned around to look at me but instead of waiting for me to join him at the altar, as he should have done, he slowly started to walk towards me with one hand stretched out in front of him, as if he was in a trance. A collective gasp was heard, but Duncan seemed oblivious to everyone else but his bride. I was so moved by his very public show of love for me that I stopped in my tracks and waited for him to come to me. My poor father decided that he might as well stand there too and just pretended that giving his daughter away to his future son-in-law half-way up the aisle, instead of at the altar, was quite normal. When the best man took a step towards the groom to bring him back, the vicar put a hand on his shoulder to stop him and simply smiled.

When Duncan reached us, my father ceremoniously took my hand and placed it in Duncan's and gave me a reassuring smile, before joining my mother in the front pew. Taking her cue from my father's actions, Jane now moved beside me, took my bouquet and handed it to Julie, my flower girl to hold. Jane then whispered to Richard to pick up the train of my wedding dress, which he had dropped, and we continued up the aisle. From that moment on the service went without a hitch, and the best man, having recovered his composure, handed over my wedding ring without any mishaps.

As Duncan and I made our vows, I felt such overwhelming happiness that I had to fight back the tears. The wedding was everything that I had hoped it would be and it was all very romantic, right up until it was time to sign the register. That's when my nerves got the better of me and I nearly wrote Leading Wren Arden instead of Mary Arden.

Once all the witnesses had returned to their pews Duncan lent down and kissed me gently on the cheek and whispered, 'Hello Mrs Ogilvie!'

We waited for Ian and Jane to make sure that Julie and Richard were in their right places and then after Ian had nodded to the organist and the familiar music of the Wedding March began, we then all walked slowly down the aisle and out of the church into the sunshine.

When everyone else came out of the church, I saw Uncle Arthur and Aunt Felicity talking to my parents. It seemed such a long time ago since I had seen them and I was so pleased that they had made the effort to come all the way from Gloucestershire. Aunt Felicity told me that she thought my veil was the most beautiful one she had ever seen and just as I was about to sing Aunt Beth's praises, she joined us. The photographer then announced in a rather bossy voice that Duncan and I had to come with him to make the most of the sunlight, so we obeyed.

After the photographer was satisfied that he had got all the photographs he wanted, Duncan and I then climbed carefully into the back seat of the Rolls, which would take us back to my parent's home for the reception. As I cuddled up to my new husband, he whispered 'I love you,' and lent his head against mine. As we drove home I realised that this was a major turning point in my life, and that nothing would ever be quite the same again.

No sooner were we back at my parent's house, than Aunt Beth whisked me upstairs to re-arrange my veil and remove any crushed flowers and leaves. As she retouched my make-up, she told me that she had wept all the way through the service and would now need to re-do her own makeup too. As I made my way back downstairs I could see that Duncan was talking to our parents. I joined them and we all hugged and embraced each other before going through to the big room to meet the guests. After the formalities were over it was then time to enjoy the delicious food and wines that my father had provided for everybody.

Some of the wines were the ones that my father had brought back from our last holiday in France just before war was declared. The food consisted mainly of vol au vents, stuffed eggs, sausages on sticks and tiny sandwiches with the crusts cut off. There was nothing too fancy because of food rationing but it was all beautifully presented. The caterers were kept busy and I noticed that Agnes was making sure that the empty plates were removed or replenished quickly and that William was handing around plates of food, although I did notice that this did seem to involve the principle of 'one for them and two for me'!

As my new husband and I wandered among our guests, it dawned on me that I was no longer alone and that from now on it would be the two of us facing the world together. I was the happiest I had ever known.

When Ian tapped a glass with his knife, the room fell silent and he announced that everybody should find a seat and make themselves comfortable, as the speeches were about to start and that the bride and groom would be cutting the cake shortly. The three-layered cake looked like a traditional wedding cake on the outside but I knew that the ingredients included radio malt, to make it sweet as there wasn't enough sugar left, and chopped plum and apricot pieces had been used to replace the now unobtainable raisins and sultanas.

With Ian in charge of proceedings my father was the first to give a speech, which he kept short. However, when he mentioned that he wished his son Peter could be here, a roar of 'Hear, Hear' echoed around the room and I could see that both he and my mother were feeling sad despite the smiles on their faces.

When it was Ian's turn to speak, Duncan whispered to me, 'Oh dear, I hope he doesn't embarrass me too much.' I didn't have to wait long to find out; Ian told some very funny stories about when he and Duncan were children and how surprised he was when it turned out that his cousin had such a passion for trees, as when he was a little boy he had got stuck up one and Ian had to rescue him. Duncan insisted that it was the other way around and the two cousins roared with laughter.

After the speeches I went upstairs to change into the pretty pink suit, and a coffee-coloured blouse and matching shoes and handbag. Just as I was admiring myself in the mirror Agnes knocked at my bedroom door and when she came in she gave me a small parcel. She said that she had noticed I hadn't eaten very much at the reception because I had been too busy talking to everybody and so she had wrapped a large slice of wedding cake in greaseproof paper for me to have later. This was typical Aggie, always thinking of others. I thanked her and gave her a big hug.

When I went back downstairs I told Duncan that we should start saying goodbye to everyone, otherwise we would miss our train. I hugged and kissed all my family and then Duncan's family, reminding them that we would be seeing each other again at the Scottish reception in Perth in a week's time.

I hugged my parents and promised them that I would ring them, once we had arrived safely at our hotel. After we had finally said all our goodbyes, we got into the back of the wedding car and started to drive off. As we waved to everyone we could hear an awful clanging noise, which was made by a few empty tin cans that had been firmly tied on to the mudguard on the back of the car by William and the other ushers.

A short time later we were on the train and on our way to London. We were both so exhausted that we just sat quietly holding hands until we arrived at Waterloo. We then took a taxi to Kings Cross station, where we left our cases in the left luggage office ready to pick up later before heading up to Scotland. We then took another taxi to a rather glitzy restaurant that my cousin Marcus had organised for us as a special treat, called Chez Pierre. It looked more like a private house than a restaurant from the outside, and when we went to knock on the door, I was amused to see that the knocker was shaped like a big frog. I wondered if the owner, Pierre, knowing that the English referred to the French as frogs had bought it as a joke.

After we had eaten our delicious meal, we talked about how lovely our wedding had been and then suddenly we heard live music being played in the basement. Duncan took my hand and said, 'Mrs Ogilvie will you do me the honour of having the next dance?' He then led me down some stairs to a dimly lit dance room where a few couples were already slowly swaying around the room, so we joined them. He held me so close that I felt I was melting into his body.

'Oh Mary,' he whispered into my ear, 'I have wanted to do this all day.'

When we left the restaurant, Duncan looked at his watch and suggested we walk for ten minutes to get some fresh air before taking a taxi to the station. We walked down the road arm in arm for a few minutes without a care in the world, and then suddenly an air raid siren screamed a warning. Everyone else in the street started running towards the nearest shelter, so we followed them and went down some stairs to find somewhere to sit.

A few minutes later we heard a loud bang and felt a shudder and then dust began to fall onto us, off the concrete ceiling. I was a little scared and held onto Duncan tightly. He pulled me close and told me not to be frightened. When the all clear sounded, everyone smiled at each other in relief. Duncan stood up and brushed the dust off his beautiful new uniform and said with a grin, 'Well, I think it was more fun being covered with confetti this afternoon, don't you darling?'

I was amazed at how calm my husband was and couldn't help but smile. He glanced at his watch and then suggested that we find a taxi quickly, so that we wouldn't miss our train.

As we drove to the station, I thought how brave these taxi drivers were, putting up with air raids day and night and carrying on their business as normal, usually with a cheery smile. They were mainly men who were either too old or physically unfit to serve in the armed forces and I really admired their courage and determination to keep London moving.

When we got to the station there was just enough time to pick up our luggage and find our sleeping berth before the train left for Scotland. When Duncan saw that our berth had only two bunks one on top of the other, his face fell as he had thought that by booking a double berth we would have a bed big enough for two.

'But it's our wedding night!' Duncan exclaimed as he talked to the attendant when he checked our tickets.

'I am sorry, Sir, but you won't find any Honeymoon suites in wartime!' the attendant chuckled. He then warned us that we shouldn't get completely undressed, just in case there was an air raid and we had to get off the train in a hurry. The look on Duncan's face was a picture and I had to put a hand over my mouth to suppress a giggle.

When the attendant left, Duncan sighed and said, 'Oh well, I suppose it wouldn't be very romantic trying to make love to you the first time on a bunk in such a bumpy train with most of our clothes on, so perhaps it's better to wait until we get to the hotel in Dunkeld.' I thought so too, as I wanted the first time to be special, and preferably somewhere a little more comfortable.

We kissed each other for a few minutes and then I told Duncan that I was feeling really tired after such a big day and he said that he was too. As he took off his uniform, I suddenly felt very shy, so asked him if he would turn his back while I took off my pink suit. He smiled and did as I requested. I then went into the tiny cubicle in our sleeper, which had a lavatory and small washbasin, and when I came back out Duncan was standing there in his unbuttoned shirt and underpants. I looked down and saw that he still had his socks on, which made me snort with laughter.

'What's so funny?' Duncan said grinning. 'Haven't you seen a man's... socks before?'

I knew he was being naughty and that made me giggle even more. While he went to the cubicle to wash, I climbed onto the bottom bunk and got under the sheets. When Duncan reappeared he was wearing a pair of tartan undershorts and started to do a highland fling. I nearly fell out of the bunk, as I was laughing so much.

'Where did you get those funny pants from?' I asked.

'They are a present from Ian and I will have you know that in certain parts of Scotland these are considered very sexy!' Duncan grinned, as he knelt down and gave me a kiss. He then stood up and leapt onto the top bunk singing, 'You take the low bunk and I'll take the high bunk and I'll be in Scotland before you!'

This was our first night as man and wife, but it obviously wasn't going to be the romantic one that I had imagined or the passionate one that Duncan might have hoped for, but I was still very happy and loved this special man with all my heart.

When we arrived in Perth the following day, Duncan collected a suitcase full of civilian clothes and two fishing rods from his parent's home, and then we got on the bus to Dunkeld. I sat next to the window, so that I could admire the glorious autumn colours and Duncan sat next to me holding my hand the whole way.

'Well, Mrs Ogilvie, here we are, at last!' Duncan said, as we arrived at our hotel. To my delight my husband had booked the honeymoon suite.

As soon as we got to our room, Duncan closed the door and started kissing me, but then there was a knock at the door. It was the housemaid bringing clean towels. Duncan sighed and I got the giggles. We waited until she left and then started to kiss again, more passionately this time, and then unbelievably there was another knock on the door.

'I don't believe it!' Duncan said exasperated. He opened the door and suddenly started laughing and so did the man standing in the corridor who had brought our suitcases to the room for us. I had no idea what was going on, and then Duncan turned to me and said, 'Mary, this is Sandy Macintosh. We have known each other for years.'

'It's an honour,' Sandy said as he shook my hand with a huge smile. Then he continued, 'Well Mr Duncan, I was hoping it was you but I didn't think that it could be, as it was only yesterday that you were a gawky young student trying to learn the names of all the trees.'

Duncan laughed and asked him if he was still working for the Duke. Sandy then explained that he was only working part-time now, as there were no game shoots, so that was why he was also acting as part-time porter and barman at this hotel. Duncan said that they would have to catch up on one another's news later, and then asked what time the bar opened. Sandy grinned and said he would open it at midday on the dot and the first drink would be on him. Duncan then told him that we had only been married for about twenty-four hours.

'You must be desperate then!' There was a moment's silence and then Sandy bellowed with laughter at his double-entendre, and said, 'For a dram I mean! I'd better open the bar straight away for you Mr Duncan.'

As our romantic moment had been interrupted twice, instead of resuming our passionate embrace we decided to unpack our cases instead. Duncan explained that while he was deciding whether to become a Forestry Officer, or a Lairds Factor, he had spent a whole summer learning the different jobs that would be involved for both and meeting all the Lairds who knew one another very well and were friends. He had also been advised to learn all the tricks of the trade from the best gamekeeper in Perthshire, and that was Sandy Macintosh.

I noticed that Sandy had called my husband Mr Duncan rather like Agnes called me Miss Mary, so wondered what the pecking order was for those who worked outside on the land and those who were servants in the houses, and whether one was grander than the other. But before I could ask, Duncan said that he was going to change into his kilt, until his leave was over. I changed into a skirt and blouse and then we went downstairs to have a drink with Sandy.

After lunch, Duncan suggested we go for a hearty walk and when we came upon a nice sunny spot, he put his jacket on the ground for me to sit on. He then sat down next to me and pulled me into his arms. We kissed gently and then lay back on the ground side by side staring up at the sun shining through the trees. It was almost like a summer's day, which was unusual for Scotland in the autumn. Duncan's hand started to explore under my skirt, which had now ridden up to reveal my suspenders, and if he hadn't heard a dog barking to warn us that someone was approaching, I think he would have taken me on the spot, but instead, he laughed and said, 'Madam, please cover your nether regions immediately. You are a wanton woman tempting a poor man by flashing your 'unmentionables' at him!'

As the dog owner walked past us, with a nod and a wave, we decided that we had better leave our continually interrupted nuptials until we were alone in our hotel room. Duncan then said that he needed to think about something else to take his mind off what he really wanted to do and started testing me on the names for different species of trees. It wasn't very romantic but it did the trick, and after ten minutes of Duncan teaching me to recognize the various names of trees, flowers and any birds that we saw in Latin, any thought of what we might have got up to if we hadn't been disturbed, were completely obliterated.

As we changed for dinner, I thought how handsome Duncan looked in his kilt and suddenly had the urge to kiss him very passionately to show him that I wanted him as much as he wanted me. After a few moments he pulled away and said, 'Well if that was the entrée, I can't wait for the main course!'

'In that case, let's go and see what's for dinner then, shall we?' I teased, knowing full well what he had meant.

We had roast pheasant with all the trimmings, which was delicious and a real treat. After dinner we had a quick nightcap at the bar with Sandy, who told Duncan that there was a 'Do Not Disturb' card in one of the drawers in the dressing table.

'I suggest that you hang it on the handle outside your door before you go to bed and then there won't be any Coitus Interruptus!' Sandy said with a cheeky grin before saying goodnight. He obviously knew Latin too.

When we got to our room, I told Duncan that I wanted to have a hot bath before we went to bed.

'I'd like one too, shall we share the bath?' he asked grinning at me.

'Yes, that's a good idea, we should be careful not to waste the hot water,' I said, not realising what he had in mind.

Duncan just chuckled to himself and sat in one of the chairs and pretended to read his newspaper, while I started to run the bath. I then added some bubble bath foam that I found on the shelf. While the bath was running,

I went back into our room and found the piece of cord I used for hanging my washing on. I asked Duncan if he could work out how I could suspend it over the bath, so that my wet clothes could dry overnight. Duncan looked a bit surprised when he realised that I really did intend to wash my underclothes and hang them over the bath on our honeymoon. However, he soon regained his composure and said with a grin, 'I will give it some serious thought later, when I am in the bath.'

When I went back into the bathroom to turn off the taps, Duncan called out for me to leave the bathroom door ajar a little, so that we could chat to each other. I then got undressed and climbed into the bath. It was lovely and hot and soon my body was completely hidden in a sea of bubbles. I started to relax completely but then felt a bit guilty enjoying all the hot water, so I washed myself as quickly as I could and then stood up to climb out of the bath. Just then, Duncan appeared in the doorway with his towel wrapped around his waist.

'You look like Venus de Milo!' he gasped.

'I hope not, she hasn't got any arms!' I replied trying not to show that I was nervous and a little frightened of being naked in front of a man for the first time in my life. 'I think you might mean Botticelli's Venus!'

'Yes that's the one,' Duncan said, obviously not really caring which Venus it was right now.

Without saying another word, he walked slowly towards me, gazing at my breasts and then he began to fondle them. When I looked down to see what he was doing, I noticed that something was moving under his towel. As the towel fell to the floor, I quickly looked away. He then he put one of his hands on my cheek, turned my face towards him, and kissed me so gently that I soon forgot my inhibitions and allowed him to kiss me all over my body. He must have stepped into the bath, while he was kissing me, as the next thing I remember was that we were both now sitting in the bath intertwined, as one.

This wonderful man had had to wait almost two years for this moment and now he could no longer control the desire that he felt welling up inside him. His hands now travelled all over my body kissing me wherever he desired, and as he did so he whispered loving words, which made me melt in his embrace. I was so overcome by this adoration that I wrapped my arms around his neck and pulled his head close to my breasts. My body began to tremble and Duncan must have thought that I was cold, so he then stood up and lifted me bodily out of the bath and wrapped me in a lovely warm towel. He then climbed into the bath and started to wash himself. It was then that I remembered that I had promised to send Jane a postcard to let her know if a man's willy sank or floated in the bath. When I took a quick peak, I was delighted to see that my husband's willy appeared to be happily floating amongst the bubbles.

I told Duncan that I was going to get into bed and warm it up for us, but unfortunately for my husband, I was now so relaxed that as soon as I got into bed, I fell fast asleep before he had even got out of the bath.

I woke at dawn and noticed that it was quite light outside already. Duncan must have pulled one of the curtains open in the night perhaps to let in some fresh air. It felt strange to see him sleeping next to me and after gazing at him for a few seconds I decided to snuggle up close to his body. His skin felt lovely and warm and then I realised he was naked. I had forgotten that he had told me that he preferred to sleep with nothing on. Suddenly he turned on his back and after checking that he was still fast asleep my curiosity got the better of me and I lifted the bedclothes to have a closer look at his willy. Very gently I touched it with my finger and then got the shock of my life. It moved! It must have a life all of its own I thought. I was fascinated and touched it again to see what would happen. This time I let out a loud gasp, as I now knew that what Jane had told me was true. Chipolatas really can turn into German sausages!

'Good morning darling!' Duncan said with a huge grin on his face.

As I emerged from under the sheet, I felt so embarrassed that for a moment I was speechless but Duncan just kissed me tenderly and then without another word, took off my nightdress and started to kiss me all over my body. I soon found myself pressing myself closer and closer to him. Duncan whispered that I was to tell him to stop if he was hurting me. When he finally entered me, I let out a little gasp but then suddenly my body yielded and we were joined together for the first time. He moved very gently to start with but as I responded he became more and more passionate and then I seemed to lose all my senses and experienced a sensation that I had never even thought was possible. He then shuddered and collapsed on top of me.

'Oh Duncan,' I cried out, 'why didn't we do this before?'

CHAPTER 16

1944

We spent a lot of time in bed making love the next day and by the evening we were feeling very hungry. While we were getting dressed for dinner, Duncan watched me attaching my suspenders to my stockings, but that wasn't such a good idea as it got him going again and soon one thing lead to another and we were late for dinner. He was still buckling up his sporran around his waist, as we hurried down the stairs to the dining room, which made us both giggle, and when the other guests looked up from their meals it was obvious that they all knew exactly what we had been up to.

After dinner, we decided to play chess and, much to Duncan's disgust, I beat him. He made the poor excuse that his eyes were playing up. 'It must be all this love making. It's making my eyes squint and I can't see properly!'

'Well, we'd better not make love anymore then,' I teased.

'No, wait a minute,' he said grinning, 'I can see again. It's a miracle!'

Before we went to bed that night, Duncan suggested that we go for a walk in the forest the following morning. I suggested that we could go fishing instead, which wouldn't involve walking quite as far. Duncan was delighted with the idea, as it would give him a chance to try out his new flies.

When we got off the bus at Blair Athol, Duncan checked with the driver that we would be able to get the return bus from the same spot later that afternoon and once he was reassured that we could, we started to walk to the river. We were heavily laden because, as well as two fishing rods, a bag and a net, we also had to carry our picnic lunch, a thermos and a jacket each, in case the weather suddenly turned cooler.

After walking for twenty minutes, we found an open grassy area, which Duncan said would be perfect spot to learn to cast without getting caught up in the bushes. He was a very patient teacher and let me cast again and again until I got the hang of it. It seemed quite easy to start with, but he told me that he was only letting me use a short line while I was learning to cast, and now he wanted me to pull out more line. I then realised how much harder it was with a longer line and immediately got it caught in a branch behind me, as I attempted a rather ambitious cast. Duncan told me to persevere and after another dozen or so attempts, I finally managed to swing the line in a lovely arc through the air. It felt very satisfying even though I never actually cast my fly anywhere near where I had been aiming and knew that I was unlikely to catch anything. I told Duncan that having him standing so close to me was putting me off and I made a complete hash of the next cast, which proved the point. I then suggested that he go further up stream to enjoy some fishing while I practised by myself.

'Are you sure you don't mind?' Duncan asked, thinking I might just be being polite knowing that he was desperate to start fishing himself.

'Absolutely,' I insisted, 'I can always sunbathe if I get bored.'

'Bored!' Duncan gasped. 'How could you possibly get bored?'

I wasn't going to spoil his day by giving him my list of reasons, so just blew him a kiss and wished him luck. Waving cheerfully, Duncan took himself upstream and I continued trying to cast again and again, thinking that once he was completely out of view I would sit down and read my book for a while.

Suddenly, I noticed a tiny ripple on the other side of the river where the water had been very still before. If I were a fish, I thought, that is exactly where I would have a siesta out of the sunlight and somewhere quiet. I held my breath and cast as far as I could reach, but the fly landed several feet too short, so the next time I let out a bit more line and, taking a deep breath, I cast again. This time to my amazement it reached exactly where I had been aiming for. A whisper of wind then moved my fly a quarter of an inch on the surface and then without any warning I felt a violent tug on the line, which bit into my hands and hurt. I then let out a gasp, as I saw a fish leap out of the water.

'I've caught a fish!' I screamed, hoping Duncan would come and help me, and then noticed the rod was starting to bend, 'No, it's not a fish it's a bloody whale!' I yelled.

I was now up to my knees in the water and my arms were beginning to ache. It was cold and wet and I felt as though I was being pulled towards the fish rather than the other way around. For a moment I was tempted to let go of the rod, but then decided I owed it to Duncan to at least try and bring this damn fish to the shore. As I tried to reel in the line as fast as I could, the fish suddenly leapt out of the river, and I could see that it was a decent sized salmon. I let out a piercing scream, which Duncan must have heard from wherever he was, as he was now running towards me to see what was going on.

'Well done that girl!' he yelled, before instructing me on what to do next. 'Hold on as tight as you can. Don't let him go.'

'Duncan! Don't just stand there, help me!' I begged.

Duncan now realised that he had left the landing net by his rod. 'I am going to go and get the net,' he told me, 'so keep playing the fish until I get back.'

'I don't want to play with a bloody fish!' I said. Duncan wasn't there to hear me but in less than a minute he was back by my side and when I asked him to take over the rod he said, 'No my girl, it's your fish and you can land it yourself, but I will help you.'

Seeing that I was about to give up he then added, 'Think how you can boast to your family that you caught a whopper on your first attempt at fly fishing.'

When the fish leapt out of the water again, I could see that it was indeed a whopper, so now, spurred on by my husband's enthusiasm I held on for dear life. Duncan took off his shoes and rolled up his trouser legs before wading into the river, and then told me to walk back towards the bank and to reel in the fish very gently.

'Slowly does it darling,' Duncan said, as he edged closer and closer to me. Suddenly the salmon began to thrash about in the net and as Duncan raised it above the water to get a better look at our catch he exclaimed, 'Well I never, this is one of the biggest salmon I have seen in a long time, you clever girl!'

Duncan gave me a very passionate kiss and put an arm around me to hold me close to him, and then realising that I was both wet and cold, he helped me get back to the bank. 'Why not take off your wet clothes and put on my shirt instead?' Duncan suggested, as he took out his penknife and removed the hook from the salmon's mouth. Having put the poor fish out of its misery, he then held it up and said, 'A fishy feast, special courtesy of Mrs Ogilvie.'

As I started to strip off my wet clothes Duncan took off his shirt and under vest and suggested that I dry myself with his vest and then put on his shirt while he hung my wet things on a tree, 'The sun and wind will soon dry them,' he assured me.

As he placed my clothes carefully over a couple of low branches, I remembered that we had brought a thermos of hot tea with us, so I started to pour some into the thermos top, which acted as a cup. When I looked up, I noticed that Duncan was staring at me and grinning.

'What's so funny?' I asked.

'You look enchanting in my shirt but it doesn't leave much to the imagination!' he chuckled.

Suddenly realising that his trousers were soaking wet, Duncan took them off and hung them on a branch near my things. Now, wearing only his underpants, he grabbed his fishing bag, put the strap over his neck, and then placed the bag in front of his private parts like a makeshift sporran. Then he put his hands on his hips like a fashion model, which made me roar with laughter.

'How do you like my new outfit?' he asked, 'It's what all the best Scotsmen are wearing this season.'

Duncan then sat down next to me, putting his bag in his lap like a portable table and started tucking into one of the sandwiches we had brought with us, as though eating a picnic practically naked was an everyday occurrence. It made me giggle so much that I suddenly needed to pee, so I popped behind a bush.

'Mind where you go, there are adders around here,' Duncan called out.

'Yes I know, I think I saw one under your bag!' I teased.

I then lay down on the grass intending to have a rest, but in doing so, Duncan's shirt must have fallen open revealing more of me than I realised, because the next thing I knew we were making love in the open air.

I thought how lovely it had been to make love out of doors with the sun on our bodies and I was just thinking how nice it would be to do it again when Duncan said, 'Darling, I think we have been a bit silly not to take precautions. I think that from now on we'd better be more careful.'

While our clothes were drying, Duncan decided to continue fishing and when he came back I saw that he had caught a couple of good-sized trout.

We then walked back to the bus stop and fortunately didn't have to wait too long for it to arrive. Unbelievably it was the same bus driver who had dropped us off earlier, but before he would continue driving he insisted on seeing what we had caught. When Duncan opened the fishing bag and showed off our catch, all the other passengers wanted to see them as well. When we finally got back to the hotel Duncan suggested that it might be better if we went in via the back door, through the kitchen, so that we could leave the fish there.

Before we went to bed that night, I noticed that I had blisters on the palms of my hands, which I must have got while reeling in my salmon. Duncan kissed them better, promising to buy me some antiseptic dressings the next day. We were both so tired that we just fell asleep in each other's arms and slept so soundly that we were still in the same position when we woke up.

After breakfast, we caught the bus to Pitlochry, where we decided to do some shopping separately. I told Duncan that while he was buying some contraceptives at the chemist, not to forget the antiseptic dressings, and that I was going to look for some small presents to give his family. We agreed to meet back at the bus stop in thirty minutes. While we were sitting on a bench waiting for the bus to arrive, Duncan suddenly leapt to his feet and ran across the road to greet a very aristocratic looking man who he brought over to introduce to me.

'Mary this is Sir Graham Ferguson,' he said and then explained that Sir Graham was the father of an old friend of his called Hamish. We chatted for a moment or two and then Sir Graham told us that his gamekeeper had told him that morning that he had spotted one of the biggest stags that he has ever seen in his life.

'How would you like to bring your lovely new wife deer stalking with me tomorrow?' Sir Graham asked.

Duncan said that we would love to come, and then Sir Graham promised to ring us at our hotel that evening to confirm what time to meet and where. Duncan told me that Hamish was a prisoner of war but that they didn't know where he was being held captive and hadn't heard from him in a long time. He was obviously feeling sad thinking about his friend, so when we got on the bus, I just held onto his hand and said nothing all the way back to the hotel.

Sir Graham called Duncan that evening to say that he would pick us up from the bus stop in Pitlochry at ten o'clock the following morning. Lady

Elizabeth, his wife then asked to speak to me. She kindly said that I could borrow a jacket, a pair of slacks and some wellington boots that belonged to their daughter, as she assumed that I wouldn't have brought anything 'sensible' to wear on my honeymoon.

'I asked my husband to give me your approximate measurements,' Lady Elizabeth said, 'but he could only tell me that you were knee-high to a bee, had golden locks and blue eyes. He was no help at all!'

Before going to bed that night, Duncan gently covered the palms of my hands with the antiseptic dressings, which eased the pain straight away.

The next morning, Sir Graham pulled up in a rather dirty old estate car. He apologised for bringing his 'doggy car', but said that this wife had taken the clean one. I sat in the back with the dogs, while Duncan sat in the front with Sir Graham, who said that his wife had remembered to put out some clothes for me and we would go back to the house first, so that I could change.

After arriving at the lovely old house, Duncan was told to show me to the spare room. As we went up the stairs, I pointed out to him that all the family portraits were of men, which I thought was strange. He explained that this was a family tradition and that all the portraits of women, were in another part of the house, which I would see later. Lady Elizabeth had laid out the clothes on the bed for me and everything fitted perfectly, except the slacks, which were a size too big around the middle and too long. I went downstairs to ask Sir Graham for a piece of string, so that I could thread it through the loops to keep them up and then tuck the legs into the wellington boots, they had also provided for me. I now looked a bit like a second-hand scarecrow in my borrowed clothing, but at least I was warm and comfortable. I was also thankful that she had thoughtfully left out a pair of gloves, which I carefully pulled over the dressings on my hands.

It took nearly an hour to drive to the spot where the last sighting of the stag had been noted. Angus, the gamekeeper, was already waiting for us and greeted Duncan like an old friend. He then introduced himself to me and suggested that we all have our picnic lunch first, as we had a long walk ahead of us. Before we set off, I looked around for a suitable tree to hide behind to have a pee. Sir Graham must have noticed, as he suddenly called out, 'Ladies to the left and gentlemen to the right!'

After we had all relieved ourselves, we began our walk and the men marched on so fast that I had difficulty keeping up with them. However, Angus, kindly fell back behind the others, until I caught up with him and then we walked on together. After about half an hour, I got a stitch in my side and had to bend down to touch my toes. Duncan, now suddenly remembering for the first time that he had his wife with him, waited for us to catch up. He gave me a quick hug and told me to go at my own pace, but not to lose sight of him. Twenty minutes later, just as I was starting to get tired, I saw Sir Graham stop and hold up his hand, as a warning that he had spotted something.

'Walk very slowly, keep your head down and do exactly what Sir Graham does,' Angus whispered beside me.

Suddenly all three men lay flat on the ground, so I did the same. The men then wriggled nearer and nearer to the brow of a hill, so I did my best to copy them, but my bosoms kept getting in the way, so I had to raise myself up on my elbows and move forward inch by inch in a rather unladylike manner, until I was right behind the others. Now I had so much grass, gorse and earth on my clothes, on my face and in my hair that I was virtually camouflaged from head to toe and very thankful that I had been able to borrow some old clothes to wear.

As I lifted my head, I could see that Duncan was looking through a pair of binoculars. He turned around and beckoned me to come towards him. I crawled on my elbows, as quietly as I could, and stopped by his side. It was only then that I realised we were virtually on the edge of a steep precipice. Duncan smiled and handed me the binoculars, pointing in the direction I should look. Initially, all I could see was miles and miles of blurry heather, but once I got used to the magnification and adjusted the focus to suit my eyes, I finally saw what was making him so happy. Right in front of us was a huge stag. Its antlers looked so heavy I thought the poor beast must have difficulty holding up its head.

The stag was now sniffing the air, so I wondered if it could smell us, but then Duncan nudged me and pointed to a group of does that were grazing quietly nearby. Then, suddenly, something must have disturbed the stag, as it shot off and disappeared over the brow of the next hill.

'Well my dear,' Sir Graham beamed, 'have you ever seen anything quite so beautiful?'

'No Sir Graham, I must admit I haven't,' I replied feeling overawed by the experience of seeing such a magnificent beast.

When we got back to the car we said goodbye to Angus and then drove back to Sir Graham's house. As he opened the front door he said, 'Why don't you two make yourselves at home, while I let the dogs out, perhaps one of you can put the kettle on? I hope you don't mind having tea in the kitchen but it's lovely and warm in there, and the drawing room is bloody freezing, so we hardly ever use it.'

As I went upstairs to get washed and changed, Duncan told me that he would meet me in the kitchen a bit later. When I put my own clothes back on, I noticed that my knees and elbows looked a bit red from crawling over all the sharp stones and thistles that afternoon. I then left the borrowed things in a neat pile on the floor because they were too dirty to leave on the chair.

I found my way back down to the kitchen, and decided to put the kettle on. Just as I was looking in the drawers for a tablecloth, Sir Graham came into the kitchen and told me where I could find one. He then suggested that I use the crockery on the dresser and that the milk, butter and jam were in the pantry.

'I will leave you to it, Mary, while I let the dogs in,' Sir Graham said.

I had just got everything ready, when the back door opened and two large Labradors charged into the kitchen nearly knocking me over.

'Sit!' Sir Graham commanded. Both dogs immediately sat down.

That's impressive,' I remarked.

'That's nothing, watch this,' he chuckled and then yelled, 'Biccies!'

The dogs then leapt up and one of them pushed the swing-door to the scullery open with its nose and they both disappeared. A moment later the two dogs returned, each carrying an empty bowl in their mouths. They then put them on the floor and pushed them towards Sir Graham, who was now rattling a box of dog biscuits, which made their tails wag with excitement.

'You want some biccies, do you then boys?' he asked. 'Say please.' The dogs both gave a loud woof in unison, so their master rewarded them with a handful of biscuits in each bowl, which were wolfed down in seconds.

While the kettle was boiling, I told our host that everything was ready but I couldn't find the tea leaves anywhere.

'I'm not surprised,' he chuckled. 'Elizabeth keeps the tea in the jar marked Sago, as it has an airtight lid.'

I was just wondering where Duncan had got to when he joined us.

'Sorry to be so long, ' he apologised, 'but I have just been talking to your gardener, and was amazed that he still remembered me after so long. He reminded me of the time when Hamish and I used to smoke behind his shed, so that Lady Elizabeth wouldn't find out!'

'Find out what?' a female voice called from the hall. A moment later a smiling Lady Elizabeth came into the kitchen and went straight up to Duncan to give him a hug saying, 'Hello dear boy, it's so good to see you again.'

She then turned to me and said, 'You must be Mary, its lovely to meet you,' and gave me a kiss on my cheek. I thanked her for lending me the clothes and told her where I had left them. Over tea, the two men talked about the difficulties of running an estate with so few men around to help, and Lady Elizabeth asked me to tell her all about my family and about the work I did in the Wrens. She then offered to show me the portraits of all the women in her husband's family. When I asked her why these paintings had been banished to a hallway right at the back of the house, she explained that many years ago one of the wives had run away with another man and since then all the paintings of any female members of the family had been hung in the remotest part of the house.

'Is there a portrait of you here?' I asked.

'No, it's in Graham's study. I have warned him that if he dares to put it with the others I will run away with the gamekeeper and that will be the ruin of his good family name!'

When it was time to leave, Sir Graham said he would take us to the bus stop in Pitlochry, and as we were getting out of the car, I spotted an elderly man running out of the post office, waving his arms and shouting Sir Graham's name. He had a small pack of letters tied together with string in his hand and as he handed them to the Laird, I heard him say, 'Here are some letters from the young master for you, Sir Graham. I was going to bring them up to your house and then I recognised your car.'

Sir Graham suddenly staggered, so Duncan put out a hand to steady him.

'Thank God,' Sir Graham sighed, 'and thank you for bringing them to me. Now I must get back and tell his mother, as she will be as relieved as I am to hear from him at last.'

Just then our bus arrived and Duncan asked me to flag it down, so that it wouldn't leave without us, while he said a final goodbye to Sir Graham.

When Duncan joined me on the bus he told me how happy Sir Graham was to get the letters from his son, as he now had an address to write to him and could arrange for Red Cross parcels to be sent to his prisoner of war camp.

By the time we got back to the hotel I was beginning to feel very stiff, so Duncan suggested that I have a hot bath. As I lowered myself into the water I let out a squeal, as not only were the blisters on my hands still hurting but now my knees and elbows were sore too. Duncan came in to see what was the matter and told me to keep my hands, knees and elbows out of the water, while he sponged the rest of me. He wasn't being entirely sympathetic, as when he had finished playing 'doctor' he got in with me, and as a result we were late for dinner again.

Before going to bed that night, Duncan re-dressed my hands and gently rubbed cold cream on my knees and elbows, and then we both cuddled up for the night.

A few days later, the honeymoon was over and we went back to Duncan's parents house in Perth. When we arrived Bumble gave me a big hug and told me that they had put a new double bed in Celia's room to replace the two twin beds, so we could sleep in there and Celia would sleep in Duncan's old bedroom, while we were all in the house together.

After unpacking, we went downstairs to have a cup of tea and Father John then said to Duncan, 'Your Uncle Freddy is going to give you a cheque son, as he thought that it might be useful once the war is over to help you both set up house.' He then suggested that Duncan went to his bank the next day to open a joint account, and that he should arrange for some of his pay to be paid into that account in case I needed to draw on it once he was back at sea. I protested, insisting that I was able to support myself with my own money.

'Yes, dear, I know you will, but the war could drag on and then you may need to leave the Wrens and set up house ready for Duncan's return,' Father John explained.

That evening I found Celia alone in the kitchen, filling her hot water bottle, so I took the opportunity to ask her if she had seen her friend, Anthony, since she'd had him to dinner. Celia told me that she hadn't, but she thought he must be away with his Regiment or on a course, as she hadn't received a letter from him either. Bumble then came in to fill her hot water bottle too, so I hugged them both goodnight and went up to our room. When

Duncan joined me shortly afterwards, I suddenly felt a bit shy, knowing that all his family were in the other bedrooms nearby, and was worried that they would hear us if we made love.

'What do you mean if?' Duncan asked grinning at me.

'I hope the bed won't rattle,' I said, so he pulled it well away from the wall, and a little while later we discovered that the bed didn't rattle at all, it squeaked!

'Hells bells,' Duncan exclaimed, 'it must be the new springs under the mattress. I will have to oil them tomorrow!'

Duncan threw the eiderdown onto the floor and then the pillows, before pulling me out of bed and onto the floor beside him. He then began to kiss me passionately. Suddenly he stopped,

'My feet are frozen!' he whispered and then got up to put his socks back on. The sight of my new husband standing naked apart from his socks made me laugh so much that the idea of making love to him that night was completely off the agenda. He could see the funny side of the situation too and we both laughed hysterically. I realised at that moment that I not only loved Duncan as my husband and lover but also as my best friend and appreciated just how lucky I was to have him in my life.

After an early breakfast, Duncan went straight upstairs to oil every spring on the bed and then started jumping up and down on the mattress to make sure it wouldn't squeak that night, while Janet and I hurriedly prepared the food for our reception. There was a lot to do and it took us most of the morning. At midday, the caterers arrived to unpack all the glasses and china that we would need the following day, and helped move the furniture.

That afternoon, Duncan and I walked into Perth to the bank, as we both felt we could do with some fresh air. It was quite a long way from the Ogilvie's house, but we still arrived on time for our appointment to meet the bank manager to open a joint bank account. When we got home, I washed my hair, while Duncan wrote a few thank-you letters. As I was drying my hair, Duncan sat on our bed and started to bounce up and down on it a few times.

'Not a squeak!' he said looking at me with a grin on his face.

'I know what you're thinking!' I said laughing.

'Well, in that case, my beautiful bride why don't you come over here and prove your telepathic powers to me!' he chuckled, so I did.

Some time later, I realised that we would have to get washed and changed very quickly, so that we wouldn't keep the rest of the family waiting, as this was a special dinner that Father John had arranged at a restaurant. This was one meal we couldn't be late for.

When we arrived at the restaurant, I was delighted to discover that the main course was roast duck, but as there were no oranges available, the chef had made a sauce using blackberries, apples and elderflowers instead. It was delicious.

While we ate, Celia said that she had been considering making enquiries about a senior teaching post in Gloucestershire. Duncan thought it was an excellent idea, as if she went to a big private school she'd make lots of new friends and would be able to come home in the holidays. I glanced over towards Father John and noticed that he was nodding his approval at the idea too, but Bumble looked a little upset. I then realised that if all her children left home, she would most probably feel rather lonely.

'I have some lovely relatives in Gloucestershire,' I told Celia. 'So if you do go there, I'll put you in touch with them. They know everyone for miles around, so you would soon make friends through them,' I assured her.

'Are they all Lords and Ladies?' Duncan teased. I had to admit that they were, and everyone laughed.

By the time we got home, we were all more than ready for bed. As we got undressed, Duncan admitted that he was feeling a bit nervous about the Scottish reception, as it would be quite frugal compared with our rather lavish English one, but I reassured him that everything would be perfect, however it turned out.

We decided to have a lazy morning to save our energy for the reception, but by noon, we were all dressed in our finery, the fire was lit to warm the big drawing room and three big chairs from the dining room had now been placed near the fireplace. I thought that they looked rather like three thrones ready to seat the elderly Great Aunts, which made me giggle.

Duncan's Uncle Freddy and Aunt Daisy were the first to arrive to the reception. I could see why Duncan loved them so much, as it was immediately obvious that they both enjoyed the good things in life. There was no sign of their sons, though, and when I asked where they were Freddy explained that they were busy helping to park the guests cars at the back of the house, 'They are all in the army,' he chuckled, 'so they know how to organise others while doing very little themselves!'

Aunt Daisy came up to me and whispered in my ear that as I was now Duncan's wife, she would look on me as the daughter she had never had. She told me that if I ever found myself anywhere near Aberdeen I was to invite myself to stay. Duncan's cousin and best man, Ian, then came in and gave me a big hug. It was so good to see him again. He then introduced me to his brother, Alan, who welcomed me to the family. 'Ian said you were a pretty, wee lassie' he smiled, 'but he didn't say Duncan had married such a beauty.' He then bent down and kissed me on both cheeks.

Ian and Alan were both charming, so I wondered whether the other brother James was too. I didn't have to wait long before finding out. As I looked towards the drawing room door I saw a very tall, dark-haired and striking man wearing a regimental kilt staring at me with a big smile on his face. He came over and gave me a huge bear hug saying 'Hello Mary, I'm James, the best looking one in our family!' His dark eyes seemed to flash with life and good humour. Duncan must have spotted James already, as I saw him pushing through all our guests to get to him. The two men greeted one another with deep joy and warmth. I was glad to see that Duncan had an extended family just like I had with my father's sister's children.

As I looked around I saw Father John hurrying into the corridor leading from the drawing room. The Great Aunts had arrived, so Duncan left me with James while he went to greet them.

The Great Aunts entered the drawing room majestically, nodding their heads here and there, as they recognised their relatives. Once they were settled in their 'thrones' near the fire, Duncan took my hand and guided me over to meet them. I wasn't quite sure if I was supposed to shake their hands or do a polite bob-curtsey, so I did the latter, first to the eldest, Great Aunt Moira and then to her two sisters. Great Aunt Moira then told me to sit next to her and tell her all about myself. She listened to me talk, but didn't seem very interested, until I told her that if I had I not joined the Wrens I would not have met Duncan, which made her smile and tell me that she thought that joining one of the women's services was a brave thing to do.

'I would have enjoyed doing something exciting like that when I was a girl, but my parents would never have allowed it,' she confided. I now felt as though I had her approval, so when the trays of food were brought into the room, I left her side to mingle with our other guests.

Despite the rationing, the food was almost pre-war standard, and I greedily had second helpings of everything that the caterers handed round, but I decided to avoid drinking any alcohol, just in case it made me talk too much or say anything inappropriate to the Great Aunts. I also needed to keep my wits about me to remember which relatives belonged to Father John's family and which ones belonged to Bumble's. James was a big help and told me who was who. He then asked me if Duncan had told me about his life when he first joined the Navy, so I told him that I knew a little but that he hadn't said very much about his time on the fishing boats near Wick.

'The so-called fishing boats, you mean?' James asked. 'I can tell you Mary, that your husband is a very brave man.'

I looked at him in amazement and was about to ask him to tell me more when there was a call for silence, as our wedding cake was carried in. Everyone now sat down for the speeches, which, thankfully, were reasonably short and some of them very funny. Janet told the assembled crowd that the cake was a gift from their local baker, whose son Alex had been at kindergarten with Duncan. He and Duncan had remained good friends until they had lost touch when the war started; sadly Alex was now a prisoner of war in a German camp. I immediately thought about our brave servicemen and women and offered up a silent prayer for them all, hoping that the war would come to an end soon.

When it was time for our guests to leave, Uncle Freddy pulled Duncan away to a quiet corner of the drawing room and the two men hugged each another with deep affection. Uncle Freddy then handed his nephew an envelope, which I presumed was our wedding present.

Duncan waited until we were going to bed before opening the envelope, and inside he found an unbelievably generous cheque; it would be enough for us to buy our first home together. Duncan was so overcome with emotions that he burst into tears.

The next day we all went to church together, and after the service Bertie drove Janet and Celia home, so that they could see to the lunch, while Duncan and I stayed behind for a while to meet some of the congregation, who were all old friends of his family. We then went home for a lovely lunch.

Halfway through our meal, the telephone suddenly rang. We all reacted with surprise, as nobody expected a call on a peaceful Sunday afternoon. When Father John asked who was calling, he was informed that it was the Admiralty and that they needed to talk to Lieutenant Commander Ogilvie urgently.

Ten minutes later Duncan came back into the dining room looking as white as a ghost. He was swaying unsteadily on his feet and having to hold on to the doorframe for support. He looked so shocked and miserable that I immediately knew that something was very wrong indeed.

Duncan then told us that the rest of his leave had been cancelled and that he had been given less than twenty-four hours to pack and get himself to Edinburgh.

'You remember that I was posted to Wick at the start of the war, to take command of a fishing boat?' Duncan began to explain. 'Well the same crew has now been given a very special mission, and they have insisted that I am their skipper.'

No one spoke for a moment, as no one quite knew what to say. Duncan continued, 'They say it's my choice, but if I decide not to go and the crew is given another skipper who they don't know or trust and then they lose their lives, I'd never forgive myself.'

It was clear to us all that there was no choice, Duncan had to go and that was the end of it. The shock of hearing that his leave had been cut short was bad enough, but now that he had explained why he had to go, I felt cold and began to tremble with fear.

Father John stood up and said, 'I'm very proud of you son. If your old crew need you then as far as I am concerned you have no choice but to go.'

Duncan nodded at his father and then bravely smiled and said, 'Well then, I'd better go and find my warm jumpers, socks and scarves, as it's going to be damn cold where I'm going!'

I felt very scared about what might happen to Duncan on this mission and felt like crying, but instead I offered to help him pack. He gave me 'that smile' and then went off in search of his winter clothes.

Father John came over to me and put his hand on my shoulder, 'I'm so sorry that your honeymoon has been cut short, my dear, but in war time we all have to make sacrifices, and try not to think of ourselves.'

That night as we lay in each other's arms, Duncan tried to reassure me that all would be well. I promised that I would write often and told him that I quite understood if I didn't hear from him for a while.

'It will be just like when I was on 'ops' on my aircraft carrier, darling,' Duncan said calmly. 'Whatever happens, these last few days have been the happiest in my life, always remember that,' he whispered, kissing my gently and holding me tight.

The following morning we all did our best to behave normally but everyone was still shocked at Duncan's sudden early posting and we all sounded a little too bright and cheerful to be convincing.

While Duncan and his father went into Perth to deposit the wedding cheques we had been given, I rang my parents to let them know what had happened and that I would be returning earlier than expected.

I was dreading the moment I would have to say goodbye to Duncan's parents who had been so good to us, turning their home upside down for the Scottish reception and making the last few days so happy and carefree, but in the end, it was such a rush to get to the station that there was only time for quick hugs and kisses and promises to ring when I was safely home. Duncan had just enough time to reassure his parents that he would use public telephones to call whenever he could, and then a whistle told us it was time to board our train.

When we arrived in Edinburgh, we found a porter to take my big case to left luggage, and then made our way to the ticket office, where we changed the date on my return ticket for the next day. We then caught a taxi to the hotel where we would spend our last night together.

Our room looked very old fashioned, but it was clean and warm with its own washbasin. The bathroom was next door. Having satisfied himself that the bed didn't squeak, Duncan suggested we make up for lost time, but first he needed to put out everything he'd need for the next day and check that he had all his papers to hand, as he would have to leave at five thirty in the morning. Then he asked me to show him that I had enough money to buy myself refreshments on the way home the next day, and also that I had enough money to tip the hotel staff. 'I have paid for our room already, darling, so don't go and do it again!' he grinned. 'Now that you are a Scottish housewife, you'll need to watch the pennies!' he teased.

We went to a pub for a quick supper, and then went back to our hotel. No sooner had Duncan's head hit the pillow than he was asleep. So much for making up for lost time, I thought, but I didn't mind and just lay close to him and looked at his handsome face, fearful that if I didn't memorise every feature I might forget what he looked like if he was away for too long. Duncan woke up about an hour later and remembering that he was still on his honeymoon and would soon have to leave me, he took me in his arms and made love to me very tenderly.

As we lay together whispering to each other afterwards, he reminded me that I must not tell anyone where he was and I was just to say that he was on a special course for a couple of weeks. 'If I'm away for more than a month, just tell people that I'm back on my carrier. Please remember, darling, other lives beside mine could be in danger if the enemy learns about what I am doing.'

I assured him that I could keep a secret, and then we both fell asleep again.

I woke with a start when I heard someone knocking at our door. It was the night porter with a tray of tea and biscuits; he called out that Duncan had three-quarters of an hour before his taxi was due. While I sat up in bed drinking tea, Duncan washed and shaved, and every now and then he would turn and smile at me, 'I'll most probably be given leave after this 'op' ends, so don't worry, I'll come and find you in Ireland I promise.'

Once Duncan was dressed, he came over to the bed and kissed me gently on the lips. He then turned to pick up his overnight case, and said, 'Don't cry, darling, even if you feel like doing so, or I will as well.' He then put on his hat, and without looking back went quickly through the door, shutting it firmly behind him. I felt as if I had suddenly been thrown into a freezing-cold bath. I put my face on his pillow and could smell his hair. Then I wept like a baby. 'Oh Duncan, please be careful and don't get killed,' I whispered, 'I wouldn't want to live without you!'

I must have cried myself back to sleep, as the next thing I heard was my alarm clock going off. It was now seven thirty. I didn't have my dressing gown with me, so I put my overcoat over my nightgown and went to find the bathroom, which thankfully, was unoccupied. I ran a bath far deeper than regulations permitted making the water so hot that I almost scaulded myself, but at least I stopped shivering and began to calm down. When I climbed out of the bath, I looked at myself in the mirror, and saw that my eyes were puffy from crying. 'Pull yourself together and stop feeling sorry for yourself,' I said to myself and then went back to my room to get dressed and put some powder on my face and a little rouge on my cheeks. I was now ready to go downstairs and face the world again.

When I eventually arrived at Woking station, I took a taxi home and when it drew up outside our house, the front door opened and there was my mother standing there with her arms wide open ready to give me a hug. How pleased I was to see her again.

Back in my own bed that night, I clutched my old teddy bear for comfort and pulled up my bed socks, feeling more like a schoolgirl than a recently married woman.

The following week I contacted Daddy-T to let him know that I was ready to leave for my new posting to Ireland. A few days later I received a letter with all the necessary papers and warrants to get to HMS Gannet enclosed, along with my commissioning letter. There was also a hand-written note from him wishing me all the best and reminding me that if I really hated it he'd bring me home again without delay. 'You will have to work very hard, and remember that you will be running two units on your own for a while, but I know you will do well, just be well organised and don't let any bossy bitches interfere or tell you that they know best. Ring me if they try it on and I'll tell them to bugger off!'

It wasn't until the last day that I suddenly remembered that I had to sew new nametapes on my uniform and underclothes, as I was now Mary Ogilvie and no longer Mary Arden. It took me all day to do it. How I wished that Aunt Beth hade been there to help me but now I was a married woman I would have to start doing things like this for myself.

As usual my father accompanied me to London where my long journey to Belfast would begin. I was very glad that he did, because he asked the guard to look after me, which he kindly did by moving me from a noisy overcrowded third-class carriage to a first-class compartment, which I shared with three American naval pilots who were also on their way to Ireland. They treated me like a little sister, looking after my every need, even letting me lie down on one side of the carriage while they all squashed up together on the other side, so that I could have a nap. Although it was a long and tiring journey, they made it fun by letting me play poker with them. They were rather surprised when I kept winning, so I explained that I had been well taught by my elder brother Peter. I then shared my sandwiches, that Mrs Green had prepared for me, and they shared their American chocolate bars, which were a real treat and whenever the train stopped at a station, the pilots would take it in turns to leap out and buy us all cups of tea.

When we finally arrived in Liverpool, one of the pilots grinned at me and said, 'Nice meeting you Mrs Leading Wren Ogilvie Ma'am. Goodbye and good luck!'

CHAPTER 17

1944-45

'Are you going to HMS Gannet or HMS Shrike?' a young Officer asked me, on the ferry to Belfast.

'Both!' I replied.

'I've seen you before, haven't I?' he said obviously trying to work out where, 'I remember now, it was at HMS Jackdaw in Scotland. You gave me a Night Vision Test!' He then found me a seat and told me to look out for transport marked Gannet or Shrike, which would be waiting for Other Ranks at the docks, 'I wanted to ask you to have dinner with me but got posted before I had the chance,' he said grinning at me.

'Too late now!' I said showing him my wedding ring. His grin suddenly disappeared and after making an excuse, he left me on my own. I must have dozed off for a while, as I suddenly woke up feeling a little seasick, so I went on deck to get some fresh air.

It was about five o'clock, when the ferry finally docked. I was feeling extremely tired, having travelled for over twenty four hours non-stop, with only two short catnaps on the way. A young sailor kindly slung my suitcase into the back of the lorry destined for HMS Gannet, and then as I tried to climb in after it, he pushed my backside to help me get in, apologising as he did so, but I don't think he was very sincere judging by the huge grin on his face.

We arrived at HMS Gannet about two hours later, and when I got off the lorry I was greeted by a rather attractive woman who introduced herself as Third Officer O'Neil. 'You look a bit pale, I hope it wasn't a rough crossing?' When I assured her that I was fine, just a bit tired, she continued, 'I've arranged for you to sleep at Swallow Cottage, which you will find very comfortable and its less than half an hour from the airbase. There are a few rules and regulations, but the other girls will fill you in when you get there.'

When I told her that I would also be working at HMS Shrike, she suggested that as I would be sleeping in a Nissen hut when I was there, it might be a good idea to take only what I needed and leave most of my belongings at the cottage. Apparently the airfields were only a few miles from each other anyway, so that was good to know.

I thanked her for being so helpful and then got up to leave, but as soon as I stood up I had to quickly sit down again, as I suddenly felt faint. She suggested that I should go to the Wrens' mess straightaway to have a hot meal, while she phoned Lieutenant Commander Mansfield. I then heard her talk to him on the phone asking him to get someone to collect my bags and take them to Swallow Cottage for me. I thanked her for being so helpful and then went straight to the mess for something to eat.

When I got there, I was amazed at the size of the helpings and even more surprised at the quality of the meal. The rationing in Ireland obviously isn't as tough as everywhere else I have been, I thought, as I tucked into my supper with relish.

While waiting for transport in the NAAFI, I found the telephone block and decided to ring my parents to let them know that I had arrived safely. I then rang Duncan's parents to see if they had any messages from him for me, but Father John told me that apart from a postcard they had heard nothing. 'No news is good news Lass,' he reminded me. 'Work hard and then the time will fly by, I promise.'

An hour later, I was on my way to my new billet, as usual in the back of a lorry. It was dark outside, so I couldn't see where we were going but as it was only a short drive to my new home, it obviously wasn't very far from the airbase. When we arrived, a rather stern looking woman who introduced herself as Mrs Donaghue, the housekeeper, was waiting for me at the side door, which was used by Other Ranks. 'Your bicycle is in the shed, and your cases are in the airing room,' she informed me.

'Thank you Mrs Donaghue, I do hope you weren't put to any inconvenience when they delivered my things here for me?' I said sincerely.

The housekeeper's frown suddenly disappeared and a smile appeared in its place, 'Not at all my dear, but thank you for asking.'

As we went upstairs, Mrs Donaghue told me how fortunate I was to have a room to myself, as all the other girls had to share three or four to a room. To my delight I discovered that I had been given a pretty bedroom overlooking the garden at the back. Mrs Donaghue then told me that the girls usually had Sunday lunch at the house, so if I wanted to do the same I would find a book in the dining room, which I would have to sign each Friday to let her know, and then she added smiling, 'You won't want to miss it, if I say so myself, as I cook the best roasts around here for miles!'

I was now feeling very tired and decided to go and fill my hot water bottle. When I saw a Wren in one of the bedrooms along the corridor, I asked her where I could fill it. She introduced herself as Hannah and told me to follow her. Several other girls were also waiting to fill their bottles. They seemed very friendly and started telling me about the house rules. They told me that breakfast was between seven thirty and eight o' clock, but had to be eaten in silence and I could have a bath at night, or a shower in the morning, but not both. I must have looked a bit tired and confused, as a girl called Eliza, said, 'Here, sleepyhead give me your 'hotty', I'll fill it for you while you have a bath, you look like you could do with one!'

I collected my sponge bag and towel and then took her advice and had a good soak. I revived almost at once, and when I got back to my room found the 'hotty' already in my bed. Bliss!

When I woke up the following morning, I wondered for a moment where I was, but once I had got my bearings, I made myself ready for my first day at HMS Gannet.

The first thing I did when I got to the Sick Bay was to make myself known to the Chief SBA, CPO O'Connor. He was a jolly middle-aged man who introduced himself with a firm handshake. He told me in a broad Irish accent that the NV Tester, Joanna Hampton, had gone home to look after her mother, as her brother had recently been killed. 'We were all very upset for her as you can imagine,' he said solemnly, and then added, 'You'll find everything, just as she left it and in working order, unless a few spiders have climbed into the machine!'

Although the office was rather dusty, nothing seemed to be missing, but when I checked the testing room, it was very cold and damp, so I thought I would ask the Chief for an electric fire. I then wondered if the NVT unit at HMS Shrike would be in similar working order and decided to ask the Chief if he could check for me. I then introduced myself to the Wren writers in their office, and just as I was about to leave, a good looking young doctor came to see if he could borrow some ink, so I asked him if he knew whether the Senior Surgeon Commander was free, as I wanted to introduce myself to him.

'You will have to introduce yourself to me first!' the doctor teased.

'I'm Leading Wren Mary Ogilvie,' I replied.

'I'm Dr Timothy Flaver, in charge of your unit,' he said. 'How on earth do you intend running two NVT units, and be in two different places, at once?'

'It might be as simple as two weeks here and two weeks there,' I explained, 'but it rather depends on how many pilots still require tests. I will work out a plan and get back to you as soon as I have one, Sir.'

'That's fine,' he said, 'come back to me if you need any help.'

I soon discovered that HMS Gannet's main task was to support the training fighter pilots, and there were quite a lot of them, so I was kept busy doing tests for the rest of the week.

On Saturday morning, I decided to get my bicycle out of the shed and look for a shortcut to the airbase. I asked Mrs Donaghue if there was a track where I could ride my bike through the woods. She thought for a moment and then said, 'Go to the bend in the road, where the Navy lorries have to go slowly due to it being so dangerous, and then look out for the big chestnut tree to the right of the road, then get off your bike in case you get yourself killed by an oncoming car, cross over the road, go down a path covered in grass, or mud if its rained the night before, until you see some blackberry bushes tumbling out over the path, and then go left and look for a stile and keep going until you see a white-washed cottage, where my friend Mrs Finnegan and her man live with their many children; you'll know it's them as they are the ones not at school, and the young ones pretend to be leprechauns!' She then took a breath before continuing, 'After that you go on to the normal tar, you'll soon arrive at the aeroplane gates.'

Five minutes later, I set off on my first Northern Ireland adventure, with Mrs Donaghue's rather odd instructions still swimming in my head. I thought that I could always turn back and use the road, if I got completely lost.

I found my way to the bend in the road easily and then, as instructed, got off my bike when I saw the big chestnut tree, just as she had described. I pushed my bicycle for a while along a muddy lane, and it wasn't long before the mud turned into a stony track, so I was then able to get back on my bike until I reached the stile, which thankfully had a gap to squeeze the bike through. I continued my journey for a few more minutes and then, just as Mrs Donaghue had said, I heard children laughing and shouting just ahead of me. A moment later, I saw a whitewashed cottage with a thatched roof, which looked in need of repair.

I then found myself surrounded by several bare-footed children wearing clean but well-worn clothes. I had never seen children as poor as this before and had to admit that I felt rather shocked. They ranged in age from about two to twelve. I wondered why the two older children weren't at school, but soon discovered why. They both had colds.

The children stood silently staring at me, so I got off my bike and smiling cheerfully at them. I said, 'Hello, I'm Mary!'

Their reaction was not what I had expected at all. Instead of saying hello back, they all crossed themselves and ran towards the house calling out, 'Mammy, the Virgin is here!'

The front door suddenly opened and a woman appeared, holding a mop in one hand and a pail in the other. After staring at me for a moment, she pointed to my head, and said, 'It'll be your hair with the sun shining through it, to be sure, looks like a bloody halo it does, and my Brian said you'd told him your name was Mary,' and then she laughed, as she added, 'and the only Mary we know is the blessed Virgin herself, so I hope you haven't come to chastise us?'

I laughed with her and then explained that I was a Wren, staying at Swallow Cottage and that I was looking for a shortcut to get to HMS Gannet.

The woman said her name was Donna Finnegan and asked me to come inside, so I rested my bike against a nearby tree and followed her into the cottage. I could see that the floor had been recently scrubbed, so I took off my muddy shoes and left them by the door. One of the younger children handed me a pair of slippers and then took me by my hand and led me towards a huge old-fashioned kitchen range. Donna told me to sit down and make myself comfortable. As I looked up at the ceiling, I saw that there was no bulb and realised that the house probably had no electricity and that the family had to use paraffin lamps and candles when it was dark. I felt as though I had suddenly been transported back in time a hundred years.

Donna then went through a door at the back of the room where I could hear her pumping water to refill the kettle. When she came back she was carrying a round loaf of bread, which looked more like a huge scone, a dish of butter and a jar of honey.

When she asked one of the older boys to get some logs for the fire, I presumed that all the children were given daily chores to do to help their mother.

I asked the younger children if they had any toys, and they scampered off in different directions, before running back to show me what they had. There was a box of hand-carved farm animals, a wooden train set and some wooden dolls dressed in knitted clothes. I then asked one of the older children if she had any colouring chalks or a paint box, but she just shook her head sadly. I will have to do something about this, when I have time to do some shopping, I thought.

The buttered soda bread and honey was delicious, but the tea was so strong it made my eyes water. As we ate, I asked Donna if there was a school nearby for the younger children, she said that there was but it was 'too far past the tar for them to walk.' She then told me that her older children were at school and doing quite well with their reading and writing, but that they still fell behind the other children in their class, because whenever they were offered work on the farm they took it, as the family needed the money.

Donna told me that her husband, Declan, was a carpenter and thankfully he had been very busy ever since the war had started, putting in cupboards and shelves at the married naval officers' homes, and that he had also been helping out at the American base nearby, but there it was, 'All passes and 'keep-your-mouth-shut'!'

Before leaving, I then asked her where the barrel of tar was. She looked blankly at me, so I explained that Mrs Donaghue had told me that I had to go to the tar before going on to the airbase. Donna chuckled and said, 'Oh you mean the tarmac road! We locals call it the tar.'

After saying goodbye, the two elder children guided me to the tarmac road and from there I found my way to the airbase. I then decided to spend the next hour exploring some of the local villages. I noticed several pubs, but didn't like to go into one on my own, so ate my sandwiches sitting on a wall, before heading back to my billet.

Once I was back at Swallow cottage, I decided to have a shower and wash my hair before changing into my uniform and getting the evening transport to Gannet for supper. I was happy to discover that there was a film on that night, but it was a love story and it made me miss Duncan so much that I cried all the way through it. I still felt upset when I got back to my room later that night, and spent a sleepless night worrying about what he might be doing on his 'op'. I just prayed that wherever he was, he would be safe.

I had to do three NV tests a day for the next four days the following week. It was exhausting but I managed to get them all done. As the next squadron wouldn't be flying in until the weekend, I asked if I could take the Friday off to go shopping in Londonderry. When I got permission, I was told that the locals preferred to call it Derry.

I was delighted to discover that the Derry shops were full of things that were no longer available in England. I bought some wool, so that I could knit a few things to give as Christmas presents, and I also bought some drawing books and crayons to give to the Finnegan children. I then wandered into a grocer's shop hoping to find some treats to send home. The grocer's wife must have noticed me looking at everything, as she asked me if she could help. I told her about the shortages on the mainland and she beckoned me to follow her to a room at the back of the shop. She then smiled and said, 'Now tell me what you need.'

'Everything, from tea, sugar, tins of meat or salmon, and anything else you can spare,' I said.

Just before I left the shop, the woman suggested that if I brought some cardboard boxes with me, like the ones that the pilots threw away after buying their flying boots, she would put the supplies in them and send them to my mother for me.

I rang my mother that evening to tell her what I was planning to do and she was delighted but warned, 'It might be a better if you pay cash each time, darling, not a cheque—just in case and Oh, the next time you go to Derry, do try and find out if there is one of those lovely Irish linen stores there. Perhaps you could do the same thing with them and arrange for sheets and pillowcases to be sent to me? I will put some extra money into your account to cover the costs.'

As it was now much colder than when I had first arrived, I decided to go to the Stores at lunchtime to get myself a heavyweight overcoat. I also bought a skirt that was one size larger than I usually wore, as I seemed to have been putting on weight recently.

The next time that I went past the Finnegan's house on the way to work, I stopped off to see Donna and gave the children the drawing books, crayons and the box of paints that I had bought in Derry. When I gave the oldest boy, a couple of model aeroplane kits, I was rewarded with the biggest smile I'd ever seen.

The evening before I was due to leave for HMS Shrike, I rang my mother and she sounded over the moon, as my first 'food parcel' had just arrived. Before going to bed, I took a look at myself in the mirror and noticed that I was putting on even more weight, so decided to put myself on a diet.

The next morning, much to my surprise, Lieutenant Commander Mansfield from the transport office was standing outside my billet and told me that he was there to make sure that I got to to HMS Shrike without any problems. After checking that my bicycle and bags were stored safely in the back of the van, he told me to climb up beside the driver and as we drove off, instead of returning my salute, he blew me a kiss.

On the way to HMS Shrike, the driver told me that many of the FAA squadrons were based there when they weren't on board their carriers, and that that there was also an anti submarine tactical school there, so it looked like I would be kept pretty busy.

When we arrived, the driver kindly carried my suitcase to the billeting office door, and then after propping my bicycle against a tree, he smiled and said, 'See you on the return trip!'

I took a deep breath before knocking on the office door, and thought to myself, Oh well, here we go again.

When I opened the door, I was relieved to see that the woman behind the desk was a Wren Officer and not a PO. At least I wouldn't be ticked-off for not having replaced my HMS Gannet hatband with an HMS Shrike one before I'd even had time to find the Stores.

'You are in Nissen hut B,' she said handing me a key and pointing to some buildings out of the window on her left. 'And you can leave your bicycle out of sight behind the hut.'

When I unlocked the door I immediately began to relax, as the hut felt more like a Wendy-house than a Nissen hut. It had pretty floral curtains in the windows with matching bedspreads on the four beds. I went to look for the ablutions block, which I found through a door at the back of the building. I couldn't help giggling to myself when I saw knickers and stockings drying on the water pipes and was delighted that this was allowed, as it would make life much easier. I had a quick wash and then went to put my cases under the bed before going to find the Wrens' mess.

As I opened the mess door, I saw a queue of girls waiting to be served. On the menu there was Irish stew with dumplings, followed by ginger sponge pudding. My diet would have to wait.

After a quick cup of coffee in the NAAFI, I got my bike and went to find the Sick Bay. When I got there, I asked a Wren writer where I could find the chief SBA. She looked at her watch and told me that he would be in his dispensary.

'Are you the new Tester?' she asked smiling, and when I nodded she pointed at another door and said, 'If you need anything our office is in there.'

I knocked on the dispensary door and was told to come in. When I entered I saw a rather jolly-looking man sipping a cup of tea. He smiled, and said 'Ah, you must be Leading Wren Ogilvie, welcome to Shrike!"

After telling me a little about the airbase, he then warned me about one of the Junior doctors called Fergal Kelly, who he thought was a very strange man, as he had a real 'thing' about cleanliness, 'Apparently he made the other Tester mop the corridor down after just one day's testing, complaining that the pilots' shoes had germs on them. He's also a Nosey Parker, Mary, so make sure you lock your filing cabinet and office door when you are not there.'

I thanked him for his advice and then went to find my new office. It was immediately obvious to me that Joanna did things in a different way to how I had been taught and I couldn't for the life of me work out her filing system, which wasn't alphabetical as I was used to. I also wondered why the bottom drawer of her desk was locked. I rattled it in case it was just stuck, and then nearly leapt out of my skin when I heard a man's voice say, 'Joanna hides the key under the typewriter!'

I looked up and saw two young men in white coats grinning at me.

'I'm Lieutenant Ingram, Geoff to my friends, and this is the junior doctor Sub Lieutenant James Nicholson also known as Doc Nick. I'm the clever one but he's better at playing rugger than me,' he chuckled.

We shook hands and then Geoff found the key to the drawer and opened it for me. Inside it there was an electric kettle, four mugs, some tea, a tin of Nescafe, a bag of sugar lumps and half a packet of biscuits. Mystery solved.

'Nick and I are usually offered a mug of tea at about three thirty,' Geoff grinned.

'Well, if I am not too busy catching up on tests I'll continue the tradition,' I assured them both, feeling pleased that I already had two new friends.

'I gather you are a married woman, which is very unfair on us vulnerable single men!' Nick said putting on a hangdog expression.

'It was a case of doing it now or not until after the war, so we chose now.' I told them, and then they left, promising to return for their tea later on.

The next thing I had to do was to report to Senior Surgeon Commander Lockhurst. When I found him, he obviously had no idea who I was, so I quickly introduced myself. He then nodded slowly and said, 'Oh, of course! You're the new Tester replacing that other poor girl whose brother has just been killed.'

I explained that I had just done three weeks at HMS Gannet, which was my main base, and would now do two at Shrike, and this would be the routine from now on depending on which squadrons were in and needed testing first. Before leaving his office I asked his permission to contact Commander Flying direct to organise the tests, as that would save time and mean that he wouldn't have to do it himself. He told me to do whatever I thought was best.

When I got back to my office, I saw a naval officer poking about in one of the stationery cupboards. I presumed it must be the 'Nosey Parker' doctor and wished that I had locked the door.

'The room is dusty, and the sill is disgusting,' the man snapped.

Ignoring his bad temper I put on my 'Lady Mary' voice and said, 'Yes, I quite agree!'

My reply made him stop in his tracks, so I continued while I still had the advantage, 'I do appreciate that our unit is in a Sick Bay and therefore needs to be spotlessly clean, so I will see to it before I leave this evening.' The surprised look on his face was so comical that I had to bite my lip to stop myself laughing.

'Yes well, see to it then,' was all he could say before he stalked out of the office. He hadn't bothered to ask who I was, or introduced himself, but it wasn't really necessary, as it was obvious that had just had my first encounter with Dr Fergal Kelly.

The day went by quickly as I had so much to organise and was just about to start cleaning up the office when Geoff and Doc Nick turned up for a cup of tea.

'Oh my goodness, is it three thirty already?' I asked them.

'Yes Mary, have you had time to bake a cake for us?' Doc Nick joked.

'Ha, ha! Very funny, I have hardly had time to sit down today,' I replied.

It was well past five before I was satisfied that there were no spiders still hiding behind the lamp for 'Nosey Parker Fergal' to find. I locked the office and then went back to my hut. I put my rug on my bed, Duncan's photo on my locker and my alarm clock and torch next to it, and then I went to have supper.

After some pre-war quality bangers and mash, I went to the shop inside the NAAFI and bought some writing paper and a few postcards. I then found a telephone and rang both sets of parents. Still no news from Duncan, much to my disappointment, but Father John repeated his mantra 'no news is good news,' and told me to keep writing to Duncan anyway. When I spoke to my mother, she told me that they had received a letter from my brother, Peter, who had said that he looked very thin but was alive and well, which was wonderful news.

Later that evening, I was just about to put my hot-water bottle into my bed when my three roommates turned up. I liked them at once. One of them asked me who the handsome man in my photograph was, but just as she was admiring the picture, the lights went out. At first I thought the lights must have fused, but then I remembered that I was in a Nissen hut, so the lights went off automatically at the same time every night.

The next morning I went into the mess for breakfast and could smell kippers, which made my tummy heave. I hoped that I wasn't about to go down with something, as that was the second time I'd felt sick since arriving at Shrike.

When I got to my office, I was surprised to find the Commander Flying waiting there for me. He said that he would be more than happy for me to organise his pilots' tests with him direct.

After the afternoon tests were finished I went back to my office and found 'Nosey Parker Kelly' rummaging through my desk drawer. I was livid and wondered how on earth he had got in, as I had locked the door before I left. To calm myself, I took a deep breath and said, 'Can I help you, Sir?' He looked a bit taken aback and said that he needed some paper clips, so I suggested that he try the Writers' office, as I didn't use them. After he left, I went straight to Chief Gentry and asked him if he would change the locks to my office.

The next day the Chief gave me a new key, and then showed me where the SBAs normally kept the spare key, which was in a cupboard marked 'Arsenic'!

As there were no re-tests that Saturday, I decided to go into Derry to look for The Irish Linen Store. When I eventually found it, the manager, Mr Patrick, showed me some of the various qualities of bed linen he stocked. He told me that it was widely acknowledged to be the finest in the world. After I told him what my mother was after, he told me to leave it to him and that he would post her a list of all their stock, so that she could order anything she wanted direct with him and that he would make sure she got it before Christmas.

When it was time to go back to HMS Gannet, I was relieved that a van was sent to take me rather than a lorry, as I was a bit worried that the petrol fumes would make me feel sick. For some strange reason, any unpleasant smells were now making me feel queasy. I decided that when I had more time I would go and see the Wrens' doctor for a check-up. Perhaps I was in need of some iron pills again, I thought.

'Welcome back! Everyone has missed you!' Chief SBA O'Connor said when I got back to my Gannet office, and then he handed me a note from Commander Flying, which read, 'Leading Wren Ogilvie, this is an SOS! Several squadrons will be flying in and out of HMS Gannet until the week before Christmas. You will need to do 'at least' four tests a day to make sure everyone is tested before they go out on 'ops'. Ring me as soon as you arrive back.'

I rang Commander Flying straight away and told him that I would be happy to forego my weekends if necessary, to ensure that all the pilots were tested. He was very grateful and said that he would make sure I had extra time off once the tests were completed.

After supper that evening I rang Duncan's father for a chat and told him that I hadn't received any news from his son yet. He then said, 'We haven't either, Mary but remember no news.'

'Is good news. Yes I know,' I said trying to sound cheerful, but I missed Duncan so much that I wanted to cry, so kept the rest of the call as short as possible without being rude.

When I was back in my comfortable bedroom at Swallow Cottage, I began to wrap up the Christmas presents I'd bought for my family in Derry, and then started to knit my father a pair of socks. I was just about to prepare for bed when there was a knock on my door and Eliza came into my room holding a pile of letters that were held together with an elastic band.

'These came for you last week, Mary, but I didn't dare send them on to you at Shrike, in case you got back here, before they got there, if you see what I mean.' With my hands now shaking like a leaf, I pulled the elastic band off and looked for anything that Duncan might have sent. Amongst the envelopes I saw not just one, but two letters from him, and immediately burst into tears, much to Eliza's concern.

'Whatever's wrong Mary?' she asked.

'I'm so happy!' I wailed, 'I haven't heard from my husband, since I've been in Ireland and these two are from him.' Eliza said she would give me some privacy and after she had left the room I starting reading his letters.

Duncan's first letter was full of love, telling me how much he missed me, that he would be finishing what he was doing fairly soon, and then he would be sent to a shore base somewhere to train to become a Commander Flying. He then added, 'I'll be able to see you quite often while I am training, as I'll not be going on any other 'ops' until spring!' I was overjoyed and proud of him for getting another promotion.

The second letter must have been written first, because it had a very different tone. He sounded rather tired and miserable, saying that he never wanted to catch fish again, was fed up with the rain and cold winds, and that he missed me so much that he couldn't sleep. 'Oh, Mary,' he wrote 'I'd give a year of my life for a squeaky bed with you beside me.' I wasn't sure whether to laugh or cry, so I did both.

Taking four tests in a row on the first day wasn't too bad, but by the end of the week, I was well behind with the reports. However, on the Saturday afternoon, I felt that I should get some fresh air and sunshine, so decided to cycle through the woods to visit the Finnegans. The children gave me some very colourful paintings they had done, which I loved and promised that I would put them up on the wall in my bedroom, as soon as I got back to the cottage.

The following week I worked until I dropped, missing lunch most days to get the reports done, so that I would have time to go to Derry one last time before Christmas to do some shopping, as I wanted to buy a few more things for my family, my roommates, and for Donna and her children.

I was given the Monday off, which gave me time to post my parents presents to them and then ride my bike to the Finnegan's house. When I got there, I told them that I had to give them their presents now, as I would be at HMS Shrike on Christmas Day.

Luckily, the presents from my family had already arrived, so I would be able to take them with me. I thought that my day bag would be perfect for me to put my presents in to take to Shrike, so I emptied out the contents on my bed to make room for them. Suddenly my eye caught sight of a small package lying on my bed, and I gasped, when I realised what it was. I had used some wedding present paper to wrap up two sanitary towels, just in case my period was early, but as I hadn't had a period since leaving England, I had forgotten they were there. It was only now that I remembered to check my diary, as I usually recorded my due dates, but had obviously forgotten to do it since arriving in Ireland. Surely, I must be due about now, I thought, and then wondered whether working so much in the dark and being a bit anaemic might be what had made me late this month.

I went to see the Wren doctor the next day, and she said that she could see from my records that I'd recently been married, and then asked, 'Did you always take precautions?'

'Oh yes, 'my husband insisted, as we wouldn't be able to afford children in wartime,' I told her honestly.

The doctor told me to roll my sleeve up, as she wanted to take a blood sample to do some tests. She then pulled down my bottom eyelids to peer into my eyes. 'I'll give you a chit for some iron pills, which should help, and then come and see me again in a week's time, as I'll have your test results by then.' I told her that I'd be at HMS Shrike until the first week in January, so I wouldn't be able to see her until then.

When I got to Shrike, I was told that I'd be in Hut 10 this time, sharing with two other girls. As one of the beds looked as if it had been recently made up, I presumed it was mine, and I shoved the case with my civilian clothes in it underneath the bed and then unpacked everything else. I then went to the NVT office to fill out some reports, but as I tried to write, I kept thinking about Duncan and how I wished we could be together for our first Christmas as a married couple, which made me start to cry.

Suddenly 'Nosey Parker Kelly' came in without knocking, demanding the key to the filing cabinet. I quickly wiped away a tear and handed him the key.

He must have realised that I was upset, as he suddenly changed his tone and asked, 'Do you ever get homesick?'

'Only a bit, Sir, but I do miss my husband terribly,' I replied.

'Is he on ops?' Fergal Kelly asked me. I nodded. Before he left, he reminded me to lock the cabinet and from that day on he always knocked before coming in.

On Christmas Eve, I rang my mother, who told me that Mr Patrick had kept his word and sent the Irish linen to her, which she was thrilled about. I then spoke to my father who said that the house would seem quiet without me this year but that they were all going to Jane's family on Boxing Day, which they were looking forward to. I then rang Duncan's parents, who were obviously missing their son as much as I was. I let them know that I had recently received two letters from Duncan and that they were the best Christmas present I could have.

There was no need for an alarm clock on Christmas morning, as it was so cold that all three of us were wide-awake by six. I suggested that we might as well open our presents as we were up, so after putting on our dressing gowns and placing blankets around our shoulders to keep warm, we began opening our presents. I had wrapped their presents in several layers of paper, like a pass the parcel game, and when they discovered that I had only bought them a lipstick each, they shrieked with laughter like small children, rather than two grown-up women. They had clubbed together and bought me a packet of Players, which I said I would save for later, but the truth was that I hadn't felt like having a cigarette for the last two months, as they made me feel a bit sick. As it was still so early, we decided to take turns to have a lovely hot shower and wash yesterday's smalls. When it was my time to shower, I inspected my breasts, as they had been feeling a bit sore lately, and let out a gasp when I saw that my nipples now looked more like blackberries than raspberries. I wondered whether I could be going down with mumps.

The whole compliment of the airbase attended a special Christmas service in the big hanger that morning, and when it was over my roommates and I made our way back to the hut to tidy up before going to lunch. When we were halfway there, I heard my name being called out over the public address system, 'Leading Wren Ogilvie to report to the First Officer's office at the double.'

I immediately went cold with fear, thinking that something terrible must have happened to Duncan.

When I got to the office, the First Officer told me to sit down. 'Leading Wren Ogilvie, I'm sorry to delay your Christmas lunch, but I'm afraid there is a change of plan and you are needed back at HMS Gannet tomorrow afternoon between fourteen hundred and sixteen hundred hours, as Commander O'Brian has three American VIPs that he wants you to test for night vision flying.'

I was so relieved that it wasn't bad news that I just grinned, and said, 'I don't mind going at all, Ma'am.'

'That's very public spirited of you Leading Wren Ogilvie, thank you.' She then picked up the phone and put me straight through to Commander O'Brian. When I heard his voice booming down the phone I could tell that he'd been at the Christmas pudding brandy bottle already. 'Thank goodness they've found you old girl! The thing is that we have these three American VIPs with us and we are at a loss as to what to do with them on Boxing Day afternoon. None of them play golf, it seems, so it was suggested that we offer them an interesting couple of hours in the NV Testing room, so we need you here you see?'

'Yes, of course Sir, I'll see if I can organise transport to get there after lunch,' I told him.

'No need to do that, its all been sorted. A car will pick you up at twelve hundred hours. Thanks for being a sport. Must fly now, the turkey is ready to be carved. Happy Christmas!' he said, and hung up before I could say the same to him.

'You are very friendly with the Commander by the sound of it,' the First Officer said, suppressing a smile.

'Well, Ma'am, we do speak most days, organising tests for his pilots.' I then leant forward and said as quietly as I could, 'I think he might have had a bit of Christmas Cheer Ma'am, as he doesn't usually call me 'old girl'.'

The First Officer burst out laughing, 'Well go and eat your own Christmas lunch now, Leading Wren, and enjoy the rest of the day.'

I ran to the Wrens' mess, thinking that I might be too late to get a seat, but as I entered, I saw one of my roommates waving at me, gesturing that she had kept a chair for me. The food was even better than the previous Christmas, so I conveniently forgot that I was supposed to be on a diet and ate everything in sight, including a marvellous tasting Christmas pudding, that I thought must have had a bottle of old stout added to the mixture, if the wonderful aroma that permeated the entire mess was anything to go by.

That evening the officers put on a hilarious Pantomime, and to my complete surprise Fergal Kelly was a natural comic. He was playing Cinderella, so his obsession with sweeping floors was put to good use!

To my utter amazement, at exactly twelve hundred hours on Boxing Day, an Officer's car came to collect me. The driver told me that he had been sent from HMS Gannet by special order of Commander O'Brian, who had insisted that I travel in comfort, as I was doing him a favour.

'The Commander asked me to tell you that one good turn deserves another,' the driver said, and then asked me if I would mind telling him what was meant by that, so I explained how I had been asked to give night vision tests to some American VIP's and, as I was working on my day off, the Commander must have been grateful that I had agreed to work today.

'Oh, I see, of course, we thought – never mind.'

I decided not to ask the driver who 'we' were or what they had thought, but knowing how men's minds worked, I suspected 'they' had thought something naughty was going on between the Commander and me.

When we arrived at HMS Gannet, I was surprised to see Commander O'Brian waiting for me. He put his arm around my shoulder and gave me a hug. 'You're a marvel, Mary. I just wanted to say a personal thank you for coming to my rescue. I will go and find our American friends and bring them to you at fourteen hundred hours. Try to keep them busy for as long as you can, as I'm hoping to get at least half a round of golf in before having to collect them!'

When I went into the NVT office, I wondered whether I should take down all the Christmas cards, but then decided against it and went to the testing room to switch on a heater instead, thinking that the Americans might feel the cold. I then sat quietly and waited for my VIPs to arrive.

At fourteen hundred hours there was no sign of them, but half an hour later a long and extremely shiny car finally pulled up in the front of the Sick Bay. After two and a half years in the Wrens I felt pretty confident that I knew which rank was which on all the service uniforms, but when the three Americans came into my office, I hadn't a clue what rank any of them were. I'd never seen so much gold braid, brass and silver buttons and medals in my life, so I wasn't sure whether to shake hands, salute or curtsy! In the end, there wasn't time to do anything, because after the Commander had quickly introduced me to them, he disappeared and left us to it.

I felt very nervous standing in front of these three distinguished gentlemen and wasn't quite sure what to say. There was a moment's silence and then the officer wearing Air Force uniform looked at my Christmas cards and said, 'My, this is a bright and cheerful room, Ma'am; we display our cards like this at home too.'

It suddenly occurred to me that they must be feeling homesick and missing their families like everyone else, which made me feel far less nervous in their company.

'I'd like to see your filing cabinet and see if your system is the same as ours, if that's possible,' the Naval Officer asked while removing his hat and placing it on top of the cabinet. Seeing the senior officer take off his hat, the other two men took theirs off too.

'Of course, Sir,' I said, opening the filing cabinet for him, but as I did so, I realised that I'd forgotten that my chocolate biscuits were in the bottom drawer filed under Z. When he saw them he grinned at me, and said, 'As I thought, just the same system as me!'

He then asked me if I had to hide them in there because the SBAs pinched them, so I told him, 'No, they are no problem, it's the naughty doctors that pinch them!'

They all laughed, and now the ice was completely broken, so I asked them to follow me down the corridor to the testing room.

'That typewriter of yours is rather out of date, Ma'am,' the Army Officer remarked as he opened the door for me.

'Everything is over here,' I replied truthfully.

I turned off the light and while their eyes were adapting to the pitch-dark room I explained to them the different ways their eyes reacted in the dark. I then handed them their boards, which I had already shown them how to use in the office.

'How did you work out the correct distance from the machine to the chair?' the Army Officer asked me.

I had no idea, so I lied and simply said, 'It took us several trials to get it right, Sir.'

All three VIPs must have been about fifty years old, but they made the same silly schoolboy remarks that the pilots and navigators, who were half their age, always did when they sat in the dark. I also noticed that they used similar swear words when losing their place on the boards!

Once the test was over I switched on the dim light first, so as not to blind them, and then unclipped their collars.

'How did we do?' the Air Force Officer asked.

'I'll tell you once we are back in the office, Sir,' I said.

When we were in my office, the Navy Officer asked, 'Could we possibly have a cup of your English tea?'

While the kettle boiled I checked the tests. Two of them had failed, but the Army Officer had passed his test with the highest marks I had ever seen. I decided to wait until each of them had a mug of tea in their hands and were enjoying all my chocolate biscuits before telling them their results.

'I do like English cookies,' the Air Force officer said, dipping a biscuit into his tea.

'I hope you don't mind my asking,' I said as politely as I could, 'but did you all have alcoholic drinks with your lunch?'

'Why, naturally,' the Air Force Officer replied with a mouthful of soggy biscuit. 'It is Christmas after all.'

'I drank some gin at the Captain's house before lunch and also some wine at lunchtime in the Officer's mess,' the Navy Officer confessed.

'I didn't have any,' the Army Officer said. 'I've been teetotal since the war began.'

When I told them their results, the Air Force and Navy Officers looked a bit worried, so I explained that we had discovered that the results were always better for the pilots who hadn't had any spirits for at least twenty-four hours before doing their night vision tests. And then in an attempt to create a slightly lighter atmosphere, I decided to tell them a funny story that one of the young pilots had told me at Shrike the week before. They all laughed so loudly that one of the SBAs came running down the corridor to see what was going on. When Commander O'Brian came to collect his VIPs, they were still laughing, sitting with their feet up on my desk, drinking mugs of tea and eating the last of my biscuits. The Commander was so happy to see that his guests were in such fine spirits that he slapped me on the back so hard that I nearly fell off my chair.

'Sorry old girl! Damn fine job! Well done,' Commander O'Brian said and then took his three VIPs away to a car that was waiting for them.

One of the junior SBAs kindly helped me wash the mugs and then after making sure that everything was turned off, I shut up shop. Just as I was locking the door, I remembered that Mrs Donaghue had told me that she was going away for a few days over Christmas, so she would lock my room up while she was away. I had completely forgotten. I now had nowhere to sleep that night, unless I could get a lift back to Shrike but that seemed unlikely at this time of night.

As I walked towards the NAAFI, I spotted a Wren Officer passing near the Entertainments hut, so I told her my problem and she told me that she was catching up with the Third Officer Billeting later that evening. So not to worry, she would find me a bed somewhere. Then I heard someone behind me call my name.

'Mary, what the hell are you doing here?'

I looked behind me and saw a group of girls walking arm in arm towards the entertainment hut where a film was being shown that night. It was my friends, Hannah and Eliza, from Swallow Cottage. They invited me to join them, so I went with them and just hoped it wasn't another love story.

When the film was over, and we went outside to get some fresh air, the Third Officer Billeting came up to me and said, 'I thought I'd find you here! I'm sorry we didn't organise a bed for you before. Commander O'Brian ticked me off at dinner and told me to put you in comfortable quarters, but it's too late to do that now, so unfortunately I have had to put you in a Nissen hut. You'll find a bed made up for you in Hut 16, which is near the wooded area; just ask one of the other Wrens.'

I was so tired that I would have willingly slept on the hanger floor.

The following morning I returned to Shrike in the same comfortable Officer's car, and as we arrived at HMS Shrike, I thought what a crazy couple of days it had been and that I'd never forget the year that I had Christmas in two places at once.

When I got to the NV Testing office, I was surprised to see a note placed on my typewriter. It said that I was to report to the Sick Bay as soon as I possible. They must have some more iron pills for me, I thought gratefully but I was wrong. When I spoke to the nurse, she told me that I had to have an examination right now. 'So you'll have to strip down to your knickers Leading Wren, and then put on a gown and wait until you're called.'

The last time I'd been told to do this was when I'd first joined the Wrens, so I wondered why I had to go through this rather undignified examination again. However, I had no choice but to do as I was told, and hoped it wouldn't take too long. I was lucky and after a few minutes I was called to the Wrens' doctor's room.

'I understand that you had a blood and urine test recently at HMS Gannet?' she asked, looking at a report on the desk in front of her. 'They have requested that I give you a full examination at once,' she said, looking up at me for the first time. 'Please go and lie down on the couch behind the curtain and call me when you have done so.'

I went behind the curtain, got up on the couch and then called the doctor.

'This won't hurt, I promise,' she said kindly, 'now please open your legs.' I did as she asked and opened my legs, but when I felt her hands push my legs open wider and realised that she was putting her fingers near my private parts, I snapped them shut, before she had time to do what I thought she was about to do, and held her arm in a vice-like grip. She just smiled and asked me if I had still been a virgin when I had got married.

'Of course,' I replied somewhat indignantly.

'I thought so,' she said. 'Now, just relax, dear, I have to do this, but I will be as gentle as I can.'

I tried to relax as she examined my lower regions, and think about something else, and fortunately it was all over quite quickly and then she told me to get up and get dressed.

'Now, Leading Wren, how long has it been since you had your last period?' she asked, with a pen poised ready to write down my answers. I told her that I had been so busy since I had been in Ireland that I hadn't even thought to check.

'Do you remember the date of your last period, before your wedding?' she then wanted to know, so I told her that that was an easy date to remember, as I had been thankful it was over before the big day. She then asked if I had experienced any giddy attacks or felt sick recently.

'Oh yes, actually both! But I expect it's probably the yummy food here and the long hours I have been doing at work, sitting in a dark room every day,' I explained.

'Have you noticed your body changing shape recently?' she said looking at me intently.

'Yes, I have worse luck! My waistline is no longer eighteen inches, it's more like twenty-four now,' I giggled, 'so I've put myself on a very strict diet,' I assured her.

'Did you use birth control methods on your honeymoon?'

I blushed scarlet, and the doctor must have realised that I was embarrassed as she said kindly, 'This is important dear. I'm not being inquisitive, I need to know.'

'Yes, we did,' I replied, blushing again, 'well except for once – when I caught my first salmon!'

She looked at me in disbelief. 'Salmon? I'm sorry you will have to explain that one to me!' So I told her all about our day fishing for salmon, and how it had ended up as a spontaneous lovemaking session. I could see that she was trying to suppress a smile, but when I then told her that I had sat in the freezing cold river after we'd 'well, you know what', as my husband had thought that would do the trick, she could contain herself no longer and laughed out loud.

'Well, Leading Wren, I'm afraid it didn't do the trick,' she said grinning from ear to ear. 'I am delighted to inform you that you are three months pregnant!'

I felt icy cold and then everything went blank. The next thing I remember was seeing several strange faces looking down at me, and a voice saying, 'It's the shock.' Another voice told me to sniff, so I did. It must have been a bottle of smelling salts, as it felt as if my nose was being burnt off, so I pushed whatever it was away.

Remembering what the doctor had just told me, as she helped me to my feet, I whimpered, 'I can't be pregnant now. It's war time and I'm too busy working, and anyway, we were going to wait until after the war to have babies.'

'I'm sorry, dear, but I'm afraid it's too late now, you'll have to go back to being a civilian as the Wrens don't keep pregnant girls on their lists,' she said, 'but there isn't time to discharge you from the Wrens until after the New Year is over, so just have a happy break and don't lift anything heavy.'

I quickly left the Wrens Sick Bay, went straight to my hut and then, thinking that Duncan would be cross with me, cried my eyes out.

That evening, I rang home to tell my parents that I was pregnant.

'That's wonderful news, darling!' my mother said. When I told her that this 'wonderful news' would mean that I would no longer be allowed to be a Wren, she calmly said, 'You've done your bit for the war, Mary, and I think the Royal Navy can most probably survive without you now, so when you are ready to come home, do so and we'll be waiting for you.'

I then heard my father, who must have been standing right next to her, say, 'Well for starters, my dear, we'd better let Duncan know!' He then told me that he still had friends in the Admiralty, so he would see to it that Duncan was contacted without breeching security, as it would take far too long for him to get the good news by post.

I was just about to ask him not to contact Duncan's family until Duncan had been informed, when my father suddenly burst out laughing.

'What's so funny?' I asked.

Still chuckling, he replied, 'I've just realised that your mother will be a Grandmother. She's not going to like being called a Granny at all!'

I then heard my mother laugh, and say, 'Don't you worry about me, Grandpa, you silly old fool!'

I was relieved that my parents were so happy for me, but didn't think that Daddy-T would be quite as pleased when he heard my news, as it would mean that he would now have to train another NV Tester to take my place. I carefully composed a letter to him later that evening, apologising for the inconvenience, and assuring him that we hadn't planned on getting pregnant until after the war. I hardly slept at all that night, as I felt that I had let him down badly and just prayed that Joanna would feel ready to resume her duties as soon as possible.

The New Year's Eve party was not much fun for me, as I was now not drinking or smoking and didn't really feel like doing much at all. However, it did give me the opportunity to say goodbye to the friends that I had made during my posting in Ireland.

Two days later, Daddy-T rang me to say that he wasn't in the least bit cross. 'Your condition isn't completely uncommon or unexpected after a honeymoon you know!' he chuckled. He then said that he'd been in touch with Joanna, who had told him that she felt ready to come back, and would replace me in a week's time. He then said that he was being posted to the Far East. This news came as a complete shock and the thought of not seeing dear Daddy-T again made me feel very sad.

Two days later a dense fog covered the base, and by lunchtime all flying had been cancelled, so I decided to write a letter to Joanna. Just as I finished writing it, I suddenly sensed that there was someone else in the room with me and wondered for a split second if it was Fergal Kelly checking up on me, but when I looked up I nearly died of fright. Standing right in front of me was Duncan's ghost!

'Happy New Year, my darling girl!' the ghost said, smiling at me.

I didn't know whether to laugh, cry or scold him for frightening me out of my wits, so I just ran up to Duncan and put my arms around him.

'I'm sorry, but I can't stay for long, my darling. The damn fog was so thick that I couldn't see the runway and I seem to have landed on one of the perimeter walls,' Duncan said casually before adding, 'so I'd better retrieve my plane before I get in trouble.' He then said how thrilled he was that 'we' were pregnant, and told me to meet him outside the Wrens' NAAFI at eight o'clock that evening to have a proper reunion. Then he was gone.

I was so overcome with relief that Duncan was alive and here with me, that I kept bursting into tears every few minutes for the next hour. When we met up again that evening, he told me that as soon as he had heard that he was going to be a father, he had become so excited that he'd flown his plane straight here from the Isle of Man, where his squadron was now based. Obviously, he shouldn't have come here without permission, so he would most probably get into trouble, especially as he had damaged his plane, which he added, was still parked on the wall!

I was horrified, but Duncan just smiled and told me that it would all work out fine, as the Station Commander was a 'very understanding man' and had told him that he would see to his plane first thing in the morning, so that he could get back to the Isle of Man before he was missed.

'Don't worry, darling,' he said laughing, 'I'll do my best not to get chucked out of the Navy!' We spent another hour together before I kissed him goodbye, wondering when I would get to see him again.

It wasn't until the next day that I realised we hadn't talked about what he'd been doing since I had last seen him. Perhaps he didn't want to talk about it, or was worried that it would upset me, especially in my current condition. He'll tell me if and when he wants to, I thought before heading back to my billet.

A week later, Joanna came back to work and told me how grateful she was that I had filled in for her while she had been away. I liked her so much, that I was sorry that we hadn't had the chance to work together, as I think we would have got on famously.

After handing over my duties to Joanna, I went to see the First Officer who told me that it was time for me to go home and that I would be contacted by the Admiralty about my discharge from the Wrens in due course.

After saying my final goodbyes to everyone in Ireland, I then made the long trip back to Woking, where I spent a whole week with my parents being thoroughly spoilt, and when it was time to go to London to be officially dismissed, my father came with me.

When we got back to Woking that night, I looked at myself in the bathroom mirror and said, 'Goodbye Leading Wren Ogilvie, Hello Mrs Ogilvie!'

CHAPTER 18

1945

The first thing I thought of, as I got off the ferry in Douglas, was that the Isle of Man was much colder than it had been in Ireland, so after Duncan had collected me and we were driving to Ramsey, which was the nearest town to RAF Andreas, where he was now training to be a Commander Flying, I asked him if he had found us somewhere warm to live, but all he said was, 'Let's just say that it's – err – a bit different!'

'I don't like the sound of that!' I said, rubbing my hands to keep warm.

'Don't worry darling,' he grinned, 'I promise it's not an internment camp, and I think you will approve of our new home once you have seen it!'

My father had told me about the internment camps before I left home. Apparently there were a number of them on the island, where refugees from the Nazis plus a number of Italians, Finns and even some Japanese would be interned until the war was over.

'Oh, and I've bought myself a second-hand bike to get to and from the airfield, so we can go for bike rides together and explore the countryside,' Duncan said, changing the subject.

'Do pregnant women ride bicycles?' I asked.

'Of course!' he replied laughing 'until they are too big to see over their tummy anyway!'

'It may be funny to you,' I told him indignantly, 'but I don't want everyone staring at my huge belly.'

'Don't worry, darling, there aren't that many people around where we will be living,' he grinned, 'so you'll only have to worry about the sheep staring at you!'

My husband then told me that my bicycle, cases and a big crate with a few of our wedding presents, had all arrived safely, and that our Landlords, Doctor and Mrs Treconner, had kindly stored them all in their 'spare' garage. I thought that our new home must be a big house if it had more than one garage and started to imagine living in a lovely Georgian house—but I couldn't have been more wrong!

When Duncan turned off the main road into a driveway lined with fir trees, suddenly all hell broke loose as dozens of crows took off at the same time and flew around us in circles, flapping and squawking and making a terrible din. I was so distracted by them that I didn't see the house until Duncan had stopped the car directly in front of it. It certainly was a bit different.

The big old house had a tower, pointed gables, and ivy growing all over the outside of it, and looked like the kind of house that Walt Disney might have drawn for a wicked witch to live in.

As Duncan helped me out of the car, he pointed to the tower and said, 'this is going to be our new home for the next few months or so. What do you think, darling?'

'I love it!' I said happily and then began to giggle as I imagined a maiden in distress being locked up in the tower who was then rescued by a knight in shining armour. A knight with lovely auburn hair like Duncan's!

Dr and Mrs Treconner, the owners of this extraordinary dwelling, welcomed us both with a smile and a handshake. They were friendly, but also made it abundantly clear that the main house was 'their' area and the wing was 'ours'. However, if we needed anything, we were to leave a note through their front door.

Mrs Treconner explained that, to get to our flat in the tower, we would have to open our front door, and then close it again, before trying to go up the stairs, because the door was so close to the staircase that there wasn't enough room in the tiny entrance hall for us to be able to move unless the door was closed.

After following these instructions and making our way upstairs, I finally got to see our flat. Duncan took me into the tiny sitting room first. There were no armchairs or sofas, but it had two loom basket chairs and a few rather dreary mud-coloured cushions. There was also a pretty fireplace with a modern gas fire in the grate, which was operated by a meter that you had to feed with shillings. I'll have to buy some new cushions, I thought as Duncan showed me the bedroom, which was quite spacious and had a big double bed. The kitchen was the size of a scullery with a sink, gas cooker, and a big cupboard across one wall. I then peered under the sink, hoping to find a rubbish bucket and perhaps an enamel bowl to do the washing up, but it was empty. The bathroom had a washbasin and a lavatory, but no bath.

'Don't worry, darling,' Duncan grinned, 'we are allowed to go into the main house on Mondays, Wednesdays and Saturdays for a bath between five and seven in the evenings. It just means taking our towels and a sponge bag. Think of how many shillings that will save!' he teased, 'By the way, darling, Mrs Treconner warned me not to use the gas fire in the sitting room at the same time as the gas oven, as they won't work at the same time; and not to put on the light on the stairs when boiling the electric kettle, as the lights will fuse!'

Duncan advised me always to have a torch handy upstairs and downstairs, so that I could find my way to the fuse box when he wasn't around, and then I would be able to fix a blown fuse on my own. He also suggested that I buy some candles, just in case all the lights fused at once.

As soon as I had unpacked, I wrote a shopping list and decided that I would try to buy everything the next day when I went to Ramsey on my bike.

Later that evening, after I had made some scrambled eggs for our supper, Duncan turned on the gas fire and we relaxed in our own little sitting room. 'Oh, by the way darling, I've made an appointment for you to see the doctor in Ramsey tomorrow, as you'll need monthly check-ups to make sure 'he's' alright.'

'What makes you so sure that it'll be a 'he'?' I asked.

'I'm just teasing,' he chuckled, 'I don't mind either way, as long as our baby is healthy.'

Duncan paused for a few moments and then asked quietly, 'Would you ask the doctor if it's still safe for us to make love and when we will we have to stop, as I don't want to hurt you, or our baby?'

When we got into bed that night, Duncan pulled up my nightdress to say goodnight to the 'bump', as he was now calling our unborn baby. 'We'll wait until you've seen the doc,' he whispered and then held me close to him. I was so happy to be with Duncan again that I was moved to tears.

The next morning as Duncan was leaving to go to work at RAF Andreas, he said, 'Oh by the way, your bicycle is in the shed behind the tower. Good luck with the shopping.' I looked out of the tower window as he cycled down the drive, and laughed when he shook his fist at the noisy crows.

After I had made the bed, I washed up and began to unpack the crate of wedding-present gifts: putting the china, toaster and kettle in suitable places in the kitchen and then arranging the china ornaments in the living room to my satisfaction. I then added to the shopping list all the other things I thought we would need to make our new home perfect: the list grew and grew.

It was almost eleven o'clock by the time I left for Ramsey. As I wobbled down the long driveway on my bicycle, the crows screeched at me, so I screeched back.

When I got to Ramsey, I asked a friendly-looking woman if she could tell me where to find the ironmonger and, as she pointed the way, she commented, 'You are the new officer's wife at the Rookery, aren't you?' so I introduced myself. It doesn't take long for the gossip to travel on this island, I thought.

After buying everything I needed at the ironmongers, I then realised that it wouldn't all fit into my bicycle basket, so I was relieved when the ironmonger offered to deliver everything the following day.

'To the tower, not the main house,' I explained.

'Yes, Madam, we know!' the ironmonger said with a grin.

I asked him if he knew of anywhere I could buy some new cushions.

'As you are only here for a short time, Madam, I'd recommend buying some second-hand ones at Mr Bright's Wartime Exchange Rooms,' he suggested.

I then went to the Grocer's and he laughed when I asked for half a pound of pepper, 'Are you sure Madam? I don't think you will need quite that much; we usually sell it by the ounce!' I confessed that I was new to being a housewife and wasn't sure of the right amounts to order.

'Yes, the Commander told us you'd been in the Wrens before you were married and were used to buying things by the dozen. Don't worry I'll help you,' he said kindly.

Mr Bright's Wartime Exchange Rooms were like Aladdin's cave. It had everything a housewife could possibly need, or no longer needed.

As soon as I walked in I found some brightly coloured second-hand cushions that were still in good condition, which I thought would replace the dreary ones perfectly and two rag-rugs for the floor beside our bed. Before I left the shop I spotted a milk jug, some cereal bowls, some wooden spoons and a box of kitchen utensils. I tied the cushions and rugs with cord onto the grid on the back of my bike, as my basket was already full with a big bunch of flowers, and then balanced two carrier bags on the handle bars before cycling to the doctor's house for the appointment Duncan had made for me.

Doctor Baker was an elderly but friendly doctor, who didn't make me take my knickers off thank goodness, and just asked me to 'pull them down below your 'balloon'!'

After he'd examined me he said that everything seemed to be developing, as it should, and then asked me if there was anything I wanted to ask him.

'Well, yes, there is actually – is it safe for the baby – if we… for us… to… eh… um,' I found that I couldn't quite express what I was trying to ask, but fortunately he could.

'Have normal marital relations?' he asked.

'Yes,' I replied, relieved that he knew what I meant.

'I don't see why not, just take it slowly and try different positions and if you feel uncomfortable in a month or two's time then stop,' he advised. 'Oh, and by the way, when you are hanging out the washing make sure the support pole is low. No stretching above your head.' I hadn't even thought about doing our washing, and would have to leave a note for Mrs Treconner to ask her where the washing line was and when I could use it.

I knew exactly when Duncan was home that evening, as the crows went mad as soon as he turned into the driveway. The first thing I did was to show him the pretty cushions, the vase of flowers and the things I'd unpacked from the crate. 'Oh, you clever girl,' he exclaimed, 'you've made our ivory tower look like a real home.'

That night we continued our honeymoon activities, but at a slightly gentler pace as advised by Doctor Baker. And the following morning everything I'd bought in Ramsey was delivered and carried up the stairs for me. Being pregnant has its advantages, I thought.

I was just putting my new rubbish bucket under the sink when there was a loud knock on the door. It was Mrs Treconner. 'I don't wish to intrude dear,' she said, balancing dangerously on the top step, 'but I received your note about the washing line and just came to tell you that you can use it at any time.'

I invited her to come in to have a cup of coffee, and as soon as she was in the flat, she said, 'I see that you've already put out your own things. I wondered what was in that crate.'

'I thought I should use a few of our wedding presents to make us feel more married!' I said, laughing.

'Do call me Jean,' she said, 'and my husband answers to Adrian when he's at home, but at work, they call him Professor!' I didn't ask her what he was a Professor of, but as he was a doctor, I assumed that it was most probably something medical.

The first week flew by, and one day, as I was bringing in the washing, I saw Jean coming towards me. 'If you need any eggs, Mary, there's a farm down the lane just behind our house. Mrs Humble would be glad to sell you some, I'm sure, as she could do with the extra money; sometimes she has extra milk and cream to spare too.'

I told Duncan about Mrs Humble later that evening, when we were sitting comfortably in our cosy sitting room.

'Good idea, Mary, fresh food is better than shop-bought things any day,' he said as he stood up to turn up the fire.

Suddenly there was a strange rustling sound, which was quite creepy, as if there was someone else in the room with us. Duncan stared at me for a moment and then checked that the door was shut. He then asked me what I thought the strange sound was, and did I know where it was coming from.

'I haven't a clue,' I told him and then felt a sudden pain in my stomach, so put both my hands on it.

'Are you alright darling?' Duncan asked me, concerned.

'The bump – our baby – it just moved!' I whispered.

'That's good isn't it?'

'Yes, of course, it just surprised me, that's all,' I replied, and then went to the bathroom for a pee.

When I came back, Duncan's face was completely white. 'What is it?' I asked him. 'What's wrong?'

'Do you believe in ghosts?' he asked.

'Why?' I said hesitantly.

'That strange rustling noise started again, as soon as you left the room,' he said looking straight into my eyes.

'Maybe it's just rooks nesting in the roof?'

'Yes, it's most probably just that,' Duncan agreed, or at least pretended to.

'Why don't I make us some cocoa?' I suggested.

Five minutes later, just as I was about to take a sip of my cocoa, I heard an even louder rustling noise than I had heard before. A shiver went down my spine.

Duncan suddenly burst out laughing. 'We are silly, darling, it's just the chairs!' he chuckled, and then explained, 'They are made of cane, so they expand and shrink with the change of temperature when the fire is on or off.' Mystery solved!

We might not have had a ghost in our part of the house, but I wasn't quite so sure that one wasn't lurking elsewhere, as I had felt a strange barrier the last couple of times I had been halfway up the big staircase that led to the bathroom in the main house. It was as if someone, or something, was trying to stop me from going up and down the stairs, whenever I attempted to get to the shared bathroom. I decided not to tell Duncan, in case he thought I was just being silly.

Humble's Farm wasn't too hard to find, I discovered when I went to buy some fresh eggs the next day. I went to the back door, as Mrs Treconner had suggested and knocked.

'Who is it?' a voice called out.

I called out that I was a new neighbour and that I'd come for some eggs. A small woman in a flower-printed overall came to the door and after looking me up and down said, 'You're the wife of the Navy Officer.'

'Yes, I am,' I smiled. He's at RAF Andreas all day, otherwise he would have come with me,' I explained. I then told her that we were renting the Treconner's Tower.

'I know,' she said, 'I seen you from the bedroom window hanging out the washing. You're expecting then?' she said, pointing at my bump. I nodded, and told her that was why I wasn't doing any war work at the moment, but I hoped to be able to do something useful for a month or two, if she knew of anyone that wanted help.

'I need help,' she said, beckoning to me to follow her to where she kept her hens.

'You do? In what way would that be war work?' I asked her.

'Land girl's gone, but we're still working on the land and I need help feeding 'em,' she said, pointing to the hens, 'and the farm hands too.'

Happy memories of helping the Bridges' on their farm where Duncan and I had first started to get to know each other came flooding back to me.

She pulled herself up and walked over to the sink, where a bucket of potatoes, carrots and onions were waiting to be peeled and chopped.

'Do you eat your own meat?' I asked her when I noticed a plate of meat waiting to be cooked.

'Oh yes, some days lamb, others beef or pork, it all depends on what has been slaughtered.' My stomach heaved for a second. 'My man Don brings in whatever is not taken away by the regulations.'

'I just about manage on my own, but it's hard this time o' year what with the lambing, calving and everything else to do,' she said. The penny suddenly dropped, she needed a kitchen maid. Well, I suppose I could tackle the vegetables, as long as I did it sitting down, and I could do the washing up too.

'I really needs a pair of willing hands,' Mrs Humble said, almost pleading, 'but we cannot pay nothing, only with your dinner and free eggs.'

'War work is free, Mrs Humble, so you won't have to pay me,' I said, 'but I would have to leave promptly at two-thirty every day, as I still have our shopping to do and my husband's evening meal to prepare.'

'I'd only need you Monday to Friday,' she explained.

'I'll ask my husband this evening, and providing he has no objection, I'll start on Monday. May I let you know tomorrow?' I asked her.

'I would be ever so grateful, as we've asked for a land girl to replace my youngest in July, so if you could give me a hand until you feel it's too hard on the baby, that would be a big help,' she said smiling. 'There's no lifting or heaving work, as a girl comes here Saturdays to scrub and clean the kitchen and scullery and wash the work clothes.' Poor girl, I thought, that sounded like real work.

That evening, Duncan said that he had no objection, as long as I promised to stop the minute I felt tired or unwell.

On the Monday morning, he walked with me to the farm, just to check everything was above board, and then he left me to get on with it.

My first job was to peel a huge pile of potatoes and carrots and then Mrs Humble asked me to chop the onions, which made cry. Out of the corner of my eye I watched as Mrs Humble prepared the meat, covering it in flour before throwing it all into a frying pan to brown. The smell was wonderful and made my mouth water. She then transferred the lot into a huge pan to which she added various herbs and stock.

By the end of my first week, I started to regret having offered to help, but a couple of weeks later I was taking it all in my stride; I now spent far less time preparing the vegetables and had all the washing up done and tidied away in no time. I even had some time to sit down and chat to Mrs Humble for a while before doing the shopping.

As my tummy had now got quite large, I needed help getting out of the bath, so Duncan would always come and help me. One night, when I was sitting in the bath, he told me that something strange had just happened to him when he was coming up the stairs. He had felt 'something' trying to stop him going any further when he was about halfway up the stairs and that he had suddenly felt so cold that he thought he must have left the door open, but when he turned around to make sure, the door was firmly shut. When I told him that I had had the same experience, but hadn't wanted to tell him in case he thought I was just being silly, he laughed and said, 'I would never think that darling, but whatever 'it' is, it's a real mystery!'

The following Saturday evening Duncan said that he had to go to RAF Andreas because a VIP was giving a lecture about Trincomalee, the base in Ceylon where he was going to be posted later that year, so I decided that while he was out, I would wash my hair. When I walked up the stairs to the bathroom, I felt 'something' try to stop me once again, which made me shiver but after a few seconds everything went back to normal and I was able to continue on my way to the bathroom. It was unnerving to say the least.

After, I had washed my hair, I went back downstairs but halfway down my way was blocked again. This time I was really frightened, but kept walking until I got to the Treconner's drawing room. When I went in, Adrian looked up at me and seeing the worried expression on my face, asked. 'Did you have difficulty getting down, Mary?' When I didn't say anything and just stared at him blankly, he asked hesitantly, 'was there... something... blocking your way?'

'So you do know about it,' I said. 'What is it?'

'Come and sit down, Mary,' Adrian said beckoning me to take the chair next to him. 'I didn't mention this strange phenomenon to you before, as it doesn't happen to everyone and I hoped it wouldn't to you either, but as it has, let me try to explain.'

When I sat down, he continued, 'About a hundred years ago, a wealthy family lived in this house; they were very well connected and were invited by the local gentry and dignitaries to many official and private parties and dinners. As their children grew up, they were invited too. There were three boys and two girls, who were both beauties, and much sought after by the sons of everyone they knew. Then, one terrible night on their way home from a ball, there was a severe storm and the family were involved in an accident. The horses bolted at the sound of thunder and their coach overturned. The eldest daughter was thrown out of the door and thrown against a tree, breaking both her hips so badly that she never walked properly again. She hated her deformed body so much that she refused to leave the house again.'

'Oh, how sad,' I said.

'Well, the story is that after a while, the youngest daughter was invited to parties on her own and this is where the trouble on the stairs all began. Every time she wanted to go down the stairs, she had to pass her crippled older sister, who would beg her not to leave her alone. This went on for months until the younger girl walked down the stairs one last time, on her wedding day and apparently, that's when all this strangeness began.'

'So you think it's the ghost of the miserable older sister on the stairs?' I asked incredulously.

'I'm not sure what to believe,' he replied. 'I'm a doctor so I always try to find a scientific answer to everything but to be honest I have no idea why this keeps happening.'

'What was her name?' I asked.

'Lydia, and apparently she starved herself to death after her sister had left home, so we asked the vicar to try to exorcise her ghost, and all was well for a while, but it started happening again, as soon as we began letting out the tower to young couples in the services.'

'Is there anything I can do?' I asked.

'Maybe you could try talking to her?' he suggested. 'Perhaps you could tell her that as she is no longer trapped in her crippled body, she is free to go… to wherever spirits go or something like that.'

'Well, it's worth a try isn't it?' I said before heading back upstairs.

A few minutes later, I was sitting on a step halfway up the stairs, trying to explain to a ghost called Lydia why it was time for her to move on. It felt a bit odd talking out loud to thin air, but I gave it my best shot and told her that she could go wherever she liked; all she had to do was let go of her life in this house.

But when Duncan told me that 'something' was still blocking his way to the bathroom, it looked as though I would have to speak to Lydia again, so the next time I went for a bath, I sat down on the staircase and tried to talk to her, as if she was really there in human form rather than just a figment of my imagination. I told her that I understood her anguish but that it was all right for her to go now and that maybe she should try to look for her little sister, as she might be missing her now that she was also a spirit.

When I went up and down the stairs the following day, I felt no barrier, no pressure, and no presence, and thankfully neither did Duncan. I will never know what the 'something' really was but would like to think that if it was Lydia's ghost, she was finally at peace now.

Duncan came home one evening looking upset and told me that he was being posted to Speke aerodrome, near Liverpool soon, where, as Commander Flying, he'd have to prepare several squadrons to fly to the Far East to fight the Japanese and then he would be sent to Trincomalee in Ceylon. Although, we both knew this day would come I had thought it wouldn't be until later in the year. I was wrong.

'I'll have to go straight away for a week to get things sorted, darling,' Duncan told me. 'But while I'm there, I'll try to find somewhere for us to live until I leave for the Far East.'

The week Duncan was away I filled my time by writing letters, knitting baby clothes and listening to the news. It sounded as though the war in Europe would soon be over, thank goodness. When I rang my parents, they told me we weren't the only ones moving house, they were too. I knew they had been planning to move after the war was over to a lovely 16th century house, called Hilltop House, which also had its own home farm on the estate, but it looked as if my father must have decided to move earlier.

Duncan telephoned me every night to reassure me that everything was fine at Speke. He'd been to see an estate agent to look for a boarding house and been advised to look a few miles outside Liverpool, where the air was cleaner, and the prices lower.

One evening Duncan told me that he'd found the perfect home for us in a small seaside town called Freshfield, near Formby. He had organised a ground floor flat for us in a big house belonging to an elderly widow, called Mrs Briars, who let out part of her house to service personnel, in preference to having evacuees.

'Mrs Briars told me that for a small extra fee her housekeeper would cook lunch for you every day, and for both of us on Sundays.' Duncan explained that the reason he'd chosen this particular flat was because he was concerned about me being on my own all day. 'Mrs Briars absolutely adores babies apparently and hopes that it's born before we have to leave!' he chuckled.

After packing all our belongings and saying our goodbyes to the Treconners, we got on the ferry at Douglas and headed for the mainland. As we looked back at the Isle of Man, I told Duncan that I would miss everyone at Humble Farm and he said that he would miss the RAF friends he'd made at Andreas, but we both agreed that neither of us would miss the noisy crows!

When we got to the mainland we got into the car that Duncan had hired the week before and drove to our new home in Freshfield. The first thing I noticed was that the house was in a lovely tree-lined street, which looked very prosperous. There were a few tulips and daffodils about to flower in the tidy beds surrounding the front garden. When Mrs Wallace, the housekeeper, let us in, I had to conceal a smile as she looked a bit like Queen Victoria, bun and all.

Mrs Wallace took us to our flat where our landlady, Mrs Briars, was waiting to show us around the small, self-contained flat. To my delight, there was a big garden at the back of the house with fruit trees, a vegetable patch, and a washing area with a line and a big pole to hold it up.

'You will need to make arrangements with a doctor who will advise you where a maternity house is situated just in case the baby comes early,' Mrs Briars advised looking at my large tummy. 'I can give you the name of mine, if you like, as he's local.' I thanked her and then asked if the shops in Freshfield were within walking distance.

'Certainly,' she replied, 'and you should walk at least a mile a day and not sit around eating biscuits like some silly expectant mothers do.'

Duncan came to my defence and said that his wife had been doing war work right up to last week.

'Good for you,' Mrs Briars said now smiling. 'If you are that kind of girl, we shall get on just fine.'

Later that evening, after I had made us something to eat, Duncan lit the fire and we played chess. After a couple of games, he asked me, 'What name should we give our son, Hamish, James or Malcolm?' and then added smiling, '—unless it's a girl, of course!'

'It won't be a girl, because before I left the farm, Mrs Humble tied a ring onto a thread and hung it over my tummy,' I told him, 'and it swung left to right, so she's sure it's a boy.'

'What old wives' nonsense!' he chuckled, 'but just in case, how about Alice?'

'Let's wait. Oh, and by the way,' I said, with a grin, 'checkmate!'

I was happy to discover that our bed was very comfortable and despite the baby keeping me awake for half the night, I still managed to get some rest. Directly after breakfast Duncan set off for the aerodrome, and I finished unpacking my things. I then made my way into Freshfield, where I found a friendly grocer who delivered locally. When I got back, I noticed that the fireplace had already been re-laid for the evening's fire and a bowl of snowdrops had been placed on the dining-room table, which made me feel very happy. That evening, Duncan took me for a drive to the beach and we had a lovely walk along the coastal road. We then found a fish and chip shop where we bought two portions 'to take home'. I popped them in our small oven and once they were piping hot we ate them by the fire, which was bliss!

When I went to see Mrs Briars' doctor, he told me that everything was fine, but that his young partner, Doctor Collins, would take care of me, as he was the obstetrics expert. Doctor Collins then gave me the name of a Maternity Hospital in Southport, and suggested that I inspect it first and then if I liked it, to book myself in for the last week of June.

'Gosh, is my baby due that soon?' I asked a little surprised.

The young doctor smiled and said, 'Well, the baby seems to think so!'

Duncan quickly got into a routine at Speke aerodrome and he seemed to be taking his new role all in his stride. I had never seen him so relaxed. And it didn't take me long to settle in either, as everything I needed was nearby and Mrs Briars and her housekeeper kept a constant eye on me.

When I next rang my mother she told me that they were settling into their new house, and that Aunt Beth had been invaluable as usual making curtains and arranging the china. Apparently my father had even managed to find a 'proper gardener', who knew how to grow peaches and grapes in the greenhouses. That will make him very happy, I thought.

The following day, Duncan received a letter from his sister Celia, but instead of being happy he suddenly went white as a sheet.

'What's wrong?' I asked.

'The stupid girl has got herself pregnant,' he whispered.

'Pregnant?' I queried. 'How? I mean she can't be, she isn't married!'

Duncan handed me the letter and then said he needed to go for a long walk, while I read it.

After waiting for weeks to hear from her boyfriend, Celia had apparently grown desperate, and had gone to see his Senior Officer to ask where he was. She was shattered to find out that he had gone on leave to be with his wife and children. I couldn't begin to imagine how she must have felt when she had found out that the man she loved was married and had a family. Father John and Bumble had obviously not been happy to hear that their youngest daughter was going to be an unmarried mother but they hadn't judged her and were being very supportive, which didn't surprise me at all. I decided that I would give her my full support too. She had put a PS at the bottom of her letter to let us know that Janet and Bertie's baby boy had been born the previous week. Poor Celia, I thought, how could that bloody man have done this to her? I burst into tears.

When Duncan returned from his walk, I could see that he had been crying too. I held him in my arms and suggested that he ask for a 72 so that he could go home. 'Tell her we love her and that we'll do anything we can to help her look after her child.'

It wasn't until he was asleep that I realised Celia's baby must be due at about the same time as ours. Our babies would almost be twins! Father John and Bumble would soon have three grandchildren, all of a similar age, only a month or two between them.

Two days later Duncan went to Perth to see what could be done to make things less upsetting for his family, and when he got home, he told me that it had been agreed that Celia would change her name by deed poll and let it be known that she was a war widow, so that when she applied for either a teaching post, or as a Housemother at a boarding school somewhere in England after the war she wouldn't be rejected for being a 'fallen woman'.

When we inspected the Christiana Hartley Maternity Hospital at Southport General Infirmary, we liked it very much. It was quite small and very clean and I felt sure it would do quite well enough for me. The Matron booked me in for mid June, telling me to check regularly with my local doctor and not to come in until the pains were at twenty-minute intervals.

'Pain?' I asked her.

'Yes dear, pain like you have never felt before,' she warned me and then thought carefully for a moment before adding, 'Imagine going to the loo when you haven't been able to for several days; it's a bit like that but a lot, lot worse!'

I didn't like the sound of that at all.

On the way home, I saw someone reading a copy of the Daily Express and stopped in my tracks when I saw the headline 'Hitler is Dead'. I bought myself a copy of the paper and read that Hitler had been killed at his command post in Berlin the day before, 'according to a Hamburg radio announcement'. I hoped that this was true and would mean the war would end soon but the paper also said that Admiral Doenitz was now the new Fuhrer and had announced that, 'The military struggle will continue,' so perhaps not.

When I discussed the news with Duncan that evening, he told me that he thought it was true that Hitler was dead, but perhaps the time, place and way he had died might not be, 'Don't believe everything you read in the papers, darling, after all propaganda tricks are employed by both sides!'

On the 8th May, 1945, Winston Churchill officially announced that the war with Germany was finally over, but in his speech he also said, 'We may allow ourselves a brief period of rejoicing; but let us not forget for a moment the toil and efforts that lie ahead. Japan, with all her treachery and greed, remains un-subdued. The injury she has inflicted on Great Britain, the United States, and other countries, and her detestable cruelties, call for justice and retribution. We must now devote all our strength and resources to the completion of our task, both at home and abroad. Advance, Britannia! Long live the cause of freedom, God save the King!'

Duncan suddenly got up, grabbed me by both hands and we started dancing around the room, but unfortunately my tummy kept getting in the way, which made us giggle like schoolchildren, so we gave that idea up and kissed each other instead. We then went out into the streets and it was quite a sight to see so many people dancing, waving Union Jacks and smiling at each other. The atmosphere was wonderful and it was a very happy day but in the back of my mind I kept hearing Churchill's words and knew that the war wouldn't really be over until the Japanese surrendered too.

'Have you any idea when you might be sent to Trincomalee?' I asked Duncan, as we were getting ready to go to bed.

'No darling, but I'll get embarkation leave first, why?'

'Well, I was wondering if the baby starts just as you are about to leave, do you think Mrs Briars would let Mummy stay here with me instead of you?'

'Why don't you ask her?' he said, 'Mrs Briars might even have a spare room in the house and I have no doubt that she'd be glad to make a bit more money!'

One evening we had a telephone call from Father John to tell us that Celia had given birth to a baby boy and that both were doing well. As both Duncan's sisters had given birth to boys, I wondered what the odds were that we would have one too, and for the first time started to think that we were more likely to have a girl.

I rang my mother to tell her about Celia's baby and afterwards she asked me how long I had before it would no longer be safe to travel, so I told her that the doctor had thought I had about a month left, but as the baby's head was down it could be sooner. She suggested that I come home to them, as soon as Duncan had his embarkation leave, which I agreed to do but a week later Duncan was told that his leave had been cancelled and that he would be needed at Speke every day until he left for Trincomalee.

As I was due a medical check up in the morning, I decided to ask Doctor Collins's advice, and he said, 'Well I think it would be a great joy and comfort for your husband if he was able to see his baby before he has to leave.'

'Well, of course I would like him to see our baby before he leaves too, but how is that possible unless it decides to arrive early?' I asked.

'Well, as your baby is head down and ready to pop out, we could arrange for it to be induced, if you like,' the doctor said smiling at me and then realising that I had no idea what he was talking about, he then kindly explained, 'That means that we can break the waters, so that the baby is born almost immediately.'

When I got home, I asked Duncan whether he thought it was a good idea to induce the baby before he left and he was over the moon at the idea. 'Oh darling, that would be splendid, as long as there are no unnecessary risks involved.'

Duncan picked me up after lunch the next day and we went straight to the Maternity hospital, expecting to have the baby that very afternoon, but of course it was never going to be quite that easy.

When we arrived, Duncan was told to go for a walk and come back in an hour. I was then taken into a room and a nurse told to remove my lower garments and wait for the hospital doctor.

'This shouldn't hurt much,' the doctor said, which was obviously a well-used lie.

'Ooo… oow!' I squealed. I half expected to see my baby's head appear any minute between my legs, but there was nothing.

'You can get dressed again now and go home,' the nurse told me.

'What happens next?' I asked feeling a bit bewildered.

'The birth will start with gentle pains, so ignore them,' the doctor ordered, 'and don't contact us again until the pains are really strong and occur every twenty minutes. Then ring us to say you are coming in'

'Can't I stay here?' I begged. 'What if the baby is born before I can get back?'

'It won't be,' he said smiling, 'and don't worry, babies usually take their time, so you'll have plenty of warning.'

When Duncan came back to collect me he was as disappointed as I was, but when I told him that I was hungry, he cheered up and suggested we have a meal at the local pub, as a treat.

'I'd rather have fish and chips at home,' I told him 'just in case'. But I needn't have worried, as there wasn't a twinge all evening.

The next morning Duncan said, as he was getting ready to leave for Speke, 'I'll ring you at lunchtime and see how you are and I'll make arrangements to be free for the rest of the day. Isn't this exciting?' I didn't agree at all, as I was terrified.

The very second that I waved goodbye to him out of the sitting room window, the twinges started, as if the baby knew I was now on my own. The twinges then turned into cramps but they weren't happening every twenty minutes, more like every thirty-five, so I tried to ignore them as I had been told to do.

By lunchtime, the pains were starting to come every twenty minutes, but there was still no phone call from Duncan, so I decided to call him at the aerodrome but as he wasn't there I spoke to one of his fellow officers instead.

'Oh I'm sorry Mary, but Duncan has been held up, as we have a visiting Admiral,' he informed me. 'May I suggest that you call for an ambulance and I'll tell him you are in labour the minute he gets in. Good luck old girl!'

As the ambulance pulled up outside the house, I had two more strong contractions. Mrs Briars let the men in and then she and Mrs Wallace started fussing over me, checking that I had everything I needed to take with me. I had packed my suitcase in advance but then suddenly remembered my sponge bag was still in the bathroom

'Take your time dear, there is no hurry,' Mrs Wallace said calmly.

'No hurry?' I shrieked, now gasping in pain. 'I'm about to have my baby!'

The pains were coming every fifteen minutes now and I just hoped that Mrs Briars had rung the Maternity hospital for me to warn them that I was on my way. Well, if she hasn't they can hardly turn me away now can they? I reasoned between gasps.

'Everything is going as it should, Mrs Ogilvie,' one of the nurses said when I finally at the hospital. 'Get undressed and put on this gown.' I was then taken to a ward, put in one of the beds and given a woman's magazine to read. I managed to survive for the next hour without making too much fuss until the pains started to come every ten minutes, and then I begged, 'Nurse please do something.'

'Right it's time to go now, have you got a dressing gown?' the nurse asked, but there wasn't enough time to put it on, as just then the pain was so unbearable that I nearly fainted.

'Ooooooow!'

The next thing I remembered was being raced down a corridor on a trolley, into a lift and then into what looked like a prison cell full of torture equipment with weird hoops on the end of straps to keep my legs in the air. I then saw some very sharp looking knives and thought… 'what the hell is happening?'

'Take a few deep breaths,' the nurse said, placing a mask over my face, 'it's a mixture of gas and air and will help relieve the pain.' I did what she suggested but it didn't help at all.

'Oh God there it is again… please no, not again, Oooow!' I screamed and then the pain suddenly stopped for a moment and everything was incredibly peaceful and quiet.

'Not long now, Mrs Ogilvie,' the nurse said, 'the pains will be different next time and we'll be asking you to push. Do you understand?'

I nodded and then mumbled to the smiling face gazing down at me, 'Can you give my husband a message from me please?'

'Yes, of course, what would you like us to tell him?' the nurse asked me kindly.

'That I will never, ever let him into my bed again,' I said crossly and then added, 'I am going back to being a virgin!'

The doctor and the nurse both roared with laughter and then the doctor said, 'Come on, one more big push, it won't hurt!'

'Liar!' I yelled and then pushed with all my might until suddenly the pain stopped and as I looked up through my tears I saw a tiny pink baby covered in blood now in the doctor's hands.

'Congratulations! You have an adorable, but very small daughter, Mrs Ogilvie. Well done!'

'By the way where is your husband?' I heard another voice say, which made me burst into tears realising that the man I loved so much had missed the birth of our first child. It wasn't his fault of course and when he eventually arrived and took our daughter in his arms for the first time, he looked at me with a big grin on his face and said, 'Lets call her Charlotte.' That's perfect I thought and as I looked at our little girl, I knew I was in love all over again.

'The doctor says she is too tiny to risk bringing her home for a few days,' Duncan said now handing Charlotte back to me, 'so I'll come and visit you whenever I can, hopefully at lunchtime and then again around this time every evening.' He then left to make sure that the Admiral, who had been responsible for him missing the birth of his daughter, was being looked after back at Speke.

When Duncan came in for a quick visit at lunchtime the following day, I told him that we still hadn't got a Moses basket or bedding or small enough baby things but he had already thought of all that. 'Don't worry darling, I rang your mother last night and she has everything at Hilltop House ready and my parents are sending a big parcel of baby things too. My mother has suggested we line one of the drawers from the chest with a pillow and blanket to go on with.'

Charlotte only weighed five pounds at birth and as she had 'arrived' two weeks early she was treated as a premature baby. My bosoms were getting sore with milk being pumped out a regular intervals and to add insult to injury my lovely daughter decided that she preferred the taste of 'Cow and Gate' to mother's milk and spat mine out!

'Never mind dear, at least with a baby bottle you know exactly how much she's taking,' the ward sister told me.

Duncan always had a big smile on his face every time he came to see us but one evening I noticed that he looked rather sad, so I asked him, 'What is it, Duncan?'

'I have to leave in two days,' he said quietly. I stared at him, as if he'd just told me that the moon had suddenly fallen out of the sky.

'Oh Duncan, you can't go, not yet. Please stay with me. I don't know how to care for our baby without you,' I cried.

Duncan then told me that he had called my mother, and that she was already on her way. 'Mrs Briars has agreed to rent the spare room to your mother and Mrs Wallace will cook all your meals, except for breakfast for as long as you both need to stay in her house until Charlotte is big enough to travel to Sussex,' he said smiling at me and mopping my eyes with his spare clean handkerchief.

After Duncan had left, the Matron came to see me and told me that if I promised to do exactly as I had been advised, I could take my baby home the following day, so that she could be with her Daddy on his last night in England. I could have kissed her!

Armed with feeding instructions, two glass bottles with teats, a tin of baby powdered milk and a set of borrowed premature baby clothes, I waited for the ward sister to come and give me some lessons on how to look after my baby. When she arrived she showed me, using a doll that she had brought with her, how to swaddle her in a shawl, 'Just like Baby Jesus!' she said kindly. 'This will make her feel safe as if she was still in your womb. You must put her down on a different side of her body after each feed to avoid pressure on her head and only wash her body, don't give her a bath until she had gained weight, as this will save energy and prevent her getting cold.' She then put Charlotte back in her little linen bed in the night nursery where she would spend the night with ten other babies, so that the mothers could get a good night's sleep.

She explained how to put the baby's arms down each side of its little body and then wrap it tightly from under the arms. She showed me the correct way to mix the powdered milk with water that had been boiled first and then cooled making sure there were no lumps. I had no idea that I would have to learn so much and hoped that I would be able to remember to do it all correctly.

'Tomorrow, before your husband leaves, ask him to go to the chemist to buy these things on the list I'm giving you, and then to an ironmonger to buy two clean buckets for the nappies. A nurse will then visit you daily until you are confident that you can manage on your own, and I understand that your mother will be staying with you after your husband has been sent overseas.'

'Yes, she will, thank goodness,' I said.

'A good routine is the essential way to help a small baby thrive. Every three hours day and night without fail, set your alarm clock, feed the baby, wind it, change it and put it down, no going out in a pram, or showing it off to friends for the first two weeks. If you start to sneeze wear a muslin mask. Do all this and within a few weeks your baby will have regained its birth weight and begin to gain several ounces a week and then you can ease up a bit,' she explained. 'After that you can change to four hourly feeds and take it out in the fresh air.' I was grateful for this advice, as I hadn't got a clue how to look after my little girl.

When Duncan arrived to take us back to our flat, the Matron patted me on the back and said, 'Next time try to go the full nine months, dear!'

'Oh there won't be a next time Matron, once is quite enough!' I said firmly.

'They all say that!' she said laughing.

That night, back at the flat, Charlotte slept in the drawer, which we filled with a pillow and a folded sheet with the blanket and a shawl to keep her warm. We didn't get much sleep that night, as feeding, winding and changing Charlotte seemed endless. In between each session we held each other close knowing that this was the last chance we would be together for a very long time.

The sound of Duncan packing his things woke me up at nine o'clock in the morning, which was just as well as it was time to feed Charlotte again. I felt really exhausted and couldn't imagine how I was going to manage each day with so little rest. Duncan made some breakfast for us and then checked the list of things he had been told to buy before he left. I had a wash, tidied my hair and put on a clean dress and then when I heard him return I took a quick look in the mirror and made myself smile, as I wanted to look my best for him, despite feeling like breaking down and sobbing my heart out.

When I saw Duncan come through the door I could see that he had not only bought the baby things while he was out but also a lovely bunch of spring flowers, 'Now darling, don't forget that your mother is arriving at five,' he said as he held Charlotte in his arms for the midday feed, looking as though he'd fed a baby all his life, 'so you won't be alone for too long and Mrs Briars and Mrs Wallace are only on the other side of that door, so don't hesitate to call them if you need anything.' I nodded, thinking how lucky we were to have found this ideal flat in such a comfortable house.

After I had managed to get Charlotte to produce a proper burp and Duncan had put her back in the drawer, Mrs Wallace called out that lunch was ready but we were both feeling far too upset to eat very much. However we managed to force a few mouthfuls down, as we didn't want to hurt her feelings.

There was now only an hour to go before Duncan would have to leave, so he moved his chair beside mine and held my hand in his. He looked close to tears, which made me feel like crying, so to try to make things a bit less tense I told him that I'd take Charlotte to stay with his parents, as soon as she was a decent weight and that I'd write to him often but to remember that if my letters took an age to reach him it didn't mean I hadn't posted them. He promised to do the same whenever he had a spare moment. Then just like on our honeymoon, one minute he was there, the next he was gone.

A Naval car had been sent to collect him and I watched through the window until it disappeared out of view and then finally I could hold on no longer, the floodgates opened and the tears began to flow. I felt like screaming and couldn't stop worrying about what Duncan would have to do, now that he had been sent to fight the Japanese.

After I had pulled myself together, I went to check on Charlotte, who looked so peaceful that it made me smile.

The District Nurse arrived just as I was in the middle of the three o'clock feed, 'You are doing it all perfectly, Mrs Ogilvie, well done.' Even though she sounded a bit patronising I didn't really mind, as it was a relief to know that I was doing everything right.

'If I were you, I would ask your mother to help with the night feeds, so that you can get a six hour break now and again at night and although your baby mustn't go out into the fresh air just yet, you should try to sit in the garden whenever you can and walk to the shops. I'll ask your Doctor to prescribe a good tonic. Once the bleeding has stopped you'll feel much better.' When she was at the door she turned to me and said, 'I'll come to see you tomorrow and then, as you are doing so well, I'll miss a day if you don't mind, as I have six other babies to check!'

I looked at my watch and realising that my mother should be here in about an hour, I thought that I'd have a rest, so that I would feel fresh when she arrived.

I was still asleep when I heard Mrs Briars talking to someone in the hall. It was my mother, apologising for having so much baggage with her. 'I brought so many baby things and food from the farm that I needed two porters!' she tittered.

I was so thrilled to see her that I ran into her arms like a child and started crying, 'Oh Mummy, thank you so much for coming.'

'There, there darling we'll soon sort it all out,' my mother said trying to comfort me. 'Leave it to me and just pretend I am a Red Cross nurse that's come to help you!'

My mother took a long look at Charlotte before smiling at me and saying, 'Oh she is absolutely adorable darling.'

412

She then lifted her granddaughter out of the drawer and put her into the new pretty frilly basket that she had brought with her, which she told me had a horsehair mattress, a waterproof sheet and flannelette under sheet.

'I see you are swaddling her, what a sensible idea,' my mother said, 'your Nanny used to do that for you when you were a tiny baby too.'

After leaving me to feed Charlotte, she went through to the main house and knocked on Mrs Briar's door who told her that the housekeeper had put her things in the spare bedroom and to please call Mrs Wallace if she couldn't find anything and then to my surprise I heard her ask my mother to join her for a sherry before supper if she wasn't too tired after the long journey.

After the next feed, I put Charlotte back in her new basket and then tied a ribbon on the hood to remind me which side she was to lie on after her next feed and then had a hot bath, which was bliss. As I changed into my nightgown and put on my dressing gown, I thought that if my mother could feed Charlotte at nine then I would be able to sleep until midnight, which would make a pleasant change.

When we had finished our supper, I showed my mother how to make up Charlotte's feed, which jug to heat the bottle in, and which pail I used for nappy soaking and which one I used for the dirty ones. She then picked up her book and told me to get some sleep while she saw to the nine o'clock feed. 'If I need help I promise I'll wake you up,' my mother said firmly.

It felt so good, knowing that I could drift off to sleep without worrying about Charlotte and that if she did suddenly wake up my mother would look after her. I could smell Duncan's aftershave on the pillow, which made me miss him terribly but I was so exhausted that any further thoughts vanished and I must have fallen straight to sleep, as the next thing I remembered was the alarm going off at midnight. I got up to feed Charlotte and then an hour or so later I went back to bed and slept soundly until the 3am feed. Thankfully my mother insisted on doing the 6am one.

After breakfast, my mother told me that she was going to the shops to buy a bottle of brandy. 'A spoonful of brandy in a cup of tea will stop us falling over with exhaustion,' she chuckled.

When she got back, she told me that the grocer had roared with laughter after she had told him that it was for 'emergency purposes', as we needed the brandy to lace our tea, while we were saving a baby's life and feeding it every three hours!

As the District Nurse had suggested that I start doing some exercise to regain my strength, I now made myself go for daily walks to the beach and back to get some fresh air. My mother took care of Charlotte while I was out, and if she was busy, my daughter's two self-appointed 'Aunties', Mrs Briars and Mrs Wallace, held the fort.

One evening I rang my cousin, Jane, to tell her all about Charlotte. She was really thrilled for me. 'Once you go to Hilltop House I'll come and see you. I can be Charlotte's godmother can't I?' she begged. This made me wonder whether I should contact Duncan's cousin, Ian, as he had told us that he would like to be one of the godfathers to our first child. Jane then told me that she had some news of her own. She had been seeing one of her cousins whenever he was on leave and it was obvious that she was very keen on him.

Three weeks later, I noticed that Charlotte seemed to be awake for longer periods and kept turning her head when she heard someone speaking. She had now caught up on her birth weight and was thriving, so the District Nurse told me that there was no need to keep doing the three am feed anymore, which was wonderful news.

When the nurse next came to see us she suggested that I take her into the garden for some sun and fresh air, which she loved but when I came back inside to give her a bath in the washbasin, she hated it and screamed blue murder. 'Wait until we can buy a baby bath where she can kick her legs,' my sensible mother suggested!

'Charlotte is doing just fine,' I was told a week later by the friendly nurse after she had weighed my tiny baby. 'You may take your baby to your mother's home now if you like, Mrs Ogilvie.'

'We'll fly from Liverpool to London' my mother said firmly, 'Daddy will meet us at the airport.'

The plane was a lot cleaner and quicker than the train. The air hostess placed the Moses basket in the aisle between the seats, and for the first time I noticed that Charlotte was now staring back at all the people who were smiling down at her. It was lovely to see her so content.

When my father saw his little granddaughter for the first time, I could see tears on his cheeks.

'Oh Blossom,' he said placing his arm tightly around my waist, 'Thank you for this wonderful gift,' That made me start crying and then when I looked at my mother she was mopping her eyes with a handkerchief. What a family!

When we arrived at Hilltop House, I could see why my father had been so anxious to live there. The house was beautiful. While my mother looked after my daughter, I had a good look around. The two tiny rooms at the top of the back staircase were perfect, as it meant that I could sleep in the room next to Charlotte. One of the rooms had been converted into a child's bedroom and decorated in primrose and cream with a frieze of farm animals on the walls. There was even a cot in one corner ready for when she grew a bit bigger and a small washbasin in the corner with a changing table and a comfortable basket chair for me to sit in while I fed her.

After I had unpacked, I went downstairs for tea. I asked my mother where Agnes was. 'She's having a much needed holiday. We sent her back to Ireland to see her family for a couple of months, as she hasn't seen them since the war started,' my mother explained, 'so we have employed a Latvian refugee called Irina until she returns.' She then told me that my father had put Irina and her two young children in one of the farm cottages, so that she had a life of her own, as she had been through hell before coming to Britain, 'I'll let her tell you herself how she escaped from Latvia and managed to get here to safety. It's quite a story.'

After getting Charlotte's next feed ready, my mother suggested we write a list of anything that I still needed to buy for her when we next went to East Grinstead, and while we did that my father held his granddaughter in his arms and told her all about the moo cows and piggy wiggies he had on his farm. It was obvious to see that he had completely fallen in love with Charlotte already.

When my father handed her back to me, he said that he was just popping down to the farm to have a chat with Fritz, the German P.O.W, who was looking after the cows, and Paulo, the Italian P.O.W, who was helping him manage the home farm. I was a bit taken aback, as my parents had never mentioned that they had prisoners of war working for them, and I wondered how long it would be before they were repatriated now that the war in Europe was over.

After breakfast, while I was sterilising Charlotte's feeding bottles, I finally met Irina, our Latvian refugee. She told me how she had managed to escape with her children from the advancing Russian army and eventually found their way to Britain. I couldn't begin to imagine what the poor woman had been through, no wonder she looked so stressed.

When I gave my daughter her first bath at Hilltop House, instead of enjoying it, Charlotte screamed blue murder.

'May I help?' Irina offered. When I nodded, she immediately took one of the muslin nappies that I had got ready to put on her once her bath was over, and laid it over her chest and then just tucked it around her upper arms. The yelling stopped at once.

'I think she not like being without clothes on! Tomorrow, you keep on her vest until she feel safe, yes?' Irina said, so for the next few days, I did as she suggested and was amazed that this trick seemed to work so well.

A few days later, Irina told me about her life in Latvia before the war. 'We lived in comfort, head held high, owing no debts and with our farm paying for itself. Then we heard that the Russian soldiers were raping all the women and young girls and sending young boys to be slave labourers in Russia, so my husband, Stephan, said go take the two young ones and stay away until the war is over and our country free. We walked from one village to the next until Allied troops saw us and gave us lift, and they... how you say?... asked no favours.' Irina then turned around to make sure my mother wasn't listening and whispered to me, 'but if I had to I would have done 'anything' to save my children from harm.' I wondered if I would do 'anything' to save Charlotte from harm and knew the answer straight away, feeling sure that every other mother would do whatever it took to protect her young too.

When I asked Irina how often she had received letters from her husband, who had remained behind with their eldest son to help care for the animals on their farm, her eyes filled with tears, as she told me she still hadn't heard from them. I felt very sad for her and putting my arms around her in a gentle embrace, I told her that she must try to be brave. It was an easy thing to say but not so easy to do. I knew only too well because I was still crying every night worrying whether Duncan was still alive.

The next day, I received an air letter from Duncan. My hands were shaking so much that I couldn't open the envelope to start with. When I finally read the letter I was overjoyed to hear that he was fit and well but had been worked off his feet, which is why he hadn't been able to write before.

'I am now in Trincomalee, which is the main launching point for British naval operations, and where I send our pilots to join their carriers from. It is a dreadful blood bath for both sides, but don't worry, we are relatively safe here.' He added a P.S at the bottom of the letter 'Please send me a photograph of you with Charlotte.'

When William came home for the holidays, I asked him to take a photograph of us and then sent it to Duncan in my next letter. My brother was thrilled to bits with the farm and spent hours working out ways to organise a better or more economical system to run it with my father. He even found out how to make clotted cream from the rich milk from the cows, teaching Irina how to leave the milk in a bowl overnight on the top of the Aga stove to warm and then skim the cream off the top to use on the strawberries and raspberries. It was lovely having William home but I wished that Peter could be here too.

One morning I woke up with a start, as I had one of my 'funny feelings' again, but this time I felt that Duncan was in distress. Obviously there was no way I could be certain but having had these strange feelings in the past, I began to fuss about all the possible things that could be wrong. When I received a letter from Duncan, two weeks later, I knew that my fears had been justified.

As I read his letter, I started crying. My mother came to see why I was sobbing, so I let her read the letter.

'While we were on a reconnaissance flight, my engine suddenly failed, so I had to try to bail out but when I grabbed the release-knob the damn hood wouldn't budge. Luckily I remembered my training and after I had reduced the speed of the plane I was able to open the hood, release my safety harness, disconnect the oxygen tube and then bail out or to be more accurate I was then thrown out of the cockpit. However, while I had been doing all this, the plane suddenly dived. As I was falling out of the plane, the tail plane must have hit the back of my left leg and my heel and also across my shoulders causing rather deep cuts, which were damn painful I can tell you. I was very grateful to see my chute open above me and when I looked down all I could see was the surface of the sea rushing up towards me. I had barely inflated my Mae West when there was a big splash and I rather unceremoniously hit the water. I went under for a moment but fortunately, as my life vest was now fully inflated, I was able to get my head above water again pretty quickly. The parachute strings had become entangled around my legs so I took off my boots and managed to get myself loose. I then inflated my rubber dinghy and once I struggled into it I suddenly remembered the dye, that we had been instructed to use, so that we could be spotted from the air, but when I tried to open the bottle it burst and instead of going into the sea it got into my wounds, which hurt like hell. However, in the end I got most of the dye into the sea and thankfully it did its job and I was eventually rescued. While I was in the ocean I must have passed out for quite a while, before I was pulled on board the ship that rescued me, because one of the crew told me that I was now an official member of The Goldfish club! Apparently if you come down in the sea and are in 'the drink' for over 24 hours this is the honour they bestow you. I would have preferred the drink! Try not to worry too much, my darling, as I'm now in hospital and in the good hands of a fine doctor called Bunton who will soon get me back on my feet again. I have to get fit quickly, as there is something big about to happen over here and I want to be in the thick of it!'

My mother put the letter down and tried to comfort me, as best she could but the tears just wouldn't stop flowing. In the end it was the sound of Charlotte crying that made me pull myself together and go to see to her.

One evening in August, on the nine o'clock news, we heard that something called an atomic bomb had been dropped on the Japanese city of Hiroshima. Apparently it was two thousand times more powerful than the largest bomb used up to now, and it had been dropped from an American B-29 Super Fortress, called the Enola Gay. I tried not to think about the amount of people who must have been killed by it, as it was too horrific.

Three days later, the Americans dropped another bomb, but this time it was on the city of Nagasaki. The bomb had been given the nickname 'Fat Man', after Winston Churchill.

On the 14th August, the Japanese surrendered and the war was finally over.

CHAPTER 19

1945-46

Before Duncan left for Ceylon, we had agreed that Charlotte should be christened while he was away, as at that time we had no idea of how long the war with Japan would go on. We had also agreed that she should be christened in England. However Duncan had insisted that his cousin and best man Ian, was there in his absence.

Both Ian and Jane had agreed to be godparents and said they could come to the christening in Sussex, but Babs, Charlottes' other godmother, was unable to come at the last minute as her husband had been wounded and was in a hospital in Edinburgh having his arm amputated, so as Aunt Beth was my godmother, I asked her if she would stand in for her, which she said she would be 'absolutely thrilled' to do.

Aunt Beth made a beautiful Christening robe for Charlotte, out of some precious lace that she had been keeping for a 'special occasion', but I had nothing special to wear, so I wore the same suit that I'd worn on my honeymoon and added a double strand of pearls around my neck. However, the overall effect was rather spoilt because I was still wearing the big nappy pin that I'd attached to the lapel of my jacket when I had to quickly change Charlotte, just before leaving for the Christening. When Jane saw what I had done she got the giggles and that set me off too. Some things never change.

An ex-naval Chaplin took the service, which went without a hitch and thankfully Charlotte didn't cry at all. After the christening we all went back to Hilltop for tea in the garden. Irina had made a wonderful cake, which was a layered sponge cake filled with strawberries from my parent's garden and cream from the cows on the home farm.

While we were clearing up Jane's boyfriend, Jim, turned up. He told us that his regiment was stationed nearby and that he had been granted a 72 pass, so we invited him to stay. Jane moved in with me, sharing the double bed, so that Jim could sleep in the spare room. This was a big mistake, as she pestered me all night to tell her exactly what to expect on the first night of her honeymoon, as Jim had just proposed to her!

When everyone had left the next day, I finally had time to write a long letter to Duncan to tell him about the christening and how well behaved his daughter had been. I missed him so much and knew he would feel disappointed that he hadn't been able to be there, so I tried to describe the day in as much detail as I could.

That evening we all listened to the news on the wireless and heard horrific accounts of what the Allied troops had found at Hitler's numerous concentration camps. We sat there in silence, completely stunned. I just couldn't understand how one human being could do such awful atrocities to another.

I was loath to take Charlotte away from the security of my parent's home, but realised that it was now time for me to be independent and look for a home for my own family. When I discussed the idea with my father he advised me not to be in too much of a hurry, as it could be months before Duncan was freed of his duties and allowed to return home.

However, I still thought that it might be a sensible idea to rent a small cottage somewhere near Duncan's parents, where I hoped it would be quiet enough for him to revise and get ready to return to University to finish his degree, so I wrote to my in-laws to ask them if it would be too much trouble for them if Charlotte and I came to stay for a week or two while looking for our new home. They wrote back straight away telling me to come whenever it suited me and that Celia would be glad of some young company. 'The two wee bairns can be together,' Father John had written 'and it will be a joy to see the cousins kicking on their blankets side by side!' I hadn't appreciated until that moment that Celia's son, Christopher, would be Charlotte's cousin and the thought made me smile.

A week later I left for Perth, and when I arrived Grandpa John and Granny Bumble, as they were now calling themselves, were over the moon to see their granddaughter. Celia was just as excited and when she hugged Charlotte, she said, 'She's not a bit like Duncan but she is the image of you!' When I saw how beautiful Christopher was and how much Celia obviously adored him, I felt very happy to be a part of this very special and loving family.

After breakfast one day, Grandpa John gave me a copy of the Scotsman and pointed to the page advertising houses and flats for rent, 'Mary, take a look at this small advertisement, it's for a cottage in Pitlochry.'

Excitedly I read the advertisement, which said that the owner wanted to have someone living in her cottage during the winter months to keep out the damp. The rent was only three pounds ten shillings a week, so I knew that we could afford to pay the rent from the money Duncan had been paying into our new joint account, so decided to go and see the cottage. Grandpa John contacted the agent for me and offered himself as a guarantor and then a few days later he drove me to Pitlochry, while Granny Bumble looked after Charlotte.

Garden Cottage was halfway up a very steep hill on the edge of the small market town and looked like something you might see in a picture book with roses around the front door and tidy flowerbeds everywhere. When we went inside, the first thing I noticed was that the kitchen had an old fashioned dryer, like my mother-in-law used with a pulley system attached to her kitchen ceiling. The whole cottage was furnished quite prettily, so all I would need to buy was a towel horse to put the nappies on to air in front of the fire overnight. I decided then and there to rent it for four months with an option for longer if required.

Before we left Grandpa John wanted to take a look in the garden shed and was pleased to see a hand mower, which he said he would use when he came to visit, so that he could keep the small lawn cut for me. I thought the shed would be a good place to leave Charlotte's pram overnight. Next to the shed was a coalhouse with fuel for the fire in the small sitting room, which we would need soon, as winter wasn't too far away.

The next weekend, Grandpa John arranged for a small carrier to take our things to Pitlochry, which consisted of Charlotte's pram and the utility cot that I'd bought for her when she out grew her basket, her bath, piles of toys and some clothes and nappies. My cases looked insignificant against all her clobber!

Both Duncan's parents came with us to drop Charlotte and me off at our new home, and when we arrived Granny Bumble said, 'Duncan will be delighted dear, it will be perfect for you all until he's in Edinburgh and it's only an hour away from us, so we can see one another often. Now don't hesitate to ring to ask for help or advice if the hot water system doesn't work or you need John to chop logs for a fire next month,' she smiled. I hugged her and said I'd ring her often to report on Charlotte's progress and once I'd got the hang of how the oven worked I'd invite them all for lunch one weekend.

I was so happy to have my own home that it never dawned on me that I might feel a bit lonely and alone here, with just Charlotte for company. I was fine to start with until I began hearing the odd creak and groan in the rafters in the evenings, which did frighten me a little, but I eventually got used to the strange sounds and soon got myself into a routine, lighting the fire every afternoon, so that the cottage was lovely and warm by the evening.

I received a letter from Duncan the following week, telling me that his leg wound was still not healing properly, but as he had so much work to do he couldn't do much about it at the moment, especially as his job of keeping the aerodrome open for planes to land with extra supplies was so crucial right now. Although he was frustrated by the slow healing process, he reassured me that he was in good spirits and then recounted a funny story he had been told by one of his junior officers.

'As they haven't got enough vehicles at the aerodrome in Ukussa, the planes are being moved around the airfield by Asian elephants, with an Indian minder sitting on top of each one to guide them. However, apparently one of the elephants took a dislike to a 'parked' Fairey Swordfish and decided to ram into it. The minder did his very best to control the animal but to no avail and by the time he got the elephant under control again there was very little left to be salvaged from the poor old Bi-plane. Apparently, the elephant got off with a reprimand, but the plane had to be 'put down'!' I laughed so much that I nearly fell off my chair. Oh how I missed my dear, funny husband.

Two whole months went by with only the occasional air letter from Duncan, and I had no idea of when he would be free to come home, so I decided to phone my parents to invite myself for Christmas, as I knew they would love to see Charlotte again. Just as I had made this decision I looked out of the window and saw a telegram boy walking up the path. Fear flooded through my whole body. Telegrams usually meant bad news.

When I opened the telegram I burst into tears. The relief knowing that not only was my wonderful Duncan still alive, but that he was on his way home was overwhelming. I didn't really take in the fact that the reason he was being sent home was because his leg wound had still not healed properly. All I could think of was that I would be with him again in a few days, so I rang my in-laws straightaway to tell them the good news.

When Grandpa John answered the phone, he didn't sound as thrilled to hear the news, as I had thought he would be. I then discovered why. He had received a long letter from Duncan telling them that he was being sent back to see a specialist, as his wound was much worse than he had let me believe and he was going to have to spend some time in hospital either in Perth or London, but wouldn't know where until he reported to the Admiralty. 'Stay where you are Mary. Duncan will ring us when he arrives and tell us his plans and hopefully he'll get a week's leave before beginning his treatment.'

'What's wrong with his leg?' I asked.

'It keeps going septic apparently, but the wound on his back has closed now, so that's something to be thankful for, isn't it?' Grandpa John said quietly.

That night I rang my parents to tell them the news, and my father told me that if Duncan had to go to hospital in London, then I should shut up the cottage and come straight back to them. Two days later, just as I was about to feed Charlotte the phone rang and it was Duncan. 'I'm on my way Mary, I want to hold you in my arms as soon as possible, I'll be with you in time for a late breakfast!' He then rang off before I had a chance to say a word. I was so happy to hear his voice again that I didn't worry that he'd hung up so quickly, and just presumed that he had to rush to catch the overnight train.

The following morning I fed Charlotte a little earlier than usual, so that I could get the washing done before Duncan arrived. I was just about to hang it on the line when I saw a taxi pull up.

When I opened the front door I saw Duncan struggling to get out of the taxi with a pair of crutches. He looked so pale and thin that I had to bite my lip to stop myself crying. I could tell that even with crutches, he was finding it hard to walk. I then heard him ask the taxi driver if he would carry his small overnight case to the cottage for him, which made me wonder where the rest of his luggage was.

When Duncan saw me he smiled and as soon as we were back inside the cottage he let the crutches fall to the floor and took me in his arms. I had tears streaming down my cheeks and sobbed in his ear, 'I'll soon have you well again, my darling.'

'Where is Charlotte?' he asked looking around for signs of his daughter.

'She's on a rug in the sitting room,' I laughed through my tears, 'she likes to be free and kick her little legs in the air before I put her in her pram for a nap.'

I handed Duncan his crutches, so that he could take himself into the sitting room to see Charlotte. As he collapsed into one of the armchairs, I noticed him wince with pain. I picked Charlotte up and put her carefully on Duncan's lap, 'She's unbelievably beautiful,' he whispered.

'If she hurts your leg let me know and I will put her back on her rug,' I told him.

'It's not my leg, it's my wretched heel,' he said with a sigh, 'it's a damn nuisance.'

Charlotte couldn't take her eyes off her father, and to me it looked as if she was trying to remember where she'd last seen him, even though I knew that wasn't possible, as she'd only been hours old when he'd last held her in his arms. Then suddenly she put out a hand and patted his cheek, which was very touching until she spoilt the tender moment with a loud burp. We both laughed and then a moment later I could see tears running down Duncan's cheeks, 'Oh Mary, I thought I'd never live to see this day,' he said quietly 'I quite expected to drift in the dinghy for days, as I was a tiny blob in a very large ocean but thank God one of the other pilots eventually spotted me.'

Duncan told me that he felt lucky, as if this had happened to him at the beginning of the war he wouldn't have survived, because it was only after the Battle of Britain in 1941 that pilots were equipped with dinghy packs, which were attached to their parachute harness. He then told me about the terrible ordeal he had been through. 'I had no idea of how high I was above the sea, or how fast I was falling but I hit the sea without being able to take a deep breath first, so it was obviously closer than I'd thought and it was damn cold! After I broke the surface and managed to get my breath back, I released myself from my parachute harness, got my dingy pack off and started inflating it. I had been told there were sharks in those waters, so despite being in extreme pain I clambered into that little dingy as quickly as I possibly could. I was far too tired to paddle, so I broke open the pack of my sea marker dye with the intention of releasing it into the sea to make a trail behind the dingy, which I hoped would make me be easily seen from the air but unfortunately as I tore the pack open the dye spilt all over my wound and it stung like hell. After floating for what seemed like many hours, my watch had packed in, so I had no idea how long I'd been in the water, a searching aircraft from my squadron did spot the trail left by the dye in the water and a ship was then directed to me and I was eventually rescued.'

As Duncan slowly recounted this traumatic event, I fought back the tears, which was hard as all I wanted to do was hold him tight and never let him out of my sight again. Charlotte broke the tension by crying and I realised it must be time for her next meal. She was now having a few mouthfuls of solid food and as long as I added a little brown sugar she would eat it; if I didn't she would spit it out in disgust.

After feeding Charlotte, I gave her back to Duncan to hold and carried his bag up to our room, wondering whether he'd manage to get up the stairs on his crutches. When I came back downstairs, I noticed beads of sweat on Duncan's brow so asked him if he had a fever, but he said it was just the pain and asked me if I would mind getting him a glass of water, so that he could swallow a couple of pain killers. 'I have to take them every four hours, less sometimes, as they help ease the pain.'

I then told him all about the Christening and how well behaved his daughter had been and how Ian had done his godfather duties so diligently, but instead of looking interested in what I was saying, he kept looking at his watch.

'Are you expecting a phone call?' I asked feeling a bit concerned.

'No darling, I'm just checking the time to see how long it will be before I can take some more painkillers,' Duncan sighed. 'Is there a lavatory downstairs? I can't manage to get up the stairs right now darling.' Thankfully there was, and while he hobbled on his crutches to go and have a pee, I finally understood why Duncan had been sent home. He was on the verge of a total collapse.

After a light lunch, Duncan said he could heave himself up the stairs on his backside one step at a time, if I wouldn't mind carrying his crutches for him. The painkillers must have taken effect quite quickly, as he managed to get to the top of the stairs without any difficulty, but when I went to lift his sore leg onto the bed, he pushed me away, and yelled, 'Don't touch it or I'll scream!'

Suddenly a strange sweet sickly smell hit me in the face, which I recognised immediately from my nursing days in Woking hospital. It was gangrene.

I waited for Duncan to fall asleep and then went downstairs to ring the doctor, but it was his assistant who answered the phone, so I told her that I desperately needed to talk to the doctor as soon as possible. When I told her why, she said that the doctor would be with me in ten minutes.

Doctor Frazer was as good as his assistant's word, and exactly ten minutes later I saw him striding up the garden path. 'Where is he?' he boomed.

'Upstairs, first room on the left,' I replied.

The doctor smiled and then said, 'Thank you, now I want you to boil some hot water for me please.'

'Yes of course doctor,' I said, thinking he must need the hot water to sterilise a scalpel or something like that. 'Is there anything else you want me to do?'

'Yes. After the water has boiled, I'd like you to pour it into a pot, add some tea and then find some milk and sugar!' he grinned. 'I think a good strong cup of tea is always the best remedy in a crisis, don't you?' He then went upstairs to see Duncan.

I felt strangely reassured by the doctor's easy-going manner. However, my sense of relief was short lived when the doctor came back downstairs and said, 'Mrs Ogilvie, there is nothing I can personally do. Your husband should have gone straight to hospital two days ago instead of coming up to Scotland to see you, so I'm sorry but he must go to the hospital in Perth now... at once!'

I stared at him in shock, as he continued talking. 'I am going to phone for an ambulance, as your husband needs immediate treatment.' He then asked me where the phone was, so I pointed to the table near the door. 'Now then, let's have that cup of tea while we wait shall we?' he said before making the call.

After he had hung up I asked him if it was all right for me to take a cup of tea up to Duncan.

'No my dear, I'm afraid not,' the doctor said and then explained why. 'Your husband may have to be operated on this evening, so its better if he has nothing to drink or eat beforehand.'

426

I longed to go up and lie beside my poor sick husband and hold him in my arms but felt it would be rude to leave this kind doctor on his own to wait for the ambulance, so instead I answered his questions as best I could. What had Duncan been doing at Trincomalee? Was he usually fit and healthy? Could I think of any reason why he didn't go straight to hospital, as soon as he had arrived in England, other than wanting to see Charlotte and me?

When the ambulance had arrived, the doctor gave Duncan an injection, which made him lose consciousness almost immediately. He was then put on a stretcher, carried down the narrow stairs, put into the back of the ambulance and driven straight to hospital. I was numb with shock and felt like screaming, but when I saw that my neighbours were watching, I rushed back indoors, before allowing myself to cry.

Doctor Frazer followed me inside the house, and said, 'I promise that I will ring you as soon as I know what the treatment is going to be, and whether he has to have an operation or not. Meanwhile is there anyone you can stay with in Perth so that you can keep his spirits up by visiting him every day?' I told him that we could stay with Duncan's parents. He said that was good to know and then left.

I was in such shock that I felt like a zombie but somehow managed to feed Charlotte and put her to bed, before ringing Grandpa John to tell him that his son was on his way to Perth hospital.

'They have taken him away in an ambulance, as his leg has gangrene and it's rotting,' I sobbed.

'Oh, I see,' Grandpa John said and then after a short pause added, 'Right this is what we are going to do, Mary. Pack a few clothes and I'll come and collect you and bring you here tomorrow and meanwhile I'll call the hospital to ask if I can see Duncan tonight, as my poor boy must be out of his mind with worry having to leave you so soon.'

I went into the kitchen to get something to eat, but when I looked in the larder and saw the chicken casserole that I'd prepared earlier, as a welcome home treat for Duncan, I started crying again.

Grandpa John rang me early the next morning to tell me that Duncan was going to be transferred to St Georges' hospital in London, as they had the very best treatment there, so instead of coming to stay with them, I should go straight back to my parents instead.

When I rang my parents to tell them what had happened, my father told me to come home at once. He then promised to get in touch with my cousin, Marcus, to ask him to keep an eye on Duncan once he had been admitted to the London hospital.

The following day Grandpa John turned up after lunch to pick us up and before we left, he made sure that everything in the cottage was turned off, so that it was safe to leave empty for however long I ended up being away. While he did that, I booked a ticket on the overnight train to London. The train journey was uneventful and thankfully Charlotte slept for most of the time, but I was too anxious thinking about Duncan to get much sleep myself.

When we eventually arrived at Hilltop House, my mother came outside to welcome us home and took Charlotte from me. My father then told me that my cousin, Marcus had rung him earlier that day to say that he was going to be allowed to confer with the specialist in charge of Duncan's treatment and not to worry, as Duncan was being sedated with morphine, so wouldn't be in any pain at the moment.

It soon became apparent that Duncan was going to be in the London hospital for quite some time, so my mother decided to employ a Norland Nanny to look after Charlotte. This would allow me to travel up and down to London to visit my husband without having to worry about our daughter all the time. I was very grateful because I thought that if Duncan could see me every day, it would help him recuperate and after all we still had a lot of catching up to do.

When the Nanny arrived she took over looking after Charlotte completely, so I was now free to travel up to London to visit Duncan. Aunt Beth insisted on coming with me the first time to give me some moral support. On the way to the hospital we stopped off to buy some sweets, magazines and flowers, and when we got there Aunt Beth said she's wait for me, so that I could have the some time with Duncan on my own.

I wasn't quite sure what to expect, so when a nurse led me to his ward and I saw him propped up by a couple of pillows in his bed, I had to force myself not to cry, as he looked truly awful and was obviously very unwell the poor man. He winced when he lent over to give me a kiss and then we talked about Charlotte for a while, until a nurse came to give him an injection, which I presumed was morphine, as he fell asleep almost at once. When Aunt

Beth came to find me she was shocked at how ill Duncan looked and suggested that we go back to her flat until it was time for me to go home.

I did the same journey to and from London every day for the next two weeks and although Duncan didn't seem to be getting any better, he kept telling me that he was 'doing just fine', so I made a big effort to remain as cheerful as I could, and made silly jokes and chatted to the other patients in the ward with him, who were mostly army officers with arm or leg wounds, before going home again.

I rang Duncan's parents every evening to keep them updated about Duncan and reassured them that I would let them know if there was any change. Grandpa John always sounded so cheerful on the phone that I wondered whether he hadn't really taken in just how ill his son was.

On my next visit, I noticed that everyone else in the ward seemed to be getting better except for Duncan, and I was now getting very concerned that he was still in such great pain, so I asked Marcus if he could talk to the doctor in charge again.

As my cousin, Jane, was now back at home with her family in St John's Wood, she suggested that we meet up for lunch the next day, so that she would then come and visit Duncan with me. On the way there, we talked about her cousin, Jim, who would soon be 'demobbed' and about their plans for the future.

When we arrived at the entrance to Duncan's ward, Marcus was waiting for us. For a brief moment, I thought that Duncan was being sent home, but when Marcus didn't smile at me, or make one of his usual funny jokes, I realised something must be very wrong.

'I am glad that Jane is with you Mary, as the specialist wants to see you,' he said quietly, 'and I'm afraid he hasn't got good news.'

I suddenly realised the seriousness of the situation and began to shake. Jane must have noticed, as she slipped her arm around my shoulder and held me close, so that I could lean my weight against her.

A moment later the specialist surgeon arrived and explained to us that Duncan's leg was not responding to treatment. They had tried everything, even radium exposure, but that had made it worse. Duncan's heel was so damaged that his foot was almost hanging off his leg and the infection was now creeping up his leg.

'The only treatment left is to amputate his left leg well above the infected area,' the specialist said slowly.

I felt faint and couldn't believe what I was hearing. I gripped Jane's hand until she gasped with pain.

'If he'd gone to hospital when he had first arrived instead of coming to be with me, would that have made any difference?' I asked him.

'No ,Mrs Ogilvie, the infection should have been treated months ago, when he was still in Ceylon,' he said. 'I think the dye that got into his wound is most probably responsible for the damage, but we can't really be certain. I'm really sorry, but if we don't operate at once he will lose his life, not just his leg.'

I felt like screaming but then Marcus gave me a gentle hug and said, 'you must try to be brave Mary and think positive. Duncan will need you more than ever after his amputation.' I knew that he was right and tried to pull myself together. He then took me to see Duncan, but he was out for the count on morphine, so I just gave him a kiss and went back to the station with Jane and Marcus, who had insisted on accompanying me to make sure I got on the right train.

'I can't possibly look after Charlotte and Duncan on my own,' I whimpered, as we got to the station, 'not now that he is going to be an invalid, it's too much responsibility.'

'Of course you bloody well can, you silly cow!' Jane said firmly. 'You managed to look after Charlotte on your own when Duncan was away didn't you? So looking after him as well won't be that much harder, will it?

'Its time to stop thinking about yourself and start thinking about poor Duncan,' Marcus added as they helped me onto the train, 'so take a deep breath and be strong.'

Just as the whistle blew and the train started to pull away from the station, Jane called out, 'I'll ring you every evening, I promise.'

They were right of course, I knew that I could manage perfectly well if I put my mind to it. I now needed to stop being selfish and start thinking about how I could make my poor husband's life easier, rather than adding to his troubles. It was time to grow up.

When I got home, my mother hugged me, and said, 'Oh my poor darling, don't give in, we've come through the war and we'll get thought this too.'

She then told me that Marcus had rung earlier to tell them the awful news, and that Aunt Beth was on her way down to give us her support.

'We must let Duncan's parents know,' I said to my parents, 'they will be devastated when they hear what has happened to him.'

'I'll ring them right now,' my father assured me, as he helped himself to a double scotch before leaving the room to make the call.

Just as we were thinking about going to bed, the phone rang. I was worried that it was more bad news, but it was quite the opposite, thank goodness. It was an Officer in Peter's regiment who had just called to tell us that that my brother was on his way back and that he'd be home by the New Year. He warned us that Peter was very thin, as he had been sick with malaria but otherwise he was fine. This was marvellous news and cheered us all up.

'Irina will soon fatten him up!' my mother said smiling for the first time since I had returned home.

Peter had not been able to keep in touch very often, during his time in the Intelligence Corp in Burma, and I wondered how he would adjust to civilian life now that the war was over. I longed to see him again and knew that he would do all he could to help Duncan and meanwhile my other brother, William, would do his best to look after me, until we were a complete family again.

The following day Marcus rang to tell us that Duncan was still recovering from his operation, so not to come and see him until he gave me the all clear. 'He needs a bit of time to come to terms with having lost one of his legs,' my cousin explained.

I was very worried how Duncan would react when he found out that his leg had been amputated and wasn't surprised that he needed some time on his own before seeing me, and to be honest I wasn't sure what my own reaction would be when I saw him with only one leg for the first time.

Two days later, Marcus rang to say that Duncan wanted to see me, so the next morning I took the train up to London. Before leaving home my mother took me to one side and said, 'Darling, try to remember that Duncan is still the same man you have always loved, so just tell him you love him. That's all he needs to hear from you right now, do you understand Mary?' I nodded. It was good advice and I did exactly what she suggested when I saw Duncan for the first time since his operation.

'I love you Duncan and I always will' I said and meant it more than ever.

A look of such joy came over Duncan's face that it made me smile and after I had lent over to give him a kiss he whispered, 'I am so lucky to have you.' He kissed me again and then said smiling, 'Well at least it just the one leg, not like poor old Tin Legs Bader!'

Douglas Bader had lost both his legs in a crash before the war, and then after being given 'tin legs' went on to become a Spitfire pilot and RAF Ace in the Battle of Britain and a national hero famous for his bravery. I felt that my husband was equally as brave, especially right now trying to make jokes so soon after his amputation just to make me feel at ease. I felt so in love with this special man at that moment, that I nearly burst into tears but having made a promise that I would put on a brave face when I was with him I stopped myself just in time.

Duncan suddenly yelled out in excruciating pain, so I called for the ward nurse.

'They call them phantom pains,' she said after she had given Duncan a sedative and then told me that perhaps I should go now and come back for a longer visit in a couple of days.

I rang Marcus that evening, and he explained that Duncan's 'phantom pain' was most likely to be a response to mixed signals to his brain. Apparently it was quite common, after an amputation.

'Chin up Mary, it could have been worse, at least his plane didn't catch fire and he hasn't ended being one of McIndoe's guinea pigs,' Marcus said before hanging up.

The next day I sat on the edge of Duncan's bed and we just held hands and talked about Charlotte, about Peter coming home, and about William demanding a stocking for Christmas despite now being sixteen!

When it was time for the patients to have their lunch, the ward nurse came to puff up Duncan's pillows, so that he could sit up to eat it and then told me it was time to leave. As I got up, Duncan told me not to come everyday but to come every other day, as then he would be able to get plenty of rest. It was obvious that he was still in a lot of pain and needed to get as much rest as he could get.

The next time I visited him, Duncan suggested that I spend Christmas Day with my family, as Marcus and Jane had said they would visit him on

Christmas morning and the hospital were putting on some special entertainment for the wounded servicemen that afternoon, so I promised that I would come the day after Boxing Day.

It was the first Christmas after the war, and also Charlotte's first Christmas, so I was very happy to be at home with my family, but at the same time I also felt sad, as I kept thinking about Duncan and hoped he wasn't suffering too much. However, when I next went to see him, he didn't appear to be in quite so much pain and seemed to be in much better spirits, so I thought that the doctor might have increased his morphine dosage over the last few days.

I spent New Year's Eve at home with my family, and while everyone wished each other a Happy New Year, I gave Charlotte her midnight feed.

'Although the war is over, my darling Blossom,' my father said quietly, 'you will need to put on a brave face more than ever this coming year, as its going to be a real challenge for you both and Duncan is going to need your full support.'

As I went to bed, my father's words still echoed in my mind. I knew my parents would always be there for me, but I also knew that the time had come for me to stand on my own two feet a bit more.

On New Year's Day 1946, Duncan's father rang me to see how we were. He then suggested that we discontinue renting our Pitlochry cottage to save money. This made good sense to me but I still felt sad at the thought that Duncan would never enjoy the home I had prepared for us. I told Grandpa John that I wasn't sure what to do with all our belongings that we had left there, however, he had already thought of that and told me that he and Bertie would collect our things and bring them back to his house, without me having to travel up there. I was very grateful and assured him that I would ring them with updates of Duncan's progress.

The next time I saw Duncan, he was sitting in a chair doing embroidery! I couldn't believe my eyes. There was my big tough husband sewing a cross-stitch cloth. He proudly showed it to me and when I took a closer inspection, I saw that the stitching on the back was as neat as the front. Whatever task he took on, he always tried his best. That was one of the many things I had always admired about him. When Duncan tried to make himself more comfortable, the knee rug that had been covering his lower half, fell to the floor and I suddenly saw just how much of his leg they had cut off. I nearly fainted at the sight but quickly managed to pull myself together and gently placed his rug over him again, tucking it around his thigh, as if he'd always only had one and a half legs.

'Don't come in tomorrow, darling, they're taking the stitches out,' he said quietly, as I lent down to kiss him goodbye, 'so I expect I will be a bit sore.'

On the way home, I thought how brave my darling Duncan was and felt an overwhelming sense of love for him.

When I got back to Hilltop House I was pleasantly surprised to see that my brother Peter had just arrived home. After giving him a long hug, I stood back to have a good look at him and was shocked to see that he had become incredibly thin and that his skin appeared to be almost yellow. He explained that this was because he had got very sick while he was in Burma but thankfully he was on the mend now. At dinner, I noticed that he hardly ate a thing, so I asked him if he wasn't feeling hungry. He told me that he still found it hard to eat normal food, as he had got so used to only having rice with whatever else could be found to add to it.

Two weeks later, when Duncan was finally allowed to leave hospital, my parents insisted that he come to Hilltop House to convalesce, until he could be fitted with a tin leg. When he arrived my father told him not to hesitate to ask if there was anything he needed.

'Well, a double scotch would be rather pleasant!' Duncan joked.

'I think we might be able manage that,' my father chuckled, 'actually I might have one too!"

I was relieved to see that Duncan was almost his old self again and that he had no difficulty getting himself around the house on his crutches. However, when it was time for us to go to bed, the stairs were too hard for him to navigate using the crutches so he heaved himself up one step at a time on his backside instead.

The following morning he offered to take Charlotte for a walk in the garden in her pram, but when he discovered that he couldn't push the pram and hold on to his crutches at the same time, he found a rope, tied it around his waist and then pulled her like a horse. She squealed with delight and cooed at him, which made him laugh. It was wonderful to see him smiling again.

Although we slept in the same bed and lay as closely to each other as we could, Duncan's leg was still too tender to move, so we supported it on a pillow, but it was too difficult for us to make love without hurting his leg. I promised him I didn't mind one bit, but he obviously did and became so stressed about it that I wondered whether it would be better if we slept in twin beds. When I suggested that idea, he whispered, 'Do you find my stump so repulsive that you didn't want to sleep with me anymore, Mary?'

'Of course not,' I told him, but I don't think he believed me.

I decided that I needed to talk to someone about this problem and decided that I would ask Archie McIndoe if he could help me, as I thought he would most probably know all about these sort of psychological problems, as his badly wounded patients had most probably had been in similar situations.

Although 'Uncle Archie' was very busy operating all day on his burn patients, he agreed to come to Hilltop House after work, and told me to not mention to Duncan that I had spoken to him about our problem, and just say that he was an old friend that wanted to meet him and see our baby.

When he arrived, he shook Duncan by the hand and then picked Charlotte up in his arms, kissed her forehead and told her she was even more beautiful than her mother. Duncan beamed with pride and offered Archie a whisky.

After the second whisky, I could tell that the two men were enjoying each other's sense of humour and getting on famously. I then overheard Archie say to Duncan, 'I was wondering if you could do me a huge favour and spare the time to come to my hospital in East Grinstead tomorrow?'

'Yes, of course, but why?' Duncan asked him.

'Well, you see Duncan, my boys get rather bored stuck in the wards, so I try to organise something interesting each day for them to help pass the time. They are mostly RAF personnel, so they would be really interested to hear about your time as a Fleet Air Arm pilot and about having to order your unruly squadron boys to toe the line and not drink before flying, you know that sort of thing!' he chuckled.

Before Duncan had a chance to refuse Uncle Archie turned to my father and asked, 'Will you drive him to us, or shall I send someone to fetch him? I'm sure that one of my recovering patients would be delighted for an excuse to drive a car again!'

My father said that he'd be happy to drop Duncan off, if someone else could bring him back, as he had a meeting at the British Legion to help organise housing for the returning troops.

'Good, that's settled then!' Archie said, turning to Duncan. 'I will expect you at twelve sharp, which will give us time for a couple of drinks before lunch with the boys and then if you are still sober you can do your talk!'

The following morning, Duncan put on his uniform, as it was the only suit that he had with him, and as I pinned the trouser leg up behind his knee on the side of his missing leg, he said that he might as well begin a new career giving lectures about the Fleet Air Arm, as it was obvious that he wouldn't be accepted as a Forest Officer now. I had never heard Duncan sound so bitter before and hoped that a day with Archie's 'guinea-pigs' wouldn't be too much for him and make things worse.

After Duncan and my father left to go to East Grinstead, I went to listen to Peter playing his viola. I had forgotten how talented he was, and wondered whether he would be able to earn a living playing in an orchestra now that he was back.

By five o'clock I started to get worried, as Duncan still hadn't returned home but a quarter of an hour later he breezed in with a young doctor by his side, both drunk as Lords, having gone to the local pub on the way home to top up a very boozy lunch. When Duncan introduced his new friend to me, there was something different about him but it took me a while to work out what it was. And then it struck me, he sounded happy.

Later that evening at dinner, my father asked Duncan, 'so how did it go with McIndoe today?'

'Guess what he said about my leg?' he asked. We all looked at him, waiting for the answer. 'He said that I can hide my tin leg inside a trouser leg, but his poor chaps can never hide their faces and some of them can't even remember what they looked like before they were burnt, poor sods. I feel so lucky compared to them.'

Meeting Uncle Archie had obviously had a positive effect on Duncan, and I decided that I would write a very grateful letter to him the next day.

As I went upstairs to get ready for bed, I overheard Duncan talking on the phone to his father, and when he said, 'I think its time I started thinking about coming back to Perth and begin swotting for my degree, if I'm going to become a Forest Officer, don't you?' I knew everything was going to be all right.

Before we left Hilltop House, Duncan spent a few hours every day with my father inspecting the hedges and ditches, as well as the farmland fences and boundaries. He then told the P.O.Ws how to get everything in good working order and how to produce fresh fruit and vegetables, so that they could be sold in the W.I village market.

As Duncan was unable to drive, at least until he had been given his artificial leg and learned how to drive one of the new specially designed cars for the disabled, I thought that it was the right time for me to learn to drive and the task fell to my brother, Peter. I was fairly confident in broad daylight, but it took me a little longer to get used to driving at night, despite my experience as a Night Vision Tester.

When it was time to leave my parents and go to Perth, my father insisted on driving us to London to catch the train. He had also made sure that Duncan had booked a first class sleeper with two lower births, which I was very glad about, as it meant that we could both sleep opposite each other and I wouldn't have to clamber up a ladder. However, Charlotte stayed wide-awake until after midnight obviously thinking that this was the perfect opportunity to 'talk' to her Daddy. 'Bow wow, cheep cheep, miaow' and so on mixed up with 'Dada' or 'Mama' and with squeals of laughter inbetween. Duncan loved every minute of it, but as I had got up at six am and it was now early morning, I was not amused and felt like throttling the pair of them.

Janet's husband, Bertie, had kindly come to pick us up at Perth station, and as Duncan wriggled himself into the front seat of the car, I took his crutches and put them on the back seat next to me and Charlotte, while our brother-in-law with the help of a porter stowed our luggage in the boot and on the roof-rack, as there was so much of it.

When we arrived, Duncan got out of the car and hobbled towards the house on his crutches. Granny Bumble was waiting to greet us but when she saw him, she immediately burst into tears. I could see her shoulders heaving, as she embraced her son. It must have been heart breaking for her, and although I knew Duncan didn't want her to pity him, he obviously understood that she needed to let her emotions out. However, later that day after she had fussed over him every time he struggled to get up, he finally snapped at her, 'I can manage, Mother!' This fussing went on for a week until she reluctantly accepted that not only could he manage, but that he would have to.

Once we were settled, Duncan and his father started searching the 'To Let' columns in 'The Scotsman' to see if there were any suitable houses, or ground floor flats to let in Edinburgh but they were all far too expensive. I began to get worried, as we couldn't stay with Duncan's parents forever.

'Why don't you and I go into the City and talk to the Estate agents?' Grandpa John suggested to me, 'and while we are there we can look for a B&B for Duncan to stay at when he has to go up for his interview.' So the next day we caught the early train to Edinburgh, promising Duncan we would be back before he noticed we had gone. But instead of finding a B&B, we found a small hotel that had a ground floor room, which would mean no steps for Duncan to have trouble with, and it was right on a bus route to the University, which would make it far easier for him to go back and forth to his studies. It was perfect.

The first Estate agent we found was a rather serious young man who told us that we would never find anything affordable that would suit our needs in the City. He then suggested that we look for a house way outside Edinburgh instead, 'I'll be sending you whatever comes in, but having a new young baby makes it far more difficult, as you'll be needing a garden to hang out the nappies and somewhere to put the pram and so on. But I'll do my best I promise.'

When Duncan was given a date for his interview to continue his BSc at Edinburgh University, I told him that I would come with him to help carry his overnight bag to the hotel, and then when he went for his interview I would 'do my own thing' and meet up with him again later for our evening meal. To my surprise Duncan didn't object. In fact he seemed relieved to have someone with him. It then occurred to me that, as he hadn't gone anywhere completely on his own since his amputation.

That night I felt Duncan tossing and turning, so I pulled his head onto my breast and held him close, just like dear Uncle Archie had once told me that 'good wives' should do, using their bosoms as a pillow to comfort their husbands. It worked and he soon relaxed and fell sound asleep.

After his interview, Duncan told me that his Professor had told him that even if he personally had to sit the examinations for all his old students himself, every single one of them who had served their country in the war would pass. He had also promised Duncan that he would give him extra tuition, if he needed it. I could see the relief on my husband's face. He would get a place at University after all.

A week before the term started, Duncan went into Edinburgh for a day with his father to visit the hospital to have a fitting for an artificial leg. While they were away, Celia and I decided that we would go for a walk with our babies that afternoon. As they had said they wouldn't be back until five, we were surprised when we got home from our walk to see that the men were already back. As soon as I opened the back door and saw Duncan's face, I knew something was wrong. He had been told that there was no way he would be able to use an artificial leg for a long time yet, as his 'stump' was taking longer to heal than expected, so he would have to go back to University on crutches.

'So what?' I said trying to sound positive. 'At least you have been accepted. I'll buy you a new fishing bag for your books and you can put it over your shoulder like a school satchel!'

'Oh Mary!' he chuckled. 'What would I do without you?' So that's what we did and I bought him a whole new set of pencils, rubbers and a fountain pen to go in his new 'school bag'.

The following morning a large envelope plopped onto the doormat, addressed to Duncan. Thinking it was just a formal letter from the hospital to confirm what they had already told him, he left it on the study table to read later. When he eventually got around to opening it at lunchtime he said, 'Well, that could be interesting.'

'What could be darling?' I asked him.

'The young Estate agent has sent us the details of a house he thinks might be suitable, but it's not in Edinburgh, it's in Peebles, which would be an hour's commute each way.' Duncan then checked the monthly rent, 'Good heavens Mary! The rent for the house is unbelievably low, so we can afford it!'

When Duncan read the description of the fully furnished house to me, he said that there were four bedrooms, a decent sized sitting room and a dining room, a kitchen plus a scullery and a walk in larder. The garden was well kept and had a stream that ran along the bottom boundary. There was a coal shed and a garden shed but no garage. As we didn't own a car yet, that was not going to be a problem. However, I thought that there must be something wrong with this house, as it was just too good to be true, especially if it was going to cost so little.

When we told Grandpa John he said, 'I'll drive you down there to see it Duncan, as I haven't been to Peebles for years and would love to see it again. I remember the town as being delightful and rather pretty. It was very prosperous at one time having busy wool mills and a cattle market, if I remember correctly.'

A few days later Duncan and his father went to view the house and when they returned Duncan warned me that it was rather old fashioned but the furniture was quite tasteful and the house looked clean.

'But you'd better see it for yourself before we sign an agreement,' he added.

'Is it right next to the gas works?' I asked him still a bit concerned that the rent was so cheap.

'No, of course not!' he replied.

'A sewage farm?' I asked.

'Mary, as if I would ever think of putting you and Charlotte near a sewage farm! No its just inexpensive because it's eh well, as I said... rather old fashioned!' Duncan said rather sheepishly.

The next day we left Charlotte with Granny Bumble, Celia and Christopher, while Grandpa John, Duncan and I took a private taxi to Peebles for the day.

The minute I saw the wide high street and the lovely shops, I thought Peebles would be a perfect place for us to live. We drove over a bridge that crossed the River Tweed, up a steep hill and then the taxi pulled up outside a large Victorian house in a street lined with trees.

Grandpa John told the driver that we wouldn't need him for at least two hours and they agreed a time for him to collect us later.

As the agent wasn't due to meet us with the key for another ten minutes, I asked Grandpa John if he thought I could have a quick peep through the little gate at the side of the house. He nodded and said, 'I think you'll be pleased'.

Pleased? I was thrilled. The garden wasn't very big but it was long and I could see a stream running along the boundary at the bottom of the lower terrace. The top terrace was covered in grass and had two posts, which would be ideal for a washing line, and on either side of the lawn there were flowerbeds with a mixed border of late summer flowers.

When I returned to the front of the house, the estate agent had arrived and ushered us inside. We went into the drawing room first, which to my delight had an open fire and in the grate was a beautiful old-fashioned coal bucket made of brass and a matching poker and tongs. I was glad to see that the carpet was clean and the sofas and armchairs looked very comfortable. The dining room was big and had a sideboard full of cutlery and glass. The agent told us that the gas fire worked well but being gas was on a meter that took shillings. The kitchen had an old stone sink and a big range, which also heated the hot water for the house. There was also a gas cooker, which the agent told us the previous family had found far easier to cook on. Thank goodness for the extra cooker I thought, as the range looked terrifying. There were some saucepans on a shelf but as they looked rather well used, I thought we could use the ones we were given as a wedding present instead. As I opened a door at the back of the kitchen, I discovered that it led to a big walk in larder, which was full of china and then I opened another door that led to a rather damp spider-ridden outside lavatory. Only to be used in an emergency I thought to myself, as I quickly shut the door again.

Duncan said that he'd wait downstairs for us, as he'd seen the bedrooms already, so I followed my father-in-law and the agent up the wide staircase to the upper floor. Two of the bedrooms had double beds, another one had a single bed and the last one was empty except for a chest of drawers. The walls all had pretty wallpaper and the rooms smelled clean and thankfully there was no sign of any rats or mice so far. The bathroom was quite large and had a big linen cupboard with a hot water tank in it, so the bathroom would be lovely and warm. Bliss! So far so good, I thought.

'How do we heat the bedrooms?' I asked the agent. There was silence for a moment and then the agent replied, 'Well Mrs Ogilvie, I believe the previous tenants used paraffin heaters and carried them from room to room in the winter. They are economical to use and just need the wicks trimming regularly.' Fortunately, I had used one at the Ugadale Hotel, when I was based at Machrihanish, and understood all about having to trim the wicks, so that wouldn't be a problem.

When we went downstairs again, I looked at Duncan's grinning face. He was obviously ready to sign on the dotted line, relieved to have found a home for his family so quickly, but first, I had to know why the rent was so low for such a big house.

'Excuse me asking,' I said, 'but why is the rent so much lower than one would expect for a house of this size? There must be a good reason.'

'Oh I'm sorry, I must have forgotten to tell you,' the agent said rather sheepishly, 'there is no electricity in the house, it's all run by gas.' And there it was!

'Gas?' I said stunned, 'how on earth will we see to read and get around in the dark?' I looked at the ceiling and saw no familiar hanging shades but when I glanced at the walls, I noticed some pretty iron brackets holding small glass shades. I took a closer look and discovered they had tiny pieces of what looked like gauze inside them.

'Those are called gas mantles and you just turn the gas on with the tap beside each set of lights and use a match,' the agent explained.

Grandpa John was just about to strike a match from his own box, when the agent stopped him, 'Please be careful sir, if you touch the mantles by mistake they disintegrate at once. May I suggest that you use a spill, which is far longer than a match, so you can light the mantle without the danger of touching it. The mantles are quite expensive to replace and only one ironmonger stocks them in the town, as most houses are connected to the electricity mains now.'

'Where is the telephone?' I asked.

'Oh there isn't one I'm afraid, they don't work on gas!' I gave Duncan a look that showed him that, like Queen Victoria, I was not amused.

'Don't worry, darling, there is a public telephone box down the road, so you can use that like you did when you were in the Wrens,' Duncan suggested.

'But I didn't have a baby when I was in the Wrens,' I said, 'so what am I supposed to do with Charlotte, when I am on the phone in the middle of winter, take her with me?'

'Well… ' Duncan started to reply but I cut him off.

'And how am I supposed to do the ironing without an electric iron?' I queried, 'Are there gas ones?'

'Well actually no... well sort of,' the agent replied, as we walked through to the kitchen where he showed me two different sized flat irons. 'All you have to do is heat them up on the gas stove and they work very well, or so I have been told... I am sure you'll soon get the hang of them, Mrs Ogilvie,' the agent said looking at the floor. I now knew why the rent was so low. The housewife would be living in the eighteen hundreds not the nineteenth century!

'It's a very economical house to run, once you get the hang of everything,' the agent told us cheerfully.

Grandpa John realising that I wasn't too happy about living in a house without electricity, offered to move in with us for a few days, so that he could show us how to manage the fires and the gas mantles, 'I remember as a wee boy that my grandmother's house was just like this,' he said trying to reassure me. 'I am sure that it will be lovely and cosy once you have the fire on and closed the curtains.'

I was still feeling a little unhappy about not having any electricity, but knew that, as we didn't have much money, I should just be grateful that we could finally have our own home together, so turned to the agent and asked, 'When can we move in?'

When we returned to Duncan's parents house, we went into our bedroom to get changed and I automatically turned on the light. Duncan immediately switched it off again and said, 'we'd better get used to living in the dark ages darling!' We both laughed and then as we sat down on the bed in the dark for a few minutes to see what it felt like, the reality suddenly hit me. This was how it was going to be from now on.

That night we risked the squeaky bed waking the rest of the household and joyfully made love. It was the first time since Duncan's amputation and he must have wanted to make up for lost time, as with each kiss he whispered, 'this is for the flat irons... this is for the gas mantles... this is for the hundred and one buckets of coal you'll have to fill each day!'

The following week we left Duncan's parents house and when I said goodbye and thank you to Granny Bumble she said, 'The house will seem so empty without you and with Celia and Christopher leaving for her new school in two weeks time too, what am I going to do with myself all day?'

'Have a much needed rest,' I said, 'and then come and stay with us for a long weekend.' She stood on the doorstep crying and waving as we drove away.

Grandpa John came with us for a few days to help us settle into our new home. He taught us how to back the range up at night or clean it out and get it going again when we pushed the wrong dampers by mistake. The shed was filled with fuel and more could be ordered on a month-to-month basis and logs could be delivered too. As for the gas mantles, I bought a dozen spares from the ironmonger, who told me to treat them like butterfly wings. I stored them carefully on the larder shelf next to piles of matches and spills and spare torch batteries.

The estate agent soon found us a wonderful daily help called Jenny, who wasn't much older than me and who insisted on doing all the housework, including scrubbing the floors. She was also willing to babysit Charlotte, so I took advantage of having her there and took some driving lessons. After I had mastered a three-point turn, done several emergency stops and reverse parked his car without bumping into a lamppost the instructor said, 'You are a natural Mrs Ogilvie, you'll pass all right.'

Duncan was so impressed that he said he'd buy a second hand car the moment I passed my test. But as it turned out I failed.

The driving test examiner said I was a good driver, but that I hadn't looked in the driving mirror to check if there were any cars behind me once, 'not even to tidy your hair!' He obviously thought this was funny but I burst into tears explaining that it was essential for me to pass, so that I could drive Duncan back and forth to Edinburgh to attend University. When we got back to our house, I invited him in for a cup of tea and when he saw Duncan hobbling around on crutches with one trouser leg pinned up behind the knee, he promised, after two cups of tea and a huge slice of my apple fruit cake, to ask for special permission for me to be allowed to re-sit the test in a month's time instead of the usual three.

'Just practise looking in the mirror, Mrs Ogilvie, and you'll pass I am sure' the instructor said, as he left.

After he had gone Duncan grinned at me and said, 'That's odd darling, you don't usually have a problem looking at yourself in the mirror!' I threw a cushion at him, which he fended off with one of his crutches.

The next week Duncan bought an old Austin and after putting two 'L' plates on the car, we started going for a drive everyday. He made a harness in the back of the car, so that Charlotte was safe. She seemed to think these drives were far more fun than being pushed around in her pram and clapped her hands with glee. Thankfully, I passed my re-test a week before Duncan was due to return to University. I wondered how he would manage having been away for so long.

Two elderly women, both called Miss Hibson, lived in the house next to us, and they absolutely adored Charlotte and cooed at her when she was sitting in her pram. Miss Hibson Number One told me that her name was Angela and that she was the older of the two by a year and that her sister, Miss Hibson Number Two, was called Daphne. When I met her younger sibling, I noticed that she had rather lovely violet eyes. I told the two Miss Hibsons that from time to time I would be calling Duncan from the phone box at the end of our street, so if they saw Charlotte sitting in the car on her own while I was on the phone not to worry, as she could see me through the window.

'We wouldn't hear of you doing such a thing dear,' Angela said, 'would we Daphne?'

'Certainly not Angela! You can make use of our telephone,' Daphne offered. 'After all we hardly ever use it do we?' So before I took Duncan to Edinburgh we made a plan that he would ring me at the Miss Hibsons house after six thirty twice a week, when Charlotte would be asleep in her cot, and then one of 'The Hibbies', as we decided to nickname them, would come over and babysit for me until I returned.

Jenny, our daily who now came three times a week, taught me how to make homemade steak and kidney pudding, cottage pie with carrots and onions, to make it go further, and also spotted dick and ginger sponge pudding. This made Duncan very happy, as they were all his favourites.

The day before I was to drive Duncan to Edinburgh, the Hibbies suggested that I leave Charlotte with them and offered to feed her for me. As she was now eating mashed food, rather than finely sieved meals, I thought this was an excellent idea, so the following morning we waited until Charlotte was asleep in her pram and then I pushed her around to our kind neighbour's house. When we drove off, I felt so awful leaving her behind that I nearly turned the car around to go back and fetch her, but as I knew that Duncan really needed my help moving in, and also needed my moral support, I held back the tears and took my brave wounded husband 'back to school'.

When we arrived at the hotel, I helped him unpack and then we had a quick lunch together. When it was time for me to go home, I could see Duncan balancing on one leg and using one of his crutches to wave goodbye. I wondered how he would cope on his own getting to and from his daily classes and whether he would find it hard with everyone else there being half his age. I hoped he would be all right.

When I got home both the Hibbies looked exhausted, but Charlotte looked as happy as a lark. She had put all her toys plus their cushions, button boxes, wooden spoons and precious ornaments on the sitting room floor and made a lovely mess.

'Thank you so much,' I said hugging them both with gratitude, 'I'd never have managed having her with me today.'

'We loved every minute, didn't we dear?' Angela said smiling at me, but I didn't hear Daphne's reply.

When I went to bed that night, I lay awake for hours worrying about how Duncan would manage on his first day back at University, and hoped that the younger students would look after him.

A letter arrived the next day from Celia, telling me about her new job and that the Headmistress at her school had been very understanding of her situation, and that Christopher was doing fine. She didn't say anything about being lonely, so I thought that if she can manage so can I.

Duncan called me one night sounding really happy, and a little drunk. 'It's a bloody miracle darling! Do you remember I told you about my two best friends at University before the war, George, the Canadian and Alastair, the Irishman? Well they are both very much alive, thank God, and guess what?' he asked. 'They are both going to be studying with me here in Edinburgh, just like we did before the war!'

Duncan then told me that Alastair had been captured by the Japanese and was forced to work on the Burma Railway, which my brother Peter had told me about, so I knew that he must have been through hell.

'He's so thin that he looks as if he hasn't eaten since I last saw him,'

Duncan sighed. 'His experiences as a prisoner of war were extremely humiliating for him and on top of everything else, he became very sick. First he had malaria, then he got dysentery and after all that, he then had to have his appendix removed in appalling conditions by a semi-trained surgeon using a penknife.'

'Oh my goodness, the poor man,' I gasped.

'And as for George, he was captured by the Italians but managed to escape with the help of the local Resistance. He then fought with them before being caught by the Gestapo.' Duncan took a deep breath and then added, 'Incredibly he managed to escape again and make his way to Switzerland.'

'What a story!' I said astonished.

'That's not the end of it Mary,' Duncan continued, 'although he was now safe he accepted another assignment and went back to help the Italian Resistance in their final push but he got captured by the Gestapo again and this time they tortured him. They took him out night after night and shot him with blanks, and each time that happened he thought that was it, his number was up. The man is a real hero, darling, and I am so proud to be his friend.'

'I am looking forward to meeting your friends,' I said sincerely. 'Tell me, are they wounded?'

'In a way, but it's more mental than physical,' Duncan told me, 'as their experiences were far worse than mine and have left them war weary.'

Duncan asked me if I would mind if we had his friends to stay at the weekends and said that as George had a car, he would be able to drive all three of them to Peebles and back, which would solve the problem of me having to drive.

When I heard a car horn hoot in front of our house on Friday evening, I picked Charlotte up, and then balancing her on one hip, I went outside to welcome my husband's friends.

I was shocked to see how desperately thin Alastair was, but surprisingly he managed to lift his luggage out of the back seat without too much difficulty. When I then looked at George, the first thing I noticed was how fit and well he looked in comparison to the other two men. He looked formidable, so I could see why he had been asked to lead the Resistance fighters. I found it hard to believe what they had both been through, as seeing them now, they looked and behaved like pre-war University students, laughing noisily and teasing one another unmercifully.

When Duncan introduced his friends to me, George smiled and said, 'Good God old boy, you've got yourself a beautiful wife!' and before I knew it he was standing next to me kissing me on both cheeks. He then looked down at Charlotte and smiled at her. I wasn't the only one hypnotized by this good-looking giant, as Charlotte just put out her arms for him to pick her up and said, 'Dada', which was not what I had expected at all. I thought she'd be shy but instead when he lifted her up high above his head she cooed with joy. She then saw her real Daddy and squealed 'Dada' again. Two Dadas then became three when Alastair gave her a huge but hideous cuddly toy, that he said he'd won as a prize at a fair, 'Ah Dada ah da ma ta da,' Charlotte said chatting away merrily, which I translated for the men as 'Thank you very much for my toy and would you like to come in for a cup of tea?' This made them all laugh and broke the ice.

'It's up to you as to who has which room,' I said when I took Duncan's friends upstairs.

'Which room has the longest bed?' George asked as he lay down on the double bed trying it out for size. As his feet were hanging over the board at the end of the bed, Alastair said, 'I'd better take that one!'

I then showed George the room with the single bed in it, which he said would suit him better as it had no board at the end of it.

'I can always put a chair at the end of the bed, so that I have something to rest my feet on!' he said laughing.

I left the men to unpack and went downstairs to find Charlotte, who was now sitting on the lap of her real Dada, patting his face and smiling at him.

'I think we'd better teach her to say George and Alastair,' I giggled after giving Duncan a real welcome home kiss, 'she can't have three Dadas!'

'Geooooorge,' Duncan said slowly.

'Oorge,' Charlotte mimicked.

'My goodness, our daughter is a genius!' Duncan said proudly.

'Alll… aas… tair,' Duncan said even more slowly.

'Oorge,' she said again

'Oh well, maybe not,' he conceded.

We were still trying to get her to say their names when the two men came downstairs to join us. Getting my rather over excited baby to sleep that night was not easy. She was in heaven having been spoilt all evening with so much attention from her three Dadas.

After supper that night there was a row of empty beer and wine bottles by our dustbin. The Hibbies must have thought an army of alcoholics had moved in with us.

When George and Alastair drove off to play golf after breakfast the next day, it gave Duncan and me a chance to be together on our own for a while, so I told him that I had noticed that Alastair had put two lumps of sugar and an apple in his pocket at breakfast and had then asked me if I could wrap up a couple of biscuits for him to take with him that morning. 'I just thought it was a bit odd, as he seems to have a very small appetite. In fact he ate less than I did at dinner last night.'

'I'm sorry, darling, I should have warned you,' Duncan said. 'As Alastair has had to live on a handful of rice or whatever they were given for several years, his stomach has shrunk and the doctors have told him to eat little and often, so that eventually he will be able to eat a full meal again.' From then on I made sure that Alastair knew where we kept the biscuit tin and where the larder was and I told him that if he felt peckish just to help himself.

The following Friday evening was much quieter, as the men had to do their homework. As all three men were tired, we went to bed early but at about two in the morning I was woken up suddenly by a loud thump followed by the sound of somebody whimpering. Thinking that Charlotte must have fallen out of her cot and was crying, I quickly got up, found my torch, and hurried to her room to check that she was all right. When I pointed my torch at her I could see that she was sound asleep, so I wondered what on earth could have woken me up with such a start. I then heard the whimpering sound again and realised that it was coming from the single bedroom. Suddenly there was a loud scream. Alastair came running out of his room and went straight into George's room. I then heard him say in a calm voice, 'It's all right old man, it's just one of your nightmares. The war is over, you are safe now.'

I lit the gas light on the landing, so that I could see better and then waited for Alastair to come back out. A few minutes later he came to the door and asked, 'Mary, do you have any spare sheets?'

'Yes… yes we do,' I replied, 'why?'

'You see, when George has on of his nightmares, he drips with sweat and well the sheets get soaked through, I'm afraid,' Alastair explained.

Having heard the commotion, my husband hobbled out of our room on his crutches to see what was amiss. After Alastair filled him in, Duncan then turned to me and said, 'Darling, I think it would be better if Alastair and I remade the bed, as it would be better if George thinks you didn't hear him.' So after giving Alastair some fresh bed linen and checking that Charlotte was still asleep, I went back to bed. When Duncan came back to bed, he told me that poor George often had nightmares about being tortured by the Gestapo, even though it was now almost a whole year since he had last escaped.

'Just imagine being taken out of your cell and then made to stand in front of a firing squad,' Duncan said quietly. 'You then hear the gunshots but nothing happens, and you realise that you are still alive. Obviously you must feel a huge sense of relief. However, when the bastards come back the next night, and the next, and do the same thing, telling you this time it's the real thing, it must make you go mad, so I'm not surprised he still has nightmares.'

The three men came to our home in Peebles every weekend from then on, and I did my best to soothe, heal and encourage each man in turn. I would often cradle Duncan like a child at night, as his wound was still not healing properly and he would weep with pain when he tried to take his trousers off. The trouser leg that was pinned behind his knee often got stuck to the wound, so it was agony for him to peel it off. I also held Alastair's head over the sink when he was being sick, as his stomach had still not got used to holding a full meal. And although George still had nightmares, he was now able to talk to me about his experiences and said that they were less frequent.

It looked as though my weekends were going to be very busy, caring for all three men and Charlotte too, and I wondered how on earth I would cope, so I rang my cousin Jane for some advice.

'You'll manage beautifully, you silly cow!' she said laughing, and then after a pause, added, 'but who would ever have imagined when we were at Finishing School, that you'd end up having to look after not one but three husbands!'

ACKNOWLEDGEMENTS

I couldn't have written this book without the help of many friends who I would like to thank for all their hard work and support.

I would like to thank Audrey Catford, Bea Tilbrook, Sue Catcher, Caroline Hampson, Rozanna Herring, Lucy Bennett and Mandi Gomez for their encouragement, advice and support.

Finally I would like to thank my youngest son, Jamie Robertson, who was my ghostwriter and edited the book down to an acceptable length for publication.

* Mary Arden is a pseudonym and some of the other characters' names have also been changed to protect privacy.